'Don't be alar

She took no not
   like a man fr
balaclava, and also remembering the hearing aid
   by the side of the bed, I raised my voice,
         shouting 'I'M THE DOCTOR!'
By now she was out of bed, had picked up an
ebony walking stick and was standing with her
back to the wall, ready to defend her honour.
   There was silence in the room as we stood
eyeing each other. During this silence a small
plaintive voice called from the room next door.
         'I'm here, Doctor.'
   I had been examining the wrong patient.

DOCTOR ROBERT CLIFFORD

Only When I Laugh, Doctor

Oh Dear, Doctor!
Look Out, Doctor!
Surely Not, Doctor!

WARNER BOOKS

A Warner Book

Oh Dear, Doctor! copyright © Robert D. Clifford 1981
Illustrations copyright © Nick Baker
First published in Great Britain by Pelham Books Ltd 1981
Published by Sphere Books Ltd 1982
Reprinted 1986, 1988, 1989

Look Out, Doctor! copyright © Robert D. Clifford 1983
Illustrations copyright © Nick Baker
First published in Great Britain by Pelham Books Ltd 1983
Published by Sphere Books Ltd 1984
Reprinted 1985, 1986, 1987, 1988, 1989

Surely Not, Doctor! copyright © Robert D. Clifford 1985
Illustrations copyright © Larry
First published in Great Britain by Pelham Books Ltd 1985
Published by Sphere Books Ltd 1986
Reprinted 1986, 1987, 1988, 1989

This omnibus edition published by Warner Books Ltd 1992

ISBN 0 7474 1170 0

Printed and bound in Great Britain by
Cox & Wyman Ltd, Reading, Berkshire

Warner Books
A Division of
Little, Brown and Company (UK) Limited
165 Great Dover Street
London SE1 4YA

Oh Dear, Doctor!

For HILDA BOOTH,

who for nine years has typed, retyped
and retyped and retyped every single
word that I have written. Grateful thanks.

Contents

Prologue

Life is a tragedy, for we are all born eventually to die. We survive our tragedies by laughing at them.

A friend once told me that when he was under the influence of ether he dreamed he was turning over the pages of a great book, in which he knew he would find, on the last page, the meaning of life.

The pages of the book were alternately tragic and comic, and he turned page after page, his excitement growing, not only because he was approaching the answer, but because he couldn't know, until he arrived, on which side of the book the final page would be. At last it came: the universe opened up to him in a hundred words: and they were uproariously funny.

He came back to consciousness crying with laughter, remembering everything. He opened his lips to speak. It was then that the great and comic answer plunged back out of his reach.

Christopher Fry

CHAPTER 1

Mistaken Identity

I hate getting out of bed to go on a call in the middle of the night. The amount of hate is in direct proportion to the lateness of the hour and the coldness of the air outside, a subjective psychological condition not unknown to general practitioners.

I knew that it had been snowing and, as I lay snugly in bed, I willed the telephone next to me to stop ringing. Failing that, that it might be a wrong number.

My wife Pam nudged me. 'Come on,' she said. 'Answer it. It might be something urgent.'

I picked up the receiver to hear a quavering, elderly female voice ask if I could come and see her. She was a Miss Hunter. She had a pain in her chest and difficulty in breathing. She apologised for having to bring me out so far, then gave me detailed instructions on how to get there. It meant my crossing to the Up-the-Hill side of the town, followed by a journey of about four miles along small lanes to her isolated house. All I had to do then, she said, was to find the key under the flower pot by the back door, take no notice of the dog – an alsatian – and come straight upstairs.

Before I ventured out I put on every scrap of clothing I could find that did not completely stop me moving my arms and legs,

11

pulled my wellingtons over some thick rugby socks, and donned an old Portuguese knitted helmet, which was a favourite of mine.

My mother had brought the helmet back from Madeira and swore to me the Portuguese peasantry wore them all the year round, ear flaps up in the summer and down in the winter. As the helmet was made of thick, heavy, oily wool, and the worst Madeira winter is about two degrees hotter than our best English summer, I wondered whether she'd got the story right. However, the helmet was beautifully warm, just right for the English winter. Mind you, with my hat pulled right down over my ears, my scarf, my duffle coat and my gum boots, I could have passed for a man from Mars.

Snow was such a rare event in Tadchester that I never thought of buying anything like chains for the car, and my journey was hair-raising. I slipped and slid up and down roads at about ten miles an hour. Having managed to scramble up the steep main road going Up-the-Hill, going down the first dip of the crest I got over-confident and spun round in a complete circle. The snow was coming down ever thicker and I seemed to be lost in a swirling curtain of flakes.

I edged my way along the lanes as the old lady had directed, came to the cross roads she had described, stepped into the white-out with my torch and stumbled to the back door. In spite of all my clothing I was already freezing, and I was not sure whether this was the house. I lifted up a flower pot by the back door. There was a key. I hoped I had got the right house; most country cottagers kept their key under a flower pot by the door.

The key turned stiffly in the lock and the door, possibly swollen by the wet weather, was difficult to open. I had to barge it a couple of times with my shoulder.

It took only a few seconds to confirm that this was the right house. A huge black alsatian, fangs bared, leapt at me as I came into the room. I was back out of the door in a flash. Strange, when I slammed the door shut it did not seem stiff at all.

I prowled round the house looking for another entrance. I could see a light on upstairs. Nobody answered or came to the window when I knocked, except the alsatian which appeared, snarling, at every window I looked into. A tentative touch on the back door knob had him snarling at the handle. I had to get past him. The noise he was making was enough to wake the dead, never mind the seriously ill. Obviously the lady was not well enough to come downstairs.

Stephen Maxwell, my partner, always carried a bottle of ethyl chloride spray for use on boisterous dogs. This is a freezing anaesthetic that comes out in a jet from a container like a scent bottle. I had used it for some local anaesthetics but had gained most of my experience with it as a medical student. The spray was capable of squirting a thin stream of freezing liquid about three feet and was ideal for assessing the reaction time of female medical students. If we were able to catch a female student from behind as she was bending over a cadaver during dissection, a well-directed squirt to the bare area between the top of the stocking and the knicker leg could produce the most dramatic results.

One athletic girl student, on receipt of a direct hit, leapt, with a high-pitched shriek, clean over the dissecting table. She was immediately signed up by the Secretary of the Hospital Athletic Club to represent the hospital in the united hospitals sports. On the day she performed she came a bad eighth out of nine. The use of an ethyl chloride spray was considered as bad as doping and fixing runners, and without it she just wasn't the same.

Although I was confident of some reaction when squirting this stuff up a girl student's skirt, I was not sure of its effectiveness against a great alsatian with dripping fangs. But I was so muffled up with protective clothing that it would be difficult for him to get his teeth in anywhere, so if I was going to test its efficacy on ravening beasts, this was the time.

I struggled back to the car, opened my midwifery bag and, with blue hands, picked up the cold glass cylinder. I experienced the euphoria that toting a gun must give: 'Keep

13

your hands in the air, Kincaid. One move and I'll drop yuh!' I would have been a lot happier if it *had* been a gun.

Boldness was my only policy. I charged the door. It crashed back on its hinges and the alsatian stood snarling at bay at the back of the room, guarding the stairs which led to my patient.

Emboldened with my phial of anaesthetic, I stared him in the face. He must have been used to that one: he stared back and lifted his lip in a silent snarl. I aimed the spray at his face. The thin jet of fluid hit him straight on the bridge of the nose, spilling into his eyes. If only we could have entered that dog for the long jump instead of our lady medical student, we would have taken away the cup.

He let out one terrified yelp and cleared the stairs from bottom to top in one tremendous leap, disappearing round the corner of the landing. As I went upstairs his head poked cautiously round the corner as if he could not believe what was happening. I only had to raise the phial and, with another yelp, he shot off to some secure hiding place.

I went through the first door I could find. There was no light on, which surprised me: I thought I had seen a light from outside. Flashing my torch on the bed, I saw an elderly, grey-haired lady, either sleeping or unconscious. There was a set of false teeth in a glass by the bed, and a hearing aid beside it, which explained why she had slept through all the din.

She looked a bit blue round the lips, so I switched on the room light, put my stethoscope on her chest and felt her pulse at the wrist. It was as if I had squirted her with the ethyl chloride. She woke with a start, screamed and struggled to get out of bed. I tried frantically to reassure her.

'Don't be alarmed,' I said, 'I am only the doctor.'

She took no notice. Remembering that I looked like a man from Mars in my Portuguese balaclava, and also remembering the hearing aid by the side of the bed, I raised my voice, shouting 'I'M THE DOCTOR!'

By now she was out of bed, had picked up an ebony walking stick and was standing with her back against the wall, ready to defend her honour.

There was silence in the room as we stood eyeing each other. During this silence a small plaintive voice called from the room next door, 'In here, Doctor.'

I had been examining the wrong patient.

There was no way of communicating with a frightened deaf lady waving an ebony walking stick, so I edged backwards to the door, hoping that the alsatian would not take advantage of the seat of my pants.

In the next room I found a frail Miss Hunter sitting up in bed, surrounded by a great white shawl, and obviously very confused by all the racket. I explained hastily, but she was too unwell to laugh. When I examined her chest, having first got rid of seven or eight grey layers of flannelette, I found the cause of her trouble. She had a trail of blistery spots coming down from high up in the middle of her back, round her side and her left breast. There was no doubt about it. She had shingles.

'How long have you been in pain like this?' I asked, now shaking with reaction from the episode of the dog and the lady in the next room.

'A good two weeks,' said Miss Hunter, 'but I couldn't sleep and I thought it would be nice to have something for the pain.'

At this point, so did I.

I fished out some pain-killing tablets and ointment from my bag, and said I would arrange for the district nurse to pop in from time to time. Nurse was a dog lover, hopefully she would have a way with alsatians.

I made my farewells and, keeping close to the wall, nipped past what turned out to be Miss Hunter's deaf sister's room, got down the stairs and out of the house without seeing the dog.

I wondered how Miss Hunter would explain it all to her deaf sister. I couldn't see the sister letting anybody into her room that night, and I envisaged her standing by the door with her walking stick, ready to let the first person entering have a good crack on the head. I hoped it was the alsatian.

I got back to the car, slithered my way home, peeled off the layers of damp clothes and jumped into bed. Pam, God bless her, had left my side of the electric blanket on. However sleepy she was, she always managed to remember to reach over and put it on for me.

'I hope it wasn't serious, darling,' she said, sleepily.

'No,' I replied. 'Just an average night call.'

* * *

I was the fourth partner in a group of five in a little Somerset town called Tadchester. Tadchester (population 6,500) stands on the estuary of the River Tad, in one of the most beautiful parts of the Somerset coast. It is a market town, with some fishing, some light industry, and a great deal of farming.

The town is split in two by the River Tad, and further split by the large hill which dominates one side of the river. The other side of the river is flat pastureland, stretching off to marshes and the sea coast. You are not just a Tadchester resident – you are strictly Up-the-Hill or Down-the-Hill. It has important social distinction: the population Down-the-Hill tends to be made up of Haves, the population Up-the-Hill tends to be the Have-nots.

16

We were the only general practice in the town, and also took care of the local hospital. The five partners each had his own area of responsibility at the hospital: Steve Maxwell, the senior partner, had a special interest in medicine; Henry Johnson, the second senior, was the surgeon; Jack Hart, the third partner, was the anaesthetist; I, as the fourth partner, was reckoned to be the expert in midwifery and was pretty good at piercing ears; and Ron Dickinson, the fifth and junior partner – an accomplished athlete who spent a great deal of his time running, jumping, swimming, sailing, water ski-ing, etc – was our ENT specialist and removed the local tonsils. We were a happy and well-balanced team.

CHAPTER 2

Amazing Grace

At the time of Miss Hunter's night call I had been living in Tadchester for about ten years. Although I was beginning to look a bit like part of the local scenery and, by virtue of being a doctor, had access to most homes and an entrée into most of society, I knew I couldn't even begin to think of myself as a 'local' until I'd been there thirty years. In spite of one decade in the town, with my hair beginning to get thinner on top and my waistline moving towards solid-citizen proportions, I was still referred to as the 'new young doctor'.

I had been a bachelor when I first arrived in Tadchester, survived the ambitions of several local ladies, and married my wife, Pam, after meeting her when holidaying with my mother in Bournemouth.

After six years in a flat Up-the-Hill, we had built a house overlooking the estuary. Thinking our family of two boys was all we were going to have, we had got our rooms worked out precisely. Jane, our daughter, was born exactly nine months after we moved. I'm sure there was a very good reason.

In our original plans we had not counted on nurseries, girls' bedrooms, etc, and the tiny study and TV room had to be knocked together to remedy this deficit. The builder said we were the only people he had ever known who started knocking walls down as soon as the house had been put up.

The birth of Jane coincided with the death of Pam's mother, Bill. Pam and her mother had been extremely close but Pam was so occupied with the new baby that frankly she-just had not the time to grieve. It was one of those strange balances of Nature which can do so much to heal the wounds of tragedy.

We both loved Tadchester and had made many good friends, chief among whom were Eric and his exotic wife Zara. Eric ran the Tadchester Radio Service and was the local expert on radio and television, while his arty wife Zara, with her bizarre dresses, set the fashion for ladies' wear in the Tadchester area. She was Pam's best friend and Jane's godmother.

Other friends we spent a lot of time with, particularly the nights when we trudged through the surf dragging a seine-fishing net, were Frank and Primrose Squires, Philip and Joan Gammon and Kevin and Janice Bird – all firm friends with whom to share good times, bad times, holidays and festive occasions. The men were all active members of the local Round Table and all had widely different occupations, Frank being a surveyor, Philip a school teacher and Kevin a farm manager.

My partners and their families were friends rather than working colleagues, and what with work and social goings on we were all well qualified to fill Kipling's *Unforgiving Minute* with sixty seconds' worth of distance run.

Over my working years in Tadchester I had developed a fairly standard routine. Four mornings a week I held a surgery in the practice house. (The closing of the local colliery at Thudrock meant that we no longer had to keep open the branch surgery we kept there.) I held an evening surgery two evenings a week and had an ante-natal clinic once a week. I visited Tadchester Hospital each day, usually in the late morning. There, as well as seeing my own patients who were in hospital I was also in sole charge of the recovery ward, which housed patients recovering from operations not needing intensive treatment and some medical cases.

John Bowler, the consultant physician from Winchcombe,

who held an out-patients' clinic at Tadchester Hospital once a week, used to cheat by admitting some patients direct to this recovery ward.

The name of the ward was supposed to cover its function, that is to say, you went there to recover in quiet surroundings after major medical or surgical illnesses, but as it was a quiet ward and beds were always at a premium, John Bowler had his acute medical patients admitted directly to these beds without having qualified by being iller somewhere else in the hospital before they were allowed in.

Once a week I did a ward round with him when he was seeing his patients. John was of great use to me when, after the round over a cup of coffee in the sister's office, he would help me catch up on all the latest developments and techniques in medicine with which, as a consultant, he had to keep up to date.

Midwifery occupied a great deal of my time. There was an increasing tendency for mothers to have their confinements in hospital; more and more were being delivered at St Mary's Maternity Home, and it was rumoured that a new maternity unit was going to be built at Winchcombe and we might lose our midwifery facilities altogether. But, home or St Mary's, I had to attend all the confinements. Although, being fundamentally lazy, I would be pleased to lose the out-of-hours calls, and hours at bedsides that midwifery involved, I looked upon it as an important part of medicine. I knew from giving up anaesthetics how soon one lost one's skills in any particular procedure.

There had been some changes in the surgery staff at Tadchester since I arrived. Gladys, our senior receptionist, seemed ageless and as if she would go on for ever. She was ably supported by her second-in-command, Mary Collaston, who did the typing and any dispensing that needed to be done. Mary's husband had been the under-manager at Thudrock Colliery and he was, for a time, out of work after it closed. We feared the couple might move to another area in their search to find work. However, the husband obtained a local post in charge of personnel at the new plastics factory. As this factory expanded, so did the population of Tadchester. This necessitated the appointment of our fifth partner, Ron Dickinson.

We had a succession of young ladies to help out with reception work in the surgery. Receptionists had a fairly high casualty rate, becoming pregnant or getting married, and in about fifty per cent of cases, doing both. We had one new full-time married receptionist – Grace Hughes – whose husband worked as a mechanic at one of the Tadchester garages, and an ever-changing stream of assistant receptionists.

Working at the surgery was a plum job for any girl, not because we paid them so magnificently, but because it was an ideal place to look for a husband. What was more, if you found somebody you fancied, you could always check up on his records to see he did not suffer from any nasty disease or unpleasant hereditary trait.

Grace Hughes was a great asset to the practice. She was outrageously outspoken and could get away with absolute murder. As Gladys was getting a bit older, it was Grace who always opened the surgery in the morning. When I came in she would be opening the mail.

'Good morning, Amazing Grace,' I would say, and this would receive a typical response like: 'Morning, Dr Bob. You look a little green around the gills. You've got to cut out this night-life a bit. Too much bed and too little sleep. Give the old woman a rest.'

Grace was ribald. I used to shudder sometimes at the things she said to patients. But she never offended and had such precise judgment that most other people, not venturing nearly as far as Grace, would get into awful trouble.

Two examples of Grace's handling of people will serve to illustrate her public-relations technique:

A dignified lady patient came up to the hatch.

'What's the trouble, luv?' asked Grace.

'I am passing my water rather frequently and it is stinging,' said the woman. 'I find it difficult to hold my water, and I've tried almost everything.'

21

'Have you tried sticking both legs into one stocking?' said Grace as she reached for the appointment book.

Anyone who dared to ask for the Family Planning Clinic which Ron Dickinson was starting as a new venture would be asked whether they had tried holding an aspirin between their knees.

Grace was always good for a laugh. There was always almost a riot going on around her. Until you knew her well, you did not realise that she had indifferent health herself and her delightful husband, Jack, had a painful spinal condition about which he never grumbled.

'No point in complaining,' said Grace. 'Life's to be lived. And I reckon a few good laughs are worth all the pills in the world.'

She was dead right. Patients would turn up at reception down in the dumps, convinced their last hour was approaching. By the time they got to me, after a quick burst of Grace's therapy, they'd be smiling broadly and almost forgetting what they'd come for.

It would be difficult to find two people more different than Gladys and Grace, and they felt for each other the attraction of opposites.

The rather fiery, prim, austere Gladys and the warm, earthy Grace got on like a house on fire. Grace would never be ribald in front of Gladys, and although Gladys shouted at most people, she would never shout at Grace.

I would sometimes come across them on a Sunday afternoon, walking their dogs together in the park, chattering away. I would love to have eavesdropped on their conversation. Henry called them the two Gee-gees and whenever he wanted assistance or some instrument taken to his room he would shout 'Gee-gee', and either Gladys or Grace (who were both a bit frightened of him) would come running.

*   *   *

One of my older friends in Tadchester was Bob Barker who kept the secondhand bookshop at Sanford-on-Sea. It was Bob who made me realise the depth of tradition and history of Tadchester. We chatted over cups of tea in his bookshop whenever I could steal half an hour from my work. He would tell me tales of his youth and of the notable figures and events that were local history. As Bob's life spanned eight decades he was himself a part of local tradition, and through him I gained some idea of the depth and strength of it.

But it was only when he took me as his guest to the Bridge Trust dinner that I realised that however long I lived in Tadchester, however warmly accepted as a doctor, I could never ever become a native.

The Bridge Trust had been founded by a man called Bernard Harding in 1600. He had set up a charitable trust – the rent from some lands – to provide monies each year for the poor of Tadchester. He had made his money from the Newfoundland cod trade. In the seventeenth and eighteenth centuries this particular trade was a very important part of Tadchester's economics and salt cod always appeared on the menu at the Bridge Trust dinners.

Senior and more important citizens of the town were honoured by being made Trustees, there being just twelve in number. It was the equivalent of a Londoner being made a Companion of Honour.

Records showed that there had been a Bridge Trust dinner and a distribution of the 'Harding Dole' every year since 1600, excepting 1640, the year of the Great Plague, when half the population of Tadchester died. The mayor and corporation fled the town, and a merchant called Robert Friend took over as mayor, organised the distribution of food, burial of the dead, and isolation of the sick. Although most Tadchestarians probably did not know the name of the current mayor, everyone knew the name of Robert Friend, the mayor who saved the town in 1640.

Every meeting of the Bridge Trustees had been recorded in a series of huge diaries which were on display at the annual dinners. They contained the names of current trustees and the names of the beneficiaries of the Harding Dole. I looked back through some of these volumes of records, some dusty old tomes with hardly legible writing, three or four hundred years old. It was interesting to note that some of the Trustees' names reappeared, generation after generation. A Barker had been a Trustee since 1647; a Hope had been a Trustee since 1700. Hope's Stores was the largest shop in Tadchester High Street, the original shop being built in 1699. And there was a Blackmore represented at every dinner from 1600, including the dinner at which I was a guest.

I felt I was extremely honoured to be asked. Each Trustee was allowed one guest. We all wore dinner jackets, and all twenty-four of us sat round a long deal table.

There was a simple ceremony, glasses were raised in memory of Bernard Harding, salt cod was served, and the business of the Trustees discussed. The meeting had an air of permanence about it: these delightful old men, surrounded by old books, carrying on traditions that had been in existence for nearly four centuries. I would not have been surprised if Sir Walter Raleigh had walked through the door. I thought to myself that if, God willing, I lived the rest of my life in Tad-chester and safely reached the age of three score and ten, I would have covered only a short span of time in relation to this town, its traditions and its fine old men who, for dozens of generations, had maintained these traditions and their charitable bequests.

I felt very humble.

CHAPTER 3

A Few Eccentrics

Tadchester had its quota of eccentric patients, and of them I seemed to get more than my share. I used to wonder what it was about me that attracted them.

One fat lady patient, Millicent Foggat, had repeated chest infections but she utterly refused to let me listen to her chest. I was allowed only to put my stethoscope on the outside of her jumper. The fact that I could hear nothing, she passed off with a little smile as irrelevant. She knew I was really wanting to see her body – all sixteen stone of it.

I once disobeyed her instructions and tried to lift the back of her jumper to put my stethoscope onto real live flesh. There was an immediate explosion. She turned round indignantly as if I had tried to rape her and yelled, 'Stop it, Doctor!'

She agreed eventually to go and have her chest x-rayed, but only on condition she kept her jumper on throughout the proceedings.

It was not the first time in my career I had been commanded to 'Stop it!' It had also happened when I was a medical student.

Once I had attained my second MB, which meant I had passed my test in anatomy and physiology, before starting on full clinical studies in the hospital, I went on what was known as a clinical introduction course.

Thirty students would be shepherded around in a group, being introduced to different aspects of hospital life and clinical teaching. We were taught how to examine a patient, or rather we were supposed to be taught: there were so many of us that only two or three of the keenest at the front ever saw or grasped what was going on.

I was secretary of the rugby club at that time and kept out of sight on the fringe of the crowd, working out who was going to play in which team on the following Saturday, where we were going to hire the coaches from, and whether the club could afford it.

We were doing a round in the surgical ward one day. I was in my usual position on the fringe when the lecturer called out, 'Hey – you at the back! Come over here and examine this breast.'

I ducked my head lower. He couldn't be wanting me. But he was. The students in front of me parted, revealing a finger pointing straight at me.

Also revealed was a large, pale-looking woman with huge pendulous breasts sitting upright like a stag at bay with thirty students crammed round her bed.

'Clifford,' said the lecturer, 'this woman complains of a lump in her breast. Come and examine it and tell us what you think about it. If you think at all, that is.'

I hadn't examined a breast before, leastways not professionally. But there had to be a first time. I stretched out some tentative fingers towards the huge breast, with all my friends crowding round expectantly. The woman eyed me mistrustfully.

I made a grab at what I thought was the lumpy area to have my fingers smacked down, accompanied by a shout of, 'Stop it, Doctor! That's enough of that!'

I was completely embarrassed, both by the woman and by my friends who broke out into disapproving mutters of 'Sexy, sexy . . .'

The lecturer had decided prudently to exit from the scene. I realised I was going to get no further with the examination, so I tracked him down. 'What did I do wrong?' I asked.

'Shouldn't manhandle them,' he said brusquely. 'And you should pay more attention.'

I never found out what was wrong with the patient. I'm ashamed to say that at the time I hoped it was something nasty.

*　　　*　　　*

Basil Small was another patient who didn't trust doctors. When he had to have surgery, he decided to keep the treatment as short as possible. He discharged himself from hospital two days after his hernia operation, when he was also carrying stitches in a large cut to his forehead (a burglar had knocked him out with a jemmy – it wasn't Basil's week!).

Always filthy and unwashed, Basil was reputed to have a large cache of money hidden somewhere in his derelict farmhouse. It was rumoured also that somewhere on his farm he kept his mother and sister in a chicken house. As he never welcomed visitors, and there were always about six ferocious dogs wandering about, nobody ventured to find out if the rumours were true.

Basil reluctantly called to see me about three months after his operation. I found that his two lots of stitches, being nylon, were still firmly in place. His hernia stitches now resembled dirty undergrowth. Those in his head were stuck together under several layers of dried blood, sweat and grime. He looked as if he had a horn sticking out of his forehead.

'Basil,' I said, 'do you know you are an endangered species? You must be one of the last of the unicorns.'

Basil didn't think that was funny at all. He wouldn't let me touch his stitches at this visit, but promised to come again sometime. All he had come for, this time, was a bottle of 'white medicine', and he wasn't going to hang about for anything else.

Basil was slow, but not all that slow – as I was to discover.

In that year he had sold the pheasant-shooting rights over his land to no less than three different syndicates.

Members of shooting syndicates tend to be pretty well-breeched, as was the case here, and there were terrible legal wrangles going on. Basil was summoned to appear in court.

He came to me terrified – at heart he was a simple country man – and even allowed me to remove the septic remnants of his stitches.

'I bain't going to court, Doctor,' he said. 'I'd ruther shoot miself. Can you fix it?'

I believe he would have shot himself if the case had proceeded, so I wrote endless letters, made dozens of telephone calls and finally managed to get the whole thing dropped.

Basil came in to thank me, as dirty as usual and leaving one of his mongrel dogs tied to the post outside the surgery.

'Thank 'ee, Doctor,' he said. 'You're a gentleman. I bain't much good with these 'ere money things.'

'You could have fooled me,' I said. 'Anybody who can sell something three times can't be all that daft. Just one word of advice: if you *are* going to have problems with people, try to avoid having them with people who have plenty of money.'

I told Steve Basil's story at coffee one morning.

Steve laughed. 'As we grow older', he said, 'it is inevitable that our faculties begin to deteriorate. But the very last faculty of all to go is the one that's concerned with money.

'Don't feel too sorry for dirty old Basil Small, the poor old man you have spent so much time and trouble on – he's probably worth about a quarter of a million pounds!'

* * *

Another of Tadchester's eccentrics – if absolute regularity of habit can be called eccentricity – was Arnold Bishop, a bachelor in middle age.

His Saturdays followed the same pattern to the minute: a perambulation around Tadchester covered market, then around the museum, followed by a crawl around the same four pubs. He always spent his holidays in the same hotel in Libya every year. He liked neither Libya nor the hotel, but at least he knew what he didn't like.

So I was surprised to learn that he had taken up astronomy in a big way, and was installing a telescope in his tiny attic flat.

'Nothing more natural, my dear chap,' he said. 'I am, as you know, a creature of habit. And there is nothing so regular as the stars in their courses. In an uncertain world it is a great comfort to observe the unchanging beauty of the heavenly bodies.'

A month later, after a discreet call from a plain-clothes policeman, Arnold sold his telescope. He had been observing heavenly bodies all right, but these were changing ones – changing their clothes in the nurses' home.

Intrigued by strange reflections from Arnold's flat one moonlit night, a nurse had used a pair of binoculars. They revealed Arnold in his darkened attic room, one eye glued to the telescope and the telescope trained directly on the windows of the nurses' home.

The story soon got around Tadchester and it took Arnold some time to live it down. The thing that seemed to bother him, however, was that his actions would seem to be some kind of deviation from the norm, something out of keeping with his usual routines.

'Nothing of the kind, old boy,' he said. 'It has always been my ambition to become a dirty old man. And this seemed a perfectly logical step in the process . . .'

*   *   *

Among my patients in Tadchester were many who did not believe in conventional medicine.

Some had explored everything that conventional medicine had to offer and were still not free of their particular malady. Others had been given a hopeless prognosis, others were just plain misfits. All went off and visited various fringe areas of medicine. Some of the fringe practitioners were well established, and some were way beyond the fringe.

I have never been able to believe, for instance, that people with inoperable diseases can go to the Far East and have tumours removed without operation and without any residual scars; much as I'd like to believe it.

A larger group than those who deserted conventional medicine were those who used it as a last resort. I once had a call from a religious sect who asked me if I would pop in and leave a death certificate for one of their members. They didn't want me to look at him. One of their beliefs was in everlasting life and they didn't want anybody as square as a general practitioner to see one of their failures.

I never minded anybody having any course of treatment that got him better, providing (a) the patient was adequately investigated and (b) he wasn't going off on some course of therapy that delayed prompt treatment by conventional methods.

One patient came to see me after his pet spinal manipulator had failed to improve the pain in his back. An x-ray showed that his spine was riddled with cancer. Although I couldn't change the course of events at this stage, I could give him something for his pain, rather than have it aggravated by unnecessary spinal manoeuvres.

31

Mind you, I have always believed that even the most conventional doctor has to be part witch doctor. The relationship between doctor and patient is terribly important, and if you really believed that the doctor who was looking after you could get you better, then you were a long way towards recovery. Similarly, I expect, if you believed that your witch doctor could lower your blood pressure by slapping you across the bottom with some stinging nettles, there would be a good chance that your blood pressure would come down if he did so.

I had read of witch doctors, herbalists and various other people coming in to save the day when conventional medicine had failed, but I didn't have any first-hand acquaintance with this until Mr. Nin, a Malaysian diplomat, bought a holiday cottage at Tadchester. Over the years he became a close friend.

Among Mr. Nin's duties was the care of Malaysian students in Britain and the arranging of medical care and treatment for senior diplomats and royalty, both in Malaysia and over here.

Mr. Nin, a small, lightly tanned man with a perpetual smile, was only too pleased to talk about unorthodox medicine as practised at home.

He told me of one senior Malaysian official who came over to Britain with a heart condition, and was told he only had a few months to live. He went back to Malaysia, saw the local Bomo (witch doctor) and was given some herbs. Twenty years later he was still happily running around and full of beans.

'Fine,' I said, 'but this is another of those second-hand stories. What have you experienced yourself?'

He smiled his inscrutable oriental smile and told me of his earliest encounter with a Bomo, which happened when he was a small boy and his sister was ill. He didn't know what the illness was, but she had been ill for a very long time and everybody assumed that she was going to die. The doctor had come and gone and all hope had been given up.

The local Bomo was called in. Straightaway he put her into a trance. She stayed in the trance for three days then sat up in bed and started to speak fluently in Malay, English, Chinese and French.

32

That would have been amazing enough, except that before the trance she spoke only Malay.

She broke off in the middle of the multi-lingual discourse to shout, 'Look out! There's a tiger downstairs!'

The house they lived in was built on stilts. Mr. Nin and the family went out onto the verandah and looked down. There, beneath the stilts, was a large tiger.

This event marked the beginning of the girl's full recovery.

Mr. Nin offered no explanation. He merely accepted it as something that had happened.

He was a social friend, rather than a medical one, and was very pleasant and easy to talk to. But one day he came to see me about his health. He wondered whether he had a touch of malaria. I did some blood tests and reassured him they were negative.

When I asked had he had malaria before, he smiled and said yes, he had had it as a teenager. He had been very, very ill and he was not responding to the normal drugs. Mr. Nin was so ill, apparently, that he wasn't taking fluid, hadn't opened his bowels for ten days and was running a high fever. The Bomo was called in but could effect no improvement.

'There is nothing else for it,' said Mr. Nin's mother. 'We will have to send for the Sensen.'

(The Sensen, apparently, was a Chinese witch doctor, whether mainland Chinese or Malayan Chinese I never discovered.)

The Sensen came, took one look at Mr. Nin, then fished in his bag. He brought out a small bottle of dirty water and told him to drink it. He then pulled out a tin can, fixed it to the light fixture above Mr. Nin's head, and filled it with water.

The tin had a small hole in the bottom. As Mr. Nin lay in bed, water dropped on his forehead. It fell drop by drop (much as I'd imagine the Chinese water torture).

That night Mr. Nin had a tremendous evacuation of his bowels. When he woke up in the morning his temperature was gone, and he was completely better.

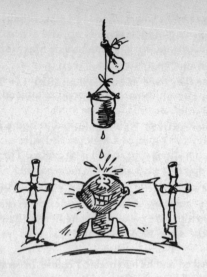

'I have no explanation for it,' he told me. 'All I can do is vouch for the truth.'

What splendid treatment, I thought. I had a number of patients I should like to have pinned to the bed with water continually drip, drip, dripping onto their heads. I am sure most of the awkward ones would be cured permanently by this treatment. The big worry would be if one of them didn't deserve it...

*   *   *

Some patients have a particular quality of cheerfulness whatever circumstances they might be in. Miss Gill, an old lady who was bedridden for forty-seven years, had it. She led a happy and successful life within the four walls of her bedroom.

Reg Dawkins, a patient with a complicated disease – pseudo-muscular dystrophy of the limb-girdle type – had it to excess. His condition meant that from his waist upwards his body worked, and from his waist downwards it worked. Unhappily the connections between the upper and lower

34

halves didn't and he was confined to a wheel chair.

I used to go to him to be cheered up, and at least once a fortnight would pop in to see Reg and his wife Mary for a chat, and a glass of their home-made wine.

From time to time he would have to go into hospital where, in spite of his disability, he was as good as a blood transfusion to the patients whose beds lay close to his.

Mary and Reg were regularly visited at home by a couple whose son, severely injured and depressed after a car accident, had the good fortune to be in bed next to Reg. They attributed their son's subsequent recovery, and regaining of the will to live, solely to Reg's cheerful encouragement and presence.

'All I did was to act daft,' said Reg. 'Once, for instance, I rattled my pills around my mouth and made choking sounds. I shouted for the male charge-nurse.

'"What's the matter?" he said.

'"My sleeping pills have gone down the wrong way, and one of my lungs has gone to sleep."

'"Silly bugger," said the charge-nurse.'

*   *   *

A third cheerful patient and perhaps the most endearing of all, was a doctor colleague, Dr. Jacqueline Dean.

Jackie had been a brilliant student, taking an honours degree in chemistry, before taking up medicine, then winning most of the hospital prizes as a medical student. She was an accomplished horsewoman and rode to hounds. She had the makings of a brilliant surgeon, and was climbing the ladder as a plastic surgeon when a severe debilitating illness forced her to give up medicine. Eventually, apart from a weekly trip round the garden with the physiotherapist, she was confined to bed.

Jackie was almost a medical museum, you name it she had it. She had bone trouble, bowel trouble, blood trouble, liver trouble and had been examined and operated on at various times by the finest specialists in the land.

She reached a relatively stable state, but was very limited in what she could do. She was looked after by her sister, who was of much the same ilk as Jackie, with weekly visits from the district nurse and physiotherapist.

Jackie was always cheerful and regaled me with stories of her days as a medical student. She was one of the first female students to enter medical school, when it became compulsory for these male chauvinistic establishments to have at least ten per cent of females in their yearly intake.

The ratio of boys to girls was about fifty to one and Jackie had a rough time. The idea of girl medical students was not a popular one: the ungentlemanly men were rude to them, propositioned them openly, and made life as difficult as they could.

'There has only been one man in my life,' said Jackie, 'and that's John Wayne. Unfortunately I've had to conduct my romance via the television and cinema screen – but if you could ever get him up into my room here, I would eat him.'

When Jackie qualified and became a house surgeon things changed very little. She literally had to fight for survival.

'There was this pesty Australian registrar,' she said. 'He thought I was a perk of the job, and should come up to his room for instructions, not all of them medical. Finally, one evening I said to him, "Having you put your hand down my blouse is not part of my duties," and I punched him on the nose. He never troubled me again.'

Even in the operating theatre, Jackie could hold her own. On being sworn at by one famous consultant surgeon, she picked up a bloodstained swab, scored a direct hit on his face mask and walked out of the theatre.

Her final disillusionment with men was when another consultant, a man she had previously admired, suggested after a particularly arduous operating session that they go for a spin in his car.

They drove out to some beautiful woodland country, stopped the car and got out. Whereupon the consultant immediately tried to press her against the nearest fir.

'I'm afraid,' said Jackie as she fought off his embrace, 'that you're barking up the wrong tree.'

36

'How would it have been,' I asked, 'if it had been John Wayne with you up there in the wood?'

'Fine,' replied Jackie with a twinkle in her eye, 'but only if he wasn't wearing his spurs . . .'

* * *

My eccentrics came in all shapes and sizes, as proven by Gladys and Ralph Dimond who kept a small greengrocery shop at Sanford-on-Sea, three doors away from Bob Barker's secondhand bookshop.

They certainly were an odd-looking couple. Gladys, who weighed in at about fifteen and a half stone, was twice the size of Ralph who was a diminutive seven stone. Their oddness was accentuated by the fact that they both always wore bowler hats. I never knew why, but thought it was in an effort to keep up with the Joneses: their nextdoor neighbour, Jones the butcher, always wore a striped apron and straw boater.

From behind, Ralph and Gladys looked exactly like Laurel and Hardy. In addition to the bowler hats, Gladys insisted that they both wore cumbersome boiler suits.

The chance of seeing them walking together was rare, however. Gladys was hardly ever seen moving at all. From early morning to closing time she sat on a high stool behind the till, shouting instructions to Ralph. Poor Ralph was kept leaping about all day with sacks of potatoes, crates of oranges and apples, swedes, turnips and tomatoes and all the other ingredients of their trade. He was a sort of greengrocer's Jimmy Wild – a flyweight, daring anything of any weight to last three rounds with him.

I wondered how he managed it: he didn't look strong enough to lift a banana skin.

The pace eventually told on him. He came to my surgery one day, after a particularly fierce battle with some sacks of potatoes.

'Doctor,' he said, 'I've a lump down below. Do you think I've got a hernia?'

I examined him. 'Yes, Ralph,' I said, 'your diagnosis is

right. I'm afraid you are going to need an operation.'

'Will the operation affect my sex life?' queried Ralph.

'No,' I replied. 'Your performance might even be better. Anyway, the operation certainly won't reduce it.'

'OH DEAR, DOCTOR!' said Ralph. 'All that sort of thing had settled down. I hope the operation isn't going to start it up again.'

CHAPTER 4

Fight the Good Fight

One of the most satisfying aspects of general practice is when a straightforward case (if there is such a thing) comes to a straightforward and reassuring end. A good example was George Ford.

George Ford staggered into my surgery, clutching his chest.

'I nearly had to break my record this time, Doc,' he said. 'There's something bad going on. I think I've had a heart attack or got pleurisy or something.'

It had been George's proud boast that in fifty years he had never had to send for a doctor. He certainly did not look well on this occasion. He was breathless, with rapid, shallow breathing, and in obvious pain.

'What has been happening to you, George?' I asked.

'I was perfectly well yesterday,' he said. 'I helped my neighbour put up some fencing. I was as fit as a flea, lifting the fencing posts around and swinging a sledge hammer. Haven't felt so fit for years. When I woke this morning,' he said, 'every time I took a breath, I got this pain in my chest and I could hardly breathe. Is it serious, Doc?'

'Take your shirt off, George,' I said. 'We'll have a look.'

I examined him carefully. His blood pressure and heart were

normal. Listening to his chest, although his breathing was rapid, both lungs appeared to have nothing wrong with them.

'Well, George,' I said, 'your heart and chest are clear. Let's have a look at the rest of you.'

I poked around in the spaces between his ribs with my finger, then I hit a point when George shouted, 'You've got it, Doc. That's the spot.' Between George's ribs I located a very tender spot which made him jump when I pressed it.

'The diagnosis is simple,' I said. 'Nothing terrible has happened. What is troubling you is the result of your fencing activities yesterday. You have torn a muscle between the ribs and every time you take a breath it stretches and causes you pain. The medical name for this condition is called intercostal myalgia, not that that will be of any help to you, but it is as painful as breaking a rib. To be absolutely certain, we ought to get your chest x-rayed, but I am pretty sure of my diagnosis. I am going to give you some simple pain relievers that will ease it, but it may take two or three weeks for it to go completely. You must avoid heavy lifting during that time, and try not to laugh or sneeze too much.'

George's x-ray was quite clear, as I thought it would be.

I found that he had worried all the time until he heard his x-ray result and, although still in pain, he immediately felt better.

So often a negative result like a normal chest x-ray makes patients improve rapidly.

I warned George that there are many conditions that can cause chest pain. Some are connected with bones and muscles, like intercostal myalgia; others are connected with the heart or with the lungs; even indigestion can give pain in the chest. I emphasised that if he should ever again get a sudden attack of pain in the chest, particularly if he found breathing difficult, he mustn't make his own diagnosis, he mustn't struggle to the surgery to see me, he must break his golden rule and ask me to come and see him wherever he was.

George, who was a carpenter, had to have ten days off work. He came to see me, smiling, for his signing-off medical certificate to start work again.

He said, grinning, 'I told my mates at work I was stabbed in the chest, fencing, Doc.

'They think I'm training secretly for the Olympic Games.'

*   *   *

Cases with an ending as happy as George's are rare. Among the routine cases that came to the surgery I usually had at least one fight on my hands coping with serious illness. Sometimes the fight was literally between life and death.

I was called one weekend to the house of a naval commander. He was obviously well-to-do: there was a substantial house, stables, and lawns running down to the River Tad.

He either had a wealthy wife, or had inherited money. Properties of that size were not come by on a commander's pay.

His message on the telephone was terse and irritating.

'I want you to come round straight away and do something about my wife – I am not going to put up with this any longer.'

Then he slammed the phone down. In the background I thought I could hear breaking crockery.

I don't like being spoken to like that. I was not one of his midshipmen.

The commander and his wife were patients of Jack Hart. I remembered Jack saying something about the wife having a psychiatric problem, but I couldn't recall the details.

I drove up the immaculately kept drive and rang the door bell.

The commander's voice shouted through the window near the door, 'Let yourself in the back door, Doctor. I daren't let go of this bitch.'

I walked round the back, in through a kitchen filled with smashed crockery, and through to a front lounge to confront a man whom I assumed was the commander. He was forcibly holding, face-down on the settee, a smartly dressed attractive-looking woman whom I took to be about thirty-five.

As I came into the room she twisted her head round and, in a

41

calm controlled voice, said:

'Thank God you've come, Doctor – see what this brute is doing to me.'

'Don't take any notice of her, Doctor,' said the commander. 'She tried to have a go at me with a knife – I want her out of here and back into hospital, but quick. Have you seen what she's done to the kitchen?'

I assumed from his 'back into hospital, quick' that something like this had happened before.

'This is silly,' said the wife in her continued calm, well-modulated voice. 'I was a bit upset, and smashed a few things in the kitchen, what woman doesn't? He was so angry I thought he was going to hit me, so I just held a knife to defend myself.

'Please will you make him let go of me so we can sit up and talk, calmly. I am afraid it's my husband who needs treatment.'

I was beginning to side with the wife; I hate violence. Here was this hulking man using physical force on her. Perhaps she had to defend herself. Anyway, I didn't like the way he had spoken to me on the telephone.

'Let your wife sit up,' I said.

'No,' he replied.

'Look,' I said, 'you have dragged me out on a Saturday afternoon – if you don't do as I say, then I shall just go and leave you to it.'

The commander reluctantly stood up, adjusting his suit that he had rumpled in the struggle.

His wife swung her legs down so she was sitting on the settee, took a compact out of her handbag, powdered her nose, touched up her hair, then smiled at me and said, 'Thank you, Doctor. It is nice to know that there is one gentleman in the house.'

I had a better look at her now: she really was extremely smart and very good looking. Poor thing, being married to such a husband.

The commander was pacing up and down. 'Doctor,' he said,

'do you realise I had to keep her tied up all last night?

'I insist that you send her to hospital.'

At the mention of the word hospital the wife was off the settee like a cat. A well-directed kick to the crotch had the commander down, and I was just in time to save him from a stiletto heel being driven into his skull.

I wrestled the shoe away and sat astride the wife, pinning her hands to the floor. She giggled, 'Do you do this often Doctor? Thank goodness I have at last managed to give that bastard what he deserves. Couldn't we sit somewhere comfortable?'

Still keeping a close grip on her I got up and led her to the settee. We sat facing each other with me still gripping her wrists.

'This is cosy, Doctor,' she said, smiling.

I couldn't help liking her, and the commander did look such an idiot groaning on the floor clutching his recently injured area.

'Look here,' said the wife, 'I've done my bit of protesting, I promise to behave now. I'll do whatever you suggest, but please could I have a cigarette and, much as I like you holding me, you are squeezing my wrists rather tightly.'

Thinking I was in control of the situation, I let go of her.

She sat rubbing her wrists thoughtfully for a minute, looked into my eyes, smiled – then punched me smack in the mouth.

I was just in time to stop her getting out of the window. 'Bloody pig!' she said. 'Didn't they tell you not to trust me?'

Suddenly I was completely on the commander's side.

We took it in turns to restrain her, whilst I made arrangements for a duly authorised officer to come. As GP I could not compulsorily order a patient to be admitted to hospital without the consent of a duly authorised officer; it was his job to do the actual committing. Our two regular officers were off duty, and I had to bring one in from some way away.

All the time we were holding the commander's wife she was sweet reasonableness. She had lost her battle, so would we let go of her?

Please could she have a cigarette?

43

She wanted to go to the toilet.

There was nothing doing. We sat firmly holding her on the settee.

I did not know the duly authorised officer who eventually arrived – he was younger than usual. Duly authorised officers who were well versed in general and mental nursing were rarely under the age of forty.

I watched this young man confidently go through the routine I had been through myself.

'You can release her now I'm here,' he said.

'Thank you, sir,' said the commander's wife. 'These two men are pigs – all I asked was to go and fetch my cigarettes.'

Like an attentive courtier the officer snapped open a cigarette case, and followed it up with a snappy lighter.

The commander's wife gave him her special intimate smile, drew deeply on her cigarette and blew the smoke out through her nose. Calm, collected, poised; as if she was a small island of sanity in a sea of idiots.

The officer was definitely on her side.

'Now what's all this about, Doctor?' said the officer. 'I was called urgently and I have come a very long way. So far I can see no reason for either the urgency or the need for my journey.'

The commander's wife literally beamed at her new champion.

I said, 'I must ask for an order for this lady for her immediate admission to hospital.'

As I said the word hospital, I was just able to duck in time to prevent the commander's wife sticking her lighted cigarette into my left eye.

'Now, my dear,' said the officer, as he put out a hand to restrain her. 'Remove your hand,' said the commander's wife ominously.

The officer had hardly mouthed his next 'Now, my dear', when the commander's wife put her head forward, sank her teeth into his thumb, jumped over the back of the settee, and was out through the open window and away.

'Quick, all outside,' said the commander. 'If we don't catch her she will be gone for days.'

'But my thumb is bleeding,' wailed the officer. 'Look, Doctor. Look at my thumb.'

I followed the commander outside. We scoured the grounds for half an hour, eventually finding his wife behind a laurel bush, quite close to the house, as if she wanted to be caught.

The duly authorised officer was still fussing about his thumb, now wrapped in a large handkerchief, when we returned.

He insisted that I gave him an anti-tetanus injection before he got on with formally committing the commander's wife to hospital.

Eventually a hospital car arrived and the commander's wife, accompanied by a very wary mental officer, drove away.

I sat for a while with the commander. 'The trouble is,' he said, 'in two weeks she will be practically running the hospital, and in a further two weeks they will send her home and it will start all over again.

'She used to be such a fine gel. Nobody seems to be able to help, or even tell me what it is.'

I felt terribly sorry for him as I left him sitting alone in his lovely house with its smashed kitchen. Poor chap, there are some types of mental illness that, as yet, we do not know how to cope with.

I subscribe to the belief that some mental conditions could be chemical or biochemical in origin and that, some day, simple remedies will be found. I take heart in the fact that disorders of the thyroid gland, too much and too little, were thought of as mental disorders until the working of the thyroid gland was understood and controlled.

I arrived home late, tired and worn; I had spent nearly seven hours all told at the commander's.

'Have you had an awful time?' Pam asked.

'Let's say it's been a struggle,' I replied.

*　　　*　　　*

But it wasn't only doctors who had to fight for a living.

John Denton, the local river bailiff, had a lot of trouble with professional poachers, especially during late spring and early summer.

They would come in small gangs by night, in cars or trucks, from as far away as London or Birmingham, armed with nets, snares, fish spears, searchlights, poison and sometimes explosives. For them it was strictly a commercial operation – they could bag dozens of salmon inside a few hours – and they had no scruples about clubbing down any bailiff or policeman who came across them.

Late one night in spring, John ran into such a gang. The first I knew of it was a phone call in the early hours.

'Bob, lad, would you mind coming out to the cottage? I've run into some villains and they've given me a fair old working over. They've hurt Biddy as well; she's in a worse state than I am, poor little sod.'

46

Biddy was John's collie – a soft-eyed, gentle bitch who went everywhere with him.

'What's the damage, do you think?' I asked.

'Couple of cracked ribs, Bob. And a broken leg.'

'God,' I said. 'I'll be right over. Make yourself comfortable. And don't move!'

I drove to the cottage as fast as I could and screeched to a stop outside the garden gate. The front door opened and there stood John, clutching his chest.

'What the hell are you playing at, John?' I yelled as I lugged out my bag. 'You shouldn't be moving with a broken leg!'

'Sorry, Bob,' he said. 'I realised as soon as I put the phone down. I've got the cracked ribs; Biddy's got the broken leg. Could you see to her first? I've phoned the vet, but he's out at a farm on an emergency.'

'OK,' I said. 'I'll treat Biddy first. But before that I'll give you a quick once-over just to make sure there are no complications setting in.'

'Complications? Such as what?'

'Such as death. Now stand there and shut up.'

Under the living-room light, John looked a lot worse than he had at the front door. He had caked blood on his scalp, a split lip and a red, green and purple eye. When he took off his shirt there was more: quite extensive bruising around the ribs and abdomen. ('Abdomen' is the polite medical term for what ballooned out over John's trousers when he took his shirt off.)

The ribs on his left side were obviously painful and almost certainly damaged. But the kidneys seemed to have missed the worst of the onslaught. John would live all right. He could be left safely for a while to sit in the armchair and kill the pain with a bottle of Scotch. Biddy, I wasn't so sure about.

'Tell me what happened, John,' I said. 'It will help me to look after Biddy.'

'I got word at the last knockings in the pub that there were villains on the river,' said John. 'Real villains. Offcomers.

'It would have been sensible to go through the proper channels – ring the police and all that – but round here you know

47

what happens: what the hell could Charlie Willis do that I couldn't?'

Police Constable Charles Redvers Willis was the local equivalent of the Flying Squad. He was getting on and creaking a bit and his pushbike wasn't much better.

'It was no use swearing in a posse at the Tadchester Arms, either. You should have seen the state of 'em. I'd have left half of 'em in the river. So, daft-like – and I admit I'd had a few – I decided to sort it out myself.'

'And?'

'They sorted me out. I never learn. There were five or six of 'em.'

'Would you recognise them again?'

'Two of 'em I would. One's got my knuckle prints right across his nose. And he's the one that kicked Biddy. I'd seen to him when his mate came up behind and dropped me. "Broken Nose" got up and the pair of 'em put the boot in. That's when Biddy came in like a good 'un, but that bastard Broken Nose kicked her twice, once in the leg and then in the belly. Then they ran off.

'If it hadn't been for Biddy, they might very well have done for me. She was carrying, you know. And she dropped her pups where she lay. Six of 'em. She was nowhere near full term, thank God, but it was bad enough. I wiped her down, best I could, then carried her home. And that's when I rang you. I've rung the police since. Happen they might pick the bastards up.'

I looked at Biddy and felt gently along her smashed hind leg. When my fingers reached the break, it obviously hurt. But she uttered no more than a stifled whimper and let me carry on. Both back legs were caked with dried blood and mucus from the loss of the pups.

I am slow to come to the boil. In my job you have to be. But I knew what I would have done if the poachers were brought before me at that moment; the thought was quite frightening.

I cleaned Biddy's hindquarters and then set the leg in the splints and pads I'd brought for John. I prided myself that I'd

48

done a good job, particularly on a patient who could not speak and whose indications of pain were muted because she knew I was doing my clumsy best. She would be as comfortable as I could make her until Andrew Thomas, the vet, could call round.

Biddy's trusting eyes reinforced my respect for vets. They are called out to attend to everything from an egg-bound budgie to a miscarrying cow, and have to do their job entirely without the question-and-answer routine which gives general practitioners the vital clues to what might be wrong.

Doctors deal with one species. Vets deal with dozens, from one end of the evolutionary scale to the other. What they do is backed by a very thorough training, but in the last analysis they have to rely on a certain amount of instinct and an ability to think themselves into the mind of the animal they are treating. It is a sensitivity I would be proud to own.

After treating Biddy, I cleaned and dressed John's cuts and bruises, strapped up his ribs and put his left arm in a sling to restrict potentially painful movement. After a Scotch and a few reassuring words for John, I drove back home to bed and collapsed into merciful sleep.

I was off duty the next day, and made the most of it by sleeping late. About noon the bedside telephone extension rang. Pam intercepted the call downstairs then came up to the bedroom. 'I'm sorry, darling, it's the police, I couldn't put them off.'

I picked up the telephone.

'Dr Clifford? Inspector Downing here, Tadchester Constabulary. I'd be grateful if you could call round to the station to attend to a casualty. Broken collar bone, I think. I understand you may be familiar with the background: John Denton and the poachers he ran into last night.'

'I'll be round straightaway,' I said. 'But how did John come to break a collar bone?'

'He didn't. Somebody else did. You'll understand when you get here.'

Muttering uncomplimentary things about John, I pulled on

my clothes, didn't bother to wash, shave, or even clean my teeth, and drove blearily to what was known familiarly as the Tadchester Nick.

'Thanks for coming so promptly, Doctor,' said the Inspector. 'The patient is in here.'

He led me down a corridor to one of a row of cells. Inside sat a large, unappetising character with a strip of sticking plaster across his nose and a left arm supported by a regulation first-aid sling.

'We strapped him up as best we could,' said the Inspector. 'But I'd be happier if he had some professional attention.'

'I think I know what happened,' I said. 'Where's John?'

'In the next cell until he cools down. You can see him when you've finished.'

I strapped up the collar bone and immobilised the arm – almost unnecessarily, since the constable who had administered first aid obviously knew what he was doing. The Inspector took me into the interview room to tell me the full story.

'After John had telephoned last night, we put the word out to the County lads. They're a bit more mobile than we are; they've got cars that work. As it happened, they'd already stopped a van and found it full of fish-snatching gear and suspicious-looking characters. Including one whose nose had come into contact with something large and heavy.'

'Such as John's fist?'

'Such as John's fist. Anyway, they brought the whole kit and caboodle down here and this morning we got John over for an identification parade. I suppose you get that feeling now and again, that you wished you'd never got out of bed?'

'Often,' I said. 'And this sounds like being another time.'

It had been a big identification parade. There were five suspects altogether, and the police had a job to muster enough villainous-looking Tadchester residents to swell the ranks. But with the help of six or so hung-over holidaymakers, some hung-over drunks who had been held overnight, and a few ex-miners from Thudrock, they managed it.

John was brought in as the only witness.

'If you recognise anyone, place your hand on his shoulder,' said the Inspector.

'My hand?' said John.

'Your hand,' said the Inspector.

'On his shoulder?' said John.

'On his shoulder,' said the Inspector.

'Right,' said John.

Walking stiffly and painfully, John approached a large man with a strip of sticking plaster across his nose. Other large men in the parade had also been decorated with sticking plaster, but John never forgot a face. Especially one he had seen so recently and had so much cause to remember.

He reached the man, raised his right hand and smashed the palm into the man's left shoulder. The man crashed back against the wall.

'That's for Biddy,' said John. Apparently so quietly and coldly that it sent a shiver up the spine of even the hardened Inspector.

'And that's for her pups,' said John, smashing his giant hand again into the man's shoulder as he rebounded from the wall.

The man finished up writhing on the floor, his collar bone smashed, and John stepped back.

'Right lads,' he said to the startled policemen, for whom everything had happened too quickly for them to move in. 'That's all the identifying I'm doing. You can take me away now – only don't put me in the same cell as that bloody swine. Not if you want two for court in the morning.'

'We had to tell the poacher that he was perfectly entitled to prefer charges for assault against John,' said Inspector Downing. 'But once he realised what he'd done to the dog, he understood John's feelings. He's got a bitch of his own, apparently, and he would have done just the same. It'll be in his favour at the trial, even though it won't be mentioned. A nod is as good as a wink and all that.

'Once you've seen John, we'll let him out. He's feeling a bit

51

sorry for himself. He's a big lad, conscious of his own strength, and he doesn't like to think he let his temper run away with him.'

'Sounds like John,' I said. 'How's Biddy?'

'Could be worse. Andrew Thomas saw her this morning. She's in a bad way, but she'll pull through. He told me to tell you, by the way, that your splinting job wasn't at all bad – for a doctor.'

'That's the finest compliment I've ever been paid,' I said. And I meant it.

'Morning, Bob,' said John, sitting bolt upright on the bench in Cell 3 and trying to ease the pain in his ribs. 'Sorry you've got involved again.'

'I'd have thought you'd have had enough, John,' I said. 'Couldn't you just let the law take its course? That's what it's for.'

'I know,' said John. 'The law will see to those buggers for

stealing the fish. But it won't do much for Biddy. All I did was to redress the balance a bit; sort of thumping by proxy. The two clouts I gave that feller were for Biddy and her pups. I had time to give him three – one for me as well – but I turned the other cheek.

'Did I ever tell you I was a pacifist. . . ?'

CHAPTER 5

Peargate

The small town of Peargate lies on a corner between Sanford-on-Sea and Tadchester, hemmed in on two sides by the River Tad before the Tad goes out to the estuary to meet the River Trip and the sea.

Facing Peargate across the Tad lies the holiday village of Stowin. There had been talk for many years of a bridge to link these two places but the expense of such a project made it quite impracticable. While the Councils of both places interminably debated the possibilities of a bridge, Jones Bros capitalised on the lack of direct communication by running an hourly ferry across the river.

Peargate was a boatbuilding town. Boats had been built there since time immemorial. The boatyard had sometimes changed hands, craft had often varied in size, but boatbuilding continued there and probably always would.

The peak of activity was during the Second World War when landing craft were produced by the hundred. Although Peargate shipyards did produce some large ships, they specialised mainly in boats of tugboat size and smaller.

The main yards were in the town near the dock. Up the river, towards Tadchester, there were smaller, family boatbuilding yards that specialised in pleasure craft, rowing boats and small fishing boats. Tadchester, not to be outdone, had its own yard to the east of the town where sophisticated hydrofoils were built.

Peargate could claim more pubs to the square yard than any other part of the Somerset coast. Although a few of the terraced houses were being taken over as holiday homes, the vast majority of Peargate people were the product of many generations who had lived in the same houses. They were a close-knit community, excellent smugglers and fishermen.

Peargate architecture was unique: a maze of narrow streets, each with a low-level drain running down the centre. The houses were in long terraces with back-to-back yards. The streets themselves were so narrow that a car could only just get along one way, the sides of the car almost brushing the windows and house doors.

Main drainage had improved the sanitation problems and made the central street drains unnecessary. However, many a noisy reveller had the contents of a chamberpot thrown over him as he walked down the street, which not only quietened him but illustrated the previous function of the central drains.

In spite of the fact that Peargate was smaller than Tadchester, there was tremendous rivalry between the two towns. Both had their own regatta, each advertised the event as the most important regatta in the west of England. Peargatians thought of Tadchester men as farmers and colliers. *They* were the only real sailors.

One sailor who sailed out of Peargate was Jonathan Blake. He was a captain and master mariner and responsible for the sea trials on all the new diesel tugs. He was a small, quiet man with a sharp, pointed beard, a completely bald head, and a weary look on his face as if he had all the world's troubles on his shoulders, which for most of the time I knew him, he usually had.

I met him soon after he arrived in Tadchester from Devonport to take up his appointment with Peargate Shipbuilders. He had arrived with five children who he somehow managed to look after on his own. I was introduced to him when he bought the house belonging to Gladys, our senior receptionist. Gladys had shared the large house with her mother. After her mother died, she moved into a flat near the surgery.

I could never work out how Jonathan Blake coped. He saw me fairly regularly in the surgery for odd aches and pains, indigestion or insomnia, all minor ailments that masked the real problem: that the situation he had on his hands was more than he could manage.

His wife had deserted him. Before deserting him, she had caused him an awful lot of worry by being wantonly promiscuous. She was quite happy to leave him to bring up their five children, three girls and two boys, whose ages then ranged from the youngest boy of four to the eldest girl of fourteen. Somehow between them they managed to do the cooking, the washing and the ironing. There was little outside help available and it was doubtful if Jonathan could have afforded it if there had been.

The two boys wet the bed every night, which must have considerably increased the laundry bill, and the general state of the house was chaotic.

Jonathan Blake's duties at the shipyard meant that when there was some new type of engine or new type of tug, he would have to go off on sea trials. Then, when the boat was ready, he would have to deliver it to the new owner and break in the crew. This meant being away from home for anything between three and six weeks. While he was away, one of the neighbours would usually keep an eye on the children. They were an unruly lot and very easily got out of hand.

When the eldest daughter became pregnant at the age of fifteen, fortunately it was by a boy who had a reasonable job and who was prepared to marry her and set up home. It meant one child less for Jonathan, but it also meant that the female head of the household had gone, thus increasing the strain on his domestic responsibilities. He would come to my surgery almost blank with fatigue, only some inner force keeping him going.

Jonathan looked desperately for another mate, as much to help with his domestic duties as to share his bed. When he could get a night off, he would go to singles clubs and dances. He had one or two near misses and one or two narrow escapes until

57

he began an intermittent affair with Sarah. Sarah was twenty-eight and had three children of her own. She was also under-going psychiatric treatment. That was Jonathan's kind of luck.

He used to discuss his lady friends with me but it was some time before I actually met Sarah. There had been a lot of to-ing and fro-ing, but eventually Sarah was installed in his home, adding her three children to his four.

At first the domestic side of the household improved but, as Sarah was prone to nervous breakdowns, she had to be admitted periodically to hospital, leaving Jonathan with seven children on his hands. He appeared to be a born loser, a sucker for punishment. But he seemed to be able to stagger on from one disaster to the next.

When Jonathan was away, Sarah was in nominal charge of the household. Mark, the elder boy, resented her. He was growing up now and did not enjoy having six brothers and sisters as opposed to three. He was a restless boy and had all sorts of brushes and problems with school authorities and the police. Mark was about sixteen when Jonathan was away on a five-week trip delivering a boat to Denmark. He had been found breaking into the local sports club and the police were called. There were various other troubles, including his inter-fering with a young girl.

A phone call from Sarah brought me news of the crisis.

Her solution to any problem was to get psychiatric help. She considered that psychiatrists were her personal friends. If Mark had been stealing, then he must see a psychiatrist. Police calling at her home were likely only to aggravate her own nervous trouble.

I did manage to get a psychiatrist to do a domiciliary consul-tation on Mark and the household in general. It was only when I received his report that I appreciated fully the home situ-ation. Sarah had thought the crisis would be helped if she took stepson Mark to bed with her and comforted him by making him her lover. She even thought that Jonathan would be pleased at how she had handled the situation.

Sarah brought Mark with her to see me at the surgery. I

could hardly recognise him. Apart from the fact that he had his best suit on, he looked tired, with bags under his eyes, and terribly bewildered. Sarah, on the other hand, was blooming, dressed up to the nines.

'Doctor,' she said, 'I have had a marvellous realisation. I have been talking to my father from his grave, and life is better than it has ever been, and I don't want it to stop. Mark has only to hold my hand and all my vibes go. I have second sight; I can read people's minds. Although I am twenty-eight, my mind is that of a woman of fifty, and my body has returned to that of a girl of sixteen.

'That is,' she concluded, 'apart from my stretch marks.'

For more than half an hour she stumbled on, attempting to tell me something, with no real idea of what she was trying to say. It was all disjointed and senseless. It was a reflection of the guilt she felt about taking Mark to bed and the worry that at some stage she would have to face the issue of his father coming home. They left the surgery with their problems unresolved.

The next night I was off duty and out at a Round Table meeting. Sarah telephoned, wanting to speak to me. Pam, used to patients by now, fended her off.

Half an hour later Sarah rang again, saying that she wasn't a patient but a personal friend of mine. Could I speak to her? Again, Pam told her I was not there.

I learnt the full story from Jack Hart the next day. He had been called by Sarah after she failed to contact me and he was left with little alternative but to get her into hospital. When she got there, having agreed to go in, she refused to be admitted. 'I have no money,' she said, 'otherwise I would quite happily go in as a voluntary patient.'

Jack Hart duly forked out £5, but when Sarah found that she could not take Mark into hospital to share her bed, she refused again.

Over the next few hours her condition gradually deteriorated. She thought she was God and had a divine message to pass, forgiving people for their sins. Eventually she had to be admitted to hospital under a compulsory order after an awful, undignified struggle, with strait jackets and tranquillising injections.

Three days later Jonathan Blake and Mark came to see me at the surgery. Jonathan had managed to get himself flown back from Denmark. He had his usual worried frown.

'I'm still trying to sort this out, Doctor,' he said. 'It's all my fault. I'll just have to fix it that I don't go away again.'

My heart bled for him. In spite of the fact that his common-law wife had just been bedding down with his elder son, had made yet one further incursion into hospital for mental break-down, with nothing to suggest that her mental instability would ever be any different, Jonathan was determined to have her home again in his chaotic household where each disaster was only a preparation for a bigger one.

Nobody could help them. We had offered every possible fa-cility available under the National Health Service and various voluntary organisations. The whole situation was a tremen-dous education to me. How *did* people in Jonathan Blake's pos-ition somehow get up and keep on going? I wondered what eventually would become of the children. As they grew older and left home, would they re-create this same environment for themselves? Where did any of them find the incentive to go on living in this complete chaos?

But when I looked back I remembered times when Jona-than's family were as happy as sandboys, when the eldest daughter's baby was christened, when they were all planning to go on a camping holiday.

I talked to wise old Steve about it.

'You must remember, Bob,' he said, 'that all people are dif-ferent and seek their own satisfactions in their own way. But,' he said with a smile, 'some are more different than others. I think you could put the Blakes in this category...'

*　　　*　　　*

Another patient who fitted well into Steve's 'different' category was Miss Monica Patterson, a spinster in her early fifties who lived in No. 5 Railway Cottages, close to Tadchester Station.

60

There were seven cottages in all and their description belied their elegant appearance. They were originally grace-and-favour houses built by the Great Western Railway for their more senior employees in south Somerset.

Although the GWR had disappeared with nationalisation, the residual families of the favoured employees were allowed to continue living there. Monica's elderly mother was the actual tenant of No. 5; Monica herself would be safe as a sitting tenant after her mother's death, as she worked in the local office of British Rail.

The health of old Mrs. Patterson merited regular fortnightly, or at least monthly, calls, and my visits to No. 5 were always traumatic. When Monica was at home, she kept up a constant tirade about her mother, saying what a cross she was to bear. Although she wished her no ill, she said, she hoped the Good Lord would take her quietly in her sleep.

When the old lady was on her own, she kept up a tirade about Monica: she never did anything round the house, she would never eat, she spent all her time smoking and drinking, and left her old mother to prepare the food, not only for themselves but also for the assortment of cats in the household.

It took me some time to realise that it was old Mrs. Patterson who was keeping the household together and doing most of the cooking and cleaning. Her eyesight was very poor and she had difficulty in getting about. She was, however, a lady of some dignity. When her husband was alive she had been able to travel all over Britain because of the special facilities offered by the railway to its employees. She was well informed, well read, well groomed, and just despaired of her daughter.

Monica was thin, round shouldered, sloppily dressed, with long, untidy hair, nicotine-stained lips and always had a cigarette, lit or unlit, hanging from the corner of her mouth.

I was always trying to encourage her to give up smoking and to eat a bit more. This usually brought a sharp retort: 'I'll stop smoking when you give your pipe up, and I'll start eating when I see you have lost a bit of weight. I wouldn't like to look like you.'

That, I thought, was a bit below the belt. Admittedly, Pam's cooking and the contentment of married life had filled out my former whippet-like outline, and my smelly old pipe might not have appealed to everybody, but I *was* the doctor, damn it.

It was an uphill struggle keeping old Mrs. Patterson going. She was coming up to ninety. I think the main reasons for her longevity were two driving ambitions – one was actually to reach the age of ninety, and the other to outlive (for some old and bitter family feud reasons) a sister-in-law.

'I want to see *her* off,' said Mrs. Patterson. 'I would also like to see the cats happily at rest before I go. I know Monica won't miss me.'

It was an unhappy household, with the daughter waiting for her mother to die to allow her to make some effort to shape her own life.

I had to admit Mrs. Patterson to hospital a couple of times but she somehow survived the worst bouts. When she was away, Monica almost stopped eating altogether and relied on nicotine and alcohol to keep her going.

On one of my routine visits to the house I was greeted by a beaming Mrs. Patterson.

'Guess what?' she said. 'My sister-in-law died yesterday.'

Forty-eight hours later I was called by Monica. She had found her mother dead in bed.

Mrs. Patterson had a look so serene that she had come as near to dying with a smile on her face as anyone I have ever seen. I wondered what had caused this bitter feud between her and her sister-in-law, but now I would never know.

Mrs. Patterson had achieved only one of her ambitions. She was still eleven days short of her ninetieth birthday.

I worried about what Monica would make of her life with her mother gone. Her dress and gait were so slovenly that I wondered how useful she was as an employee. Although there was no medical need to visit Monica, I used to pop in from time to time just to make sure that she was eating. My suspicions about her worth as an employee were confirmed six months after her mother died, when Monica was retired prematurely.

Without her mother and without the discipline of work, Monica steadily deteriorated in just about every way. She seemed to have no friends. Anybody who tried to help her got a very sharp rebuff. I would find her sitting in a chair, smoking, with a few bottles of drink by her side. When I tried to encourage her to take an interest in things outside the house she would respond sharply: 'I'll live my own life in my own way, Doctor, thank you very much. I just want to outlive the cats, then it's a handful of sleeping pills and I'm out of this world.'

Monica did less and less. Her sharp tongue gradually cut her off from almost all offers of help. Only one selfless neighbour struggled on to do things for her.

There were reports of Monica being found drunk in the street, but when I questioned her about her bruises, she said she had fallen down the stairs.

Twice she had to be admitted to hospital for attacks of pneumonia. She discharged herself as soon as she was on her feet. 'They wouldn't let me smoke in my oxygen tent,' was her chief complaint.

Relatives called and offered to take her back with them. She refused. She became even slacker both in her personal hygiene and her dress. Her clothes were stained and the general air of offensiveness was such that the pubs she used to visit, one by one, refused to serve her. It was exactly like the latter half of *The Rake's Progress* – a remorseless deterioration of body and mind.

She was continually falling. In one of her falls, she broke her hip. I had hoped a longer stay in hospital would give her time to pick up, but she came home looking more emaciated, hardly able to walk, having once more discharged herself against medical advice.

In a way, I was quite fond of her. She didn't make life easy for me, and had deteriorated into an awful, filthy mess. But she always enquired about my own health and that of the family, scolded me for working too hard and encouraged me to take things easier.

Though the hip had mended, there was some limitation of

her walking and she moved even less often. She would sit in her armchair, surrounded by bottles of booze, cigarettes and a few bars of chocolate, with a cat on her knee.

I found calls to Nature no longer roused her enough to leave her chair. I made the mistake one day of sitting on a chair she had recently vacated, to feel rising damp penetrating my own trousers after I had been sitting for a few minutes. It meant I had to go home, change, and send my trousers to be cleaned. This was an experience I had had before with much older patients: with Monica it was a horrifying sign of premature degeneration.

I arranged for the district nurse to come every day to attend to Monica. The one faithful neighbour still came in each day also, but I could not stop the decline. Most of the brass and assorted pottery that her mother had so proudly displayed round the house began to disappear as Monica sold them to keep up with the cost of her drinking and smoking. The electric fire was kept burning day and night, with the Electricity Board pressing for payment of bills which she made no attempt to settle.

She lingered on somehow, still bright enough to tell me off, but slowly and progressively getting weaker, until she lapsed into coma and was once more admitted to hospital.

It was after she had been admitted for what, in fact, turned out to be her last illness, I learnt the full story of Monica.

'She wasn't always like this, you know, Doctor,' said Mrs. Wilkinson, her neighbour. 'She used to be very smart. She was away on Government service during the war. When she came back to the railway, she had a friend here at work ... a very good looking woman. They used to have a right wild time of it. They were inseparable, always went everywhere together. They had planned to retire a bit early and share a home. Then one week her friend gave in her notice, left the district and went off to live with a lady solicitor.'

It was from then on, apparently, that Monica started to go downhill. She had never mentioned any of this to me, if indeed she had discussed it with anyone.

It all made sense now – the deterioration, lack of will to live, lack of interest. Monica had been suffering from a broken heart – broken by another woman.

Monica never regained consciousness and died three days after this last admission to hospital. But she still had one surprise in store.

Mrs. Wilkinson came to see me. 'There is a letter for you, Doctor, left by Monica in case she died.'

I opened the letter. It was the real old Monica again.

'Doctor Bob,' she wrote, 'You have got to do something for me. You know better than anyone else what a useless life I have led these last years. I want you to make certain that my body is left for medical science. Just make sure you get on with it. I can, perhaps, at last do something useful for somebody.'

Then followed strict instructions that there was to be no funeral.

There was a PS: 'Thank you for looking after me.'

I had never arranged for anyone's body to be used for medical science before; usually the deceased had arranged it beforehand.

I found it far from easy, I rang several of the teaching hospitals and they were not interested. If Monica had had some obscure condition, they would have been very interested, but the poor woman had just died of neglect.

I rang the anatomy professor at my own hospital and explained the position. He at first said no, then, when I said she had left this express message and he was my last hope, he replied 'Right ho.' I was able to leave it to him to see that her body was transferred to the anatomy dissection room, where students could learn from her poor, wasted form.

I was so pleased and relieved that I had at last been able to arrange this. Somewhere, I could sense Monica smiling. Once again, and for the last time, she had had her own way. Some young and hopeful medical student, setting out to become a doctor, would now have a sounder base from which to go on and do his clinical medicine. Thanks to Monica.

What better memorial could anyone have?

CHAPTER 6

Innocents Abroad

Pam's father, Gerry, had been a lost soul since the death of his wife. He found it extremely difficult to settle down without her. He came over to us and stayed frequently but refused to come and live with us permanently, saying that we had our own lives to lead and he did not want to interfere.

His delightful wife, Bill, had died of cancer just four days before our daughter Jane was born.

Gerry lived at Winchcombe, fifteen miles away, and drove back and forth along the estuary road to see us. He still played his violin with various orchestras but, as he had only moved down from Leatherhead to Winchcombe a few years before, he had few local friends and depended on us a great deal for his social life.

When we visited him we could see that the general care and upkeep of his house was beginning to deteriorate; it lacked a woman's touch and was really more than he could manage. After a great deal of thought he decided to advertise for a housekeeper. He put an advertisement in *The Lady* and one or two other magazines. It must have been one of the very few advertisements ever for a musical housekeeper. It read: 'Housekeeper wanted. Must be a proficient piano player.' Gerry wanted somebody to accompany him with his violin.

During the next few weeks he travelled all over the south-west of England interviewing potential housekeepers. He came back after one particular sortie saying, 'She was a fine woman ... lovely home ... cooked a marvellous meal ... but when I asked her to sit down at the piano, she banged out "Home, Sweet Home". I wouldn't have her touch my piano.' Gerry had a baby grand that was his pride and joy, although he never played it. It was destined for Pam when he no longer wanted it.

At last, Gerry found himself a housekeeper – Vera – a diminutive, rather quiet woman who came from South Wales. It was all fixed up without our help. And Vera was a good piano player! What we did not find out until later was that she was a hopeless cook and knew nothing about housekeeping.

Gerry had been quite happy about this and was fully aware of it. 'I'll do the cooking and cleaning,' he said, 'providing she plays the piano properly.' He had never suffered fools gladly, and we were very worried for Vera's sake because she had sold up house and home and her own piano to join him.

It worked marvellously for the first month. As far as I could gather, they played music virtually all day, with Gerry nipping off to prepare food between bars. After that we saw the relationship gradually deteriorate.

In all, the association lasted four months. We liked Vera. She was an unobtrusive, pleasant woman and I think she had an awful time.

We did not even hear that they had parted until Gerry came over one day and airily said, 'Oh, I gave her a week's notice a fortnight ago. I don't know where she has gone.'

'Why did you do it?' we asked, feeling concerned that Gerry was now back to square one.

'Well, listen to this,' he said.

He produced a tape recorder from his pocket, and on it was a recording of them both at practice.

The recording was awful. There was a strident, out-of-time violin playing discordant notes which were held together by virtue of finely balanced piano playing from someone with an immaculate touch.

Gerry was not nearly as good on the violin as he used to be. I think he entered another world as soon as he picked up his bow, and his faculties for criticising his own playing seemed to be the first thing he left behind.

'Well? What do you think of it?' asked Gerry.

'I have heard better,' I answered, guardedly.

'I should think so,' said Gerry. 'She was bloody awful. Just not up to my standard. She had to go.'

Poor Vera. We did not know where she had gone. Somewhere she would be trying to set up home again, and without her cherished piano that Gerry had made her sell before she joined him.

We racked our brains about how to cope with Gerry and looked at properties nearby so we could keep a closer eye on him. In the end it was Eric who made the suggestion.

'You have plenty of land down here by the river,' he said. 'Why don't you tack on a flat for your father-in-law?'

It meant knocking down one or two precious trees, but Gerry was all fired with the idea. After planning permission and the usual ups and downs of dealing with bureaucracy, we began to build a bungalow with a door into the side of our house. It had a kitchen, bathroom and bedroom, a separate garage for his car and a huge picture window in the lounge, overlooking the estuary.

The building work seemed to go on for ever. There was dirt and mud that daily found its way into the house. Gerry came over every day, breathing down the workmen's necks.

*   *   *

Finally it was done, and he moved in. By this time we were all in a state of complete exhaustion. We needed a holiday. Pam yearned for the sunshine. Jane was a bit too young to take abroad, but we knew that Zara, her godmother, would take care of her.

John Bowler offered to lend us a Volkswagen dormobile which would sleep four.

Our friends Peter and Jane Churchill offered us the use of a villa in Grasse for a week, and we planned a circuitous route down to the French Riviera, spending the middle of the holiday in the villa.

Gerry looked on wistfully as we made our arrangements.

'I've always wanted to go on a trip like that to France,' he said '... and I'd like to see Peter and Jane again. I'd pay my share of expenses.'

We had little alternative but to ask him to join us, so signed him on as ballast, philosopher and financial backer.

We had the Volkswagen for a few days before we left. John Bowler had assured us that it would cruise effortlessly down French motorways at more than sixty miles an hour and we could do five hundred miles a day without really trying.

At last the great day came for our departure, the boys jumping around with excitement – they had never been abroad before. It was a wrench leaving Jane with Zara, but we knew she would be well looked after. So we all climbed aboard and set off for Southampton.

The Volkswagen was so easy to drive. The driver was high above the road with a good view of all that was going on, and the passengers could sit comfortably round a table in the back – very similar to a dining compartment of a railway carriage.

Cards and other games could be played on the table and, with the stove at the back, a running buffet and refreshments could be served all the time.

There was a small luggage rack on the roof and, as usual, we travelled heavily. We piled up the rack with folding seats, cricket bats and tennis rackets, and a tent. The luggage rack was right over the driver's seat and, with the accumulated pile set on top, in distant silhouette we looked like a four-wheeled unicorn.

The sleeping space in the van was limited, hence the tent. The idea was that Pam and I would sleep in the body of the vehicle, with the table and everything collapsed to make a bed. This was Pam's particular bête noire: the more we collapsed things, the less room we seemed to have, and we ended up almost standing on our heads before we got some sort of order out of the blankets and mattresses, knowing that we would have to take them all up in the morning and repeat the procedure the next night.

The boys were to sleep on two stretchers under the canvas canopy which could be extended above the top of the Volkswagen. The stretchers were similar to railway luggage racks but narrower and more uncomfortable. Gerry was to sleep in the tent.

We crossed the Channel by night ferry and arrived at Le Havre at seven in the morning, with a whole day's driving ahead.

With a bad experience of a camping trip to Spain behind me, I had selected a superior, five-star-plus site near Vichy for our first night in France.

Vichy is only about 350 miles from Le Havre. Knowing the capabilities of the machine I was driving, I knew that the journey would pass like a flash. I had noticed in England how smoothly the vehicle went, and we had clocked a steady 35 miles an hour. I was now looking forward to letting it rip on the straight French roads.

I kept a gentle cruising speed until we were clear of Le Havre. Then, with an endless, straight, wide road ahead of me,

I plunged the accelerator into the floor and waited for the Volkswagen to take off.

Our speed rose steadily – 35, 36, 37, 38, 39, 40 miles an hour. The wind was whistling past the windows. Then a slight upward slope. With my foot still pressed down the speed registered 40, 39, 38, 37, 36, 35 – and this was the fastest the damn thing would go.

I looked forward to a full and frank exchange of views with John Bowler when I got back, but I realised that this was three weeks and many wearisome miles away.

To make our scheduled spot, we had to drive solidly all day, hardly daring to stop for refreshment, and eventually arrived in Vichy at about eight o'clock that night.

It was Easter, there was a bit of a nip in the air, and we looked round hungrily for this super camping site. There was a restaurant marked in the guide so we would not be cooking this evening. We followed the signs expectantly. As it grew darker the signs led us to a field containing one caravan.

I checked and rechecked. No mistake. This was the camping site with all the stars. The closed grey buildings at the far end of the field must have been the restaurant, showers and shop. I checked my guide once more and discovered what was wrong: the site did not open until June.

*   *   *

I was weary and saddlesore; the children were cold, hungry and fractious. Gerry, on his first camping holiday, at the age of seventy-five, was beginning to look a bit grey round the lips. I started to put up his tent whilst he sat shivering in the driving seat of the Volkswagen. I put up a camp bed in the tent and zipped two sleeping bags together on top. I undressed Gerry, who had now stiffened in his long johns, threaded him into the sleeping bag and pushed a hot water bottle in with him. I gave him a huge tot of whisky and zipped up the tent ... wondering whether he would still be with us in the morning.

I stumbled back in pitch darkness to the Volkswagen to find

Pam in hysterics, trying to make a bed on the floor of the vehicle. On the front seat the boys were whimpering that they were cold, tired and hungry . . . and when could they go to bed? Please?

Eventually we got everybody sorted out, had a cup of coffee made from the rest of the water in the kettle that had been boiled for Gerry's hot water bottle, and settled down for the night.

I woke to a chilly morning, with a watery sun shining through the mist. The children were stirring. By lighting a little cooking stove in the van we soon created enough fug to make it warm enough to get dressed.

I had to face the question of whether Gerry was still alive. I walked to his tent to find it empty.

'Oh, God!' I thought. 'What next?'

In the distance I could see something bobbing up and down above the waist-high boards of the gentlemen's urinals so dear to the French. It was the top half of Gerry. Thank God. Presumably both halves were alive and functioning.

We put up a table outside for breakfast. Gerry, to whom food was very important, walked up and down, beating his arms on his chest, with a small dribble of saliva from one corner of his mouth in anticipation of the forthcoming bacon and eggs.

Gerry was one of those rare people who prefer to eat standing up. On this occasion he excelled himself, standing at a table in the middle of a French field with the spring sun shining on him, dressed in a peaked cloth cap, tweed overcoat, red and white spotted bow tie, yellow cardigan, and black leather gloves.

Nattily attired, he stood eating his bacon and eggs with relish. A passing Frenchman on a bike almost dropped off in astonishment. '*Ces Anglais!*' he muttered. Yes, we could still show them a thing or two . . .

After a wander round Vichy we packed up and headed for Avignon. The further we travelled south, the warmer it became, and we began to pass through vineyard country, with rows and rows of grape-covered hills – or what would be grape-covered hills, for at this time of year the vines were just short

brown sticks, like thousands of small soldiers standing in order, waiting to be reviewed.

For the first time since we had left Southampton I began to feel cheerful, but had my cheerfulness cut short by Gerry. I am no mechanic, but Gerry had once run a garage of his own. He sowed a seed of doubt in my mind about whether the foot brake was working properly. I was sure it was, but once having been unsettled I was testing the brake every few minutes and knew that I would be apprehensive until we had made our night stop. I also knew that Gerry would not settle until we had the whole thing re-checked by the Volkswagen agent – if there was one – in Avignon. Knowing Gerry, this could easily put us a day behind schedule.

I approached Avignon heartened by the sunshine but chilled with the thought that the next camp site was one star less than the miserable site at Vichy.

I checked in the guide. The site was supposed to be open all the year round, but I had begun to lose confidence in myself as a planner.

We found the place easily. It was spacious, the sun was still shining, there were trees and green grass, and all the things the Vichy site hadn't – a shop, showers, toilets, and a restaurant.

The blueness had started to leave Gerry's lips as we reached the warmer climate. He now had two dribbles of saliva, one in each corner of his mouth, brought on by the knowledge that we were going to dine at a French restaurant that night. To mark the improvement in our situation he deigned to take off his tweed overcoat, but firmly stuck to his cap, bow tie and leather gloves.

We chose a pleasant spot to pitch our tent, and parked the Volkswagen. There was hardly anyone in the camping site. We went up to the restaurant in the evening and had the full works: potage, moules marinière, rosbif and chips, a dessert and some delicious Camembert, all accompanied by a litre of wine and followed by coffee.

It was the first proper meal we had had for a couple of days. Trevor and Paul managed to make two mountains of chips disappear, diluted with several bottles of Coca-Cola. Gerry was able to bed himself down this night. He was improving.

Next morning Gerry and I shunted around Avignon for the Volkswagen agent. Eventually we found the garage, who thought the brakes were perfectly all right. Gerry, however, insisted that they should be bled and a whole day was wasted going through this unnecessary procedure. The frustrated workman who carried out the bleeding operation under Gerry's eagle eye must have thought he'd got a right couple of bleeders here.

In a happier frame of mind we set off the next day for the Mediterranean coast. I now accepted that we would be flashing through the countryside at 35 miles an hour and once I had reconciled myself to the idea, it made the driving that much easier. I still could not get Gerry to take his cap off.

We wanted to camp as near to the sea as possible and found the most delightful, tree-lined camping site in the beautiful little bay of Agay, halfway between St Raphael and Cannes.

We pitched our tent twenty yards from the water and parked

the Volkswagen next to it. Here we had everything – a restaurant, bar, clothes washing-machine, washing-up places, showers, and a shop, as well as the sun and the sea. It was even warm enough for Gerry to take off his cardigan and jacket, but he stubbornly stuck to his cap and gloves. The only time on the whole trip he had been without these two protectors was when we had our meal at the restaurant in Avignon. Even then I had to remind him to take them off before he sat down.

'This holiday's getting better all the time,' he said.

We had several days in this camping site, exploring the villages nearby and on day trips to St Tropez and St Raphael. The sea was cold but we all managed (except Gerry, of course) to have a swim. I think he felt that if he had gone into the water his cap and gloves would never have dried out.

We then packed up the tent and Volkswagen and travelled north-east to Le Rouret, a village near Grasse, where Peter and Jane Churchill were providing a villa for us.

The sun-bathed villa was picturesque: there were grapes on the outside walls, olive trees in the garden, and Gerry found he had an interior sprung mattress to sleep on.

'This is heaven,' he said.

It must have been, because he took off his cap, took off his gloves and settled in a deckchair in the sunshine with a bottle of wine by his feet and a handkerchief with a knot in each corner thrown over his head.

There were flowers to greet us in the villa, and we were completely spoilt by the Churchills. They showed us where to shop, bought us wine, and Peter had a day off work to take us all for a picnic.

Peter was one of the most delightful, spontaneous, warm men that I have ever met. He had an infectious gaiety about him; there always seemed to be a party wherever he was, and I can understand how willing people would have been to work for him during his heroic wartime exploits with the French Resistance. He was generous to a fault, kind and patient. He and his sweet wife Jane made a pair of perfect hosts.

Our picnic outing was a day to be remembered. Peter got up

early and went to Cannes market to buy trout for lunch. He was running an estate-agent's business at this time and actually had a bar in the boot of his car for entertaining customers. On lifting the lid of the boot you saw an array of bottles and glasses which would compete with most cocktail cabinets.

Peter was amused by the French sense of humour, or lack of it. He told me that one day in Cannes he was reprimanded by a gendarme for not having his parking disc. He apologised profusely to the gendarme, then said, 'How can I put this right? Have you ever had a rum and Coca-Cola?'

'No,' said the gendarme.

'Aha!' said Peter. 'It will be my pleasure to introduce you to it.'

So, in the middle of a busy Cannes street, he lifted the lid of his boot to open the bar and poured a good measure of rum and Coca-Cola. The gendarme loved it.

'Have another one,' said Peter.

'*Merci*,' said the gendarme.

So Peter poured another measure of rum and Coke, which

the gendarme began to drink with obvious enjoyment.

'Will you have a cigarette?' asked Peter.

'Good heavens, no,' said the gendarme, his manner changing as he came briskly to attention. 'I couldn't possibly smoke – I am on duty.'

Peter said the main point of the story is that whenever he tells it in France, nobody laughs or sees anything funny in it.

We all packed into Peter's large car to go up to the Gorge du Loupe for our picnic. A friend of Peter's from the Resistance days had the gravel rights to a canyon, and it was to be our private picnic place for the day. A stream threaded its way between the tall cliff sides of the canyon, joining together deep pools. The blinding sunlight was broken by patches of shade as the canyon ran its irregular course.

We jumped out of the car and ran to the edge of the canyon. Looking back, we saw Gerry still sitting in the car and waving, so we waved back and hurried on. We looked back again to see if Gerry was coming, and he was still waving. I thought it was strange, even for Gerry, for him to be sitting inside a car at a spot like this on a blazing hot day. On looking back once more I saw that the waves were becoming quite agitated.

We rushed back to find that Gerry had not been waving, he had been beckoning for help. As we had jumped out of the car the door had closed on his thumb, trapping it. If the door edges had not been lined with rubber piping, he could easily have lost his thumb. I wondered how he was going to get his glove on over his sore thumb on the journey home.

We had a marvellous day. Peter grilled his trout over charcoal by the side of the canyon. We had an unlimited supply of drink from Peter's bar, the sun shone, and the owner of the canyon, who was a marksman in the French Olympic rifle team, came to have a drink with us.

The boys had the time of their lives racing up and down cliffs, jumping into pools and throwing stones into the blue, crystal-clear waters of the gorge.

To try and repay, to some small extent, Jane's and Peter's hospitality, we took them out for a meal one night. An attraction at the restaurant was a tame rabbit which could drink with the best. The boys made a great fuss of it. The wine and conversation flowed. It got later and later, until we suddenly realised that two rosy-cheeked little boys in their red blazers were fast asleep in their seats.

We stayed as long as we could in our villa in Le Rouret, deciding to make the trip back to Le Havre with one night's stop only. We parked that night in the grounds of a château. As we had to make another long drive next day, we didn't put up the tent. Trevor slept on the front seat of the Volkswagen, Pam went up into one of the luggage racks, and I shared a bed with Gerry. It was an unforgettable experience – he actually kept his cap and gloves on in bed.

Pam says it was the most uncomfortable night she had ever had in her life. She had backache for weeks afterwards and now, many years later, still swears if she has backache that it started that night in the Volkswagen.

And so back home. Mission accomplished.

'What about next year?' said Gerry. 'Now I know what is involved, I will be able to get some proper gear.'

I wondered what that meant ... bowler hat, gauntlets, and cricket pads?

CHAPTER 7

Home Town

One of the drawbacks of Tadchester was that anyone with ambition had to leave. By virtue of the town's size and position, there were limits as to how far people could go in many careers. In such fields as engineering, planning, journalism or the arts, the ceiling was soon reached in Tadchester. Fortunately this did not apply to general practitioners: in fact we were particularly lucky in having access to our own hospital.

I attended many farewells of bright young Tadchesterians, leaving the warm comforts of mother Tadchester to venture abroad. Abroad meant anywhere more than fifty miles' distance of Tadchester: it could be Taunton, Salisbury, or even London, though some of course did go overseas.

At least two thirds of the ambitious young men who left Tadchester eventually returned. It wasn't because they had failed in whatever profession or work they had chosen, it was because they had never ever really settled outside the town.

Most often it meant coming back to jobs in Tadchester that carried less kudos, and certainly less money than they had when they were working away. It meant a reduced style of living, but none were looked on as failures. The very fact that they had returned to Tadchester confirmed in the eyes of all the local people what bright young men they were.

Those who returned all said the same thing: it was quite a good idea to go away and have a look round other places if only to realise that there was no place on earth better than Tadchester.

And there was much in what they said.

*   *   *

Tadchester was a friendly town, which enjoyed many amenities – the country, the river, pleasant houses – and was not too far away from some of the larger centres. Most important of all, Tadchester was a community, a familiar community where you knew most of the people who lived there.

It was the comfort of belonging that brought people back, and belonging and mattering is perhaps more important than anything.

I welcomed back many of these bright young men. Sometimes they brought a wife from outside Tadchester, bringing fresh stock to the community. Most of them had taken a Tadchester wife with them before they left giving a double incentive for their return.

One person whom I was not pleased to see returning to Tadchester was Marjorie Charteris.

Before her marriage, Marjorie, daughter of Commander and Mrs. de Wyrebock, was one of a trio of ladies who had made my life uncomfortable in Tadchester. Her ambition at the time was to be Mrs. Clifford . . . and it was only because of constant vigilance and evasive action on my part that she didn't achieve it.

Poor Marjorie had the disadvantage of having one of the largest sets of prominent teeth that I have ever seen. Her passion was horses (which she closely resembled), and before her marriage she had run one of the Tadchester riding schools. She had become engaged to her husband Paul Charteris about the same time Pam and I had become engaged. I think Pam was as relieved as I was.

Marjorie and Paul had moved away some time after her

parents' deaths and I was surprised when she came back, alone, to Tadchester. Later I gathered that she was divorced. She bought her old riding school back and with her two small daughters went to live in a house in its grounds. Her two children, poor things, had inherited their mother's rows of prominent teeth.

Marjorie was very formal about her return and sent us cards letting us know she was back. Pam said we would have to ask her round for a meal. I hated the thought. Marjorie took a bit of shaking off once she had set her cap at you, and now here she was again, fancy-free and presumably looking for somebody to help share her riding school.

We had a little dinner party for her with Kevin and Janice, Zara and Eric, and the enigmatic Mr. Nin. For some reason, possibly the smell of horses that seemed to follow Marjorie wherever she went, our Cairn terrier Susie just would not leave her alone. We eventually had to shut Susie in the kitchen.

I felt something furry squeeze past my legs. Susie! She must have sneaked back into the room when Pam had brought in the food. I put my hand down under the table to see if I could find her.

As I felt around, a delighted smile appeared over Marjorie's face. Susie was nosing the inside of her thigh.

Kevin noticed my groping around, and Marjorie's smile, and almost exploded with laughter into his soup. I dragged Susie out, but for the rest of the evening Marjorie kept smirking at me. The rest of our guests could hardly restrain themselves from giggling. Even Mr. Nin looked far from inscrutable.

I was worried that, after what appeared to be an attempted indecent assault by me, Marjorie might launch into Operation Wedding Bells again, Pam or no Pam. But I was saved by a small dark stranger.

Two months after she had moved in, Marjorie was joined by a diminutive and weatherbeaten jockey, who had apparently been the cause of the divorce. They made an incongruous-looking couple: the large toothy Marjorie and her tiny bandy-legged partner. It was difficult to see what they had in common

81

but perhaps he hoped one day to ride her in the Grand National.

*   *   *

Tadchester had had a hospital of some sort for at least as long as written records had been kept. The present hospital was a compact, two-storey building erected in 1938.

This hospital was the town's pride and joy. It had been financed by the town, and built by the town, and its running costs were carried by the town.

Before it was built, the doctors and surgeons somehow managed to work from St. Mary's Maternity Home. It must have been hard work, making do with no lifts, narrow staircases and a very primitive operating theatre.

Before the National Health Service, people paid for their hospital treatment if they could afford it. If they had no money, there were sponsored beds and special funds to see that no one lacked medical care.

The doctors attending gave their services to the hospital for nothing (having honorary appointments) apart from three private rooms out of the seventy beds available, where they treated their private patients.

Steve Maxwell and Henry Johnson remembered these days well.

'My god, we knew what work was in those days, Bob lad,' roared Henry. 'There were no weekends off then, just two weeks' holiday a year.'

Apparently the most time anybody could take off each week was a half day, and then only when things were slack. There were surgeries both Saturday morning and Saturday evening, and early Sunday morning the doctors did a round of the hospital before spending the rest of the morning doing the week's major operating list.

The senior partner of the group before the war was a Dr. Tubb, the first man in Tadchester to have a car. He was apparently a giant of a man with a huge head, and was referred to affectionately by his patients as 'Old Golliwog'. He was in practice in Tadchester for nearly fifty years, and lived well; in those days doctors were very important members of the community, with large houses and servants.

He, like Henry Johnson, had been Mayor of Tadchester, and was still well remembered by the older patients of the town.

Dr. Johnson used to work under Dr. Tubb. He learnt a lot from him, they said. (I couldn't imagine Henry working under anyone. I would have loved to have seen it.)

We were very fortunate to have the hospital facilities. It allowed us to be real doctors, taking overall care of our patients and treating them both in and out of hospital. Henry Johnson was an excellent surgeon, good enough to know when surgical conditions would be better treated in more specialised centres such as Winchcombe, Bristol or London. Many of his contemporary GP surgeons would have a go at anything, regardless of the result. Henry Johnson could cope with all emergencies, but he knew his limitations. He reckoned that if you had to have something like your stomach out, you were better having it done by someone who did this operation about a hundred times a year, as opposed to his once or twice in an emergency.

The coming of the National Health Service caused some changes in the running of the hospital. Every patient had free treatment and free medicine, which was welcomed. The doctors who had previously worked for nothing were paid for their services. Although some found this rather *infra dig*, on the whole it was welcomed. The administrative staff, which had consisted of two hard-pressed secretaries before nationalisation, increased to four. It had risen to fifteen when I joined the practice and has been steadily rising since.

A great boon was that expensive new equipment could be obtained on demand, and the hospital no longer had to go round cap in hand. But strangely, it was this last benefit that the town reacted to most. Many of the functions held by the town were to raise money for the hospital. The Carnival held during the summer when the town was full of holidaymakers was the year's big money maker. Now, without a major fund-raising incentive in the community, the town lost some of its direction. It was as if the hospital had been taken out of the townspeople's hands. The x-ray machine that they had struggled and skimped and saved for now belonged to someone else.

The Carnivals went on each year, but never quite on the same scale, or with quite the same enthusiasm. There were many other worthy causes to donate to, but it was not the same as keeping your own hospital alive.

Tadchesterians had always looked after their own, and found it difficult to accept that someone was taking over their responsibilities. There would be a gap in their lives until they found something else to worry about and expend their energy on.

It was very much like a family looking after a dying relative at home. While the loved one was still alive, they didn't really have to make decisions: every waking moment was devoted to taking care of the patient.

Often it would appear, especially in the case of a very old and mentally confused relative who had taken a lot of looking after over a long period, that loss would be a relief to the family, that the bereavement would let them get up and get on with their business.

In fact this was seldom so. The loss of an elderly relative who had been looked after for a long time, too often left a void, a lack of direction. The relatives who had been doing the nursing never quite got going again. They had lost their corporate discipline, and sometimes this led to the break-up of even close-knit families.

*   *   *

Henry Johnson *was* Tadchester Hospital. He was on every committee, had a finger in every pie, and ran the whole concern as a benevolent dictator, National Health Service or no National Health Service. No hospital or group secretary could ever tell Henry what to do.

But there was a wind of change blowing. More consultants were being appointed at Winchcombe and appearing at Tadchester to do sessions in the specialities. As GP hospital consultants retired, they were being replaced by full-time consultants. It suited me: for about twelve years I had given anaesthetics at Tadchester Hospital – always conscious of the fact that I had not been trained in this speciality – and was crushed when I lost a child during an operation. I welcomed the appointment of a full-time anaesthetist which enabled me to retire from anaesthetics altogether. But Henry was concerned with the wider issues.

'We have a fight on our hands lad,' he said. 'One day they will be wanting to shut this place down.'

'Rubbish, Henry,' I replied. 'They couldn't do without the casualty services we give – especially in the summer – apart from all the other care that's available here.'

Henry's predictions began to come true. It was insidious at first. A new maternity hospital was built at Winchcombe and St. Mary's Maternity Home was shut down.

Everybody welcomed that, both doctors and patients. St. Mary's had no proper facilities and was in a poor state of repair. Once I even had a dog come into the labour ward and lift its leg against a table when I was just delivering a baby. The whole situation was very unhygienic but strangely, and I don't know why, we never had a cross-infection amongst the babies.

The patients looked forward to having their babies in this brand new Winchcombe hospital, with specialist care to hand. We doctors, although we were loath to admit it, looked forward to being called out of our beds less often, and were pleased to have the responsibilities of difficult confinements taken off us.

Unfortunately the first mothers to go to Winchcombe were delivered by a doctor who could not speak English, and obviously was not as gentle with women as the Tadchester doctors. And in Winchcombe's sterile surroundings there would be outbreaks of cross-infections between babies that had never occurred in the very unsterile surroundings of St. Mary's.

The Tadchester GPs found they had lost a precious area of communication without their young mothers and babies; they were also losing some of their skills, as the number of babies we delivered became fewer and fewer.

Though it was clearly progress to have babies born in the best surroundings in the best and most specialised hands, it took several years for both doctors and patients to adjust to the new regimes.

I bemoaned the situation to Steve one day.

'Yes, Bob, I know how you feel,' he said. 'But like everything else, if you don't keep moving forward you tend to move backwards. And remember, nothing is ever always pure gain. If you gain something, then you are bound to lose something else. It may not be much, but in the widest terms, there is no such thing as pure profit.'

The next news was of a five-year plan. A large new hospital was to be built at Winchcombe and all the small hospitals in the surrounding twenty miles would be phased out or used for some other purpose. This was national policy. All hospitals were going to be big hospitals. It was the only economic and efficient way to run a proper health service, said the planners; small personal hospitals were expensive to run and inefficient.

Tadchester Hospital was to be run down, and eventually turned into a home for the chronic elderly sick, covering a much wider catchment area than Tadchester and its surroundings.

There was tremendous uproar locally, protest meetings and a Save Our Hospital fund. Henry especially was furious. 'Nobody's going to touch my hospital while I'm alive,' he said.

I asked Steve's opinion again. 'Change is bound to come, Bob,' he said. 'We must keep on exploring. I think in time this over-centralisation will prove to be a mistake – but it's got to be tried.'

'What about Tadchester Hospital?' I asked.

'I reserve judgment on that,' Steve said with a twinkle in his eye. 'I've yet to see anybody get the better of Henry.'

One by one, all the small hospitals began to be shut down. Tadchester, ruled by the fiery Henry, held out in its normal function until his retirement, when it was turned into a geriatric unit.

Many years later, when practically every small hospital had been shut down, one of the powers-that-be, some nameless and faceless person – probably an accountant – had a brilliant idea.

With the high cost of keeping patients in the large hospitals, it would be a good idea if small hospitals were opened in some small communities. Patients who did not need major medical or surgical treatment could be looked after by their own general practitioners, by nurses from their own communities, and close to their homes so their families would not have problems in visiting them.

I thought this was absolutely marvellous: as soon as they had managed to shut all the small hospitals they were starting to open them again. One step forward, one step backwards . . . or was it the other way round?

One evening I sat down and wrote a letter to the Ministry of Health:

'Dear Minister,' I wrote, 'I have an excellent suggestion for a building that would make an ideal community hospital for the town of Tadchester . . .'

CHAPTER 8

Life and Death

Fay Thurton died suddenly and unexpectedly one night. Pam and I were out to dinner and came back to find a note that Jack Hart had pushed through the door, breaking the sad news.

Fay Thurton was a plump, bustling little woman, aged sixty-seven, and had gone to work the morning of the day she died. Her life was centred round the care of her husband, Ernest. Ernest was ten years older and one of those patients with chronic chest disease who somehow keep struggling on, year after year, with hardly any physical reserves. There were recurring battles during many nights to revive him with varieties of intravenous injections that miraculously brought him back from the almost dead. If anybody at any time had asked me about his life expectancy, I would have said it was two or three months – and I would have said the same thing over a period of six or seven years.

I had come to know the Thurtons quite well as they were almost neighbours of ours. Our new riverside house, although still in the town of Tadchester, enjoyed a village-type atmosphere, the fifty or so houses around us making up a community. And Fay and Ernest were two of its members.

The two had married when Fay was in her late twenties and

Ernest was in his late thirties. Before her marriage, Fay had worked behind the bar in the Star pub on the road between Tadchester and Sanford-on-Sea. After her marriage she worked every morning cleaning at a boys' boarding school at Sanford-on-Sea and, as well, did the cleaning of St. Mark's Church, the small church that served our small community.

In her busy life Fay still found time to bake all her own bread. Whilst I fancied myself as a breadmaker and would from time to time make a batch of wholemeal loaves, if I ever swapped one of my loaves for one of Fay's I would find out what real breadmaking was all about. The first windfalls from our apple trees went to Fay in return for pounds and pounds of her stewed-apple preserve.

Ernest was one of the nicest types. In the time I knew him, he was well enough in his better phases to keep his allotment going. He had a greenhouse by the back door of their cottage in which he could potter around even on days when his breathing was especially difficult.

When I called round after receiving the news of Fay's death, I found poor Ernest completely bemused. He was the one who had been battling with death for so many years; it was unbelievable that his plump, vigorous little wife, so cheerfully involved with life, should be the first to go.

'She went to work this morning, Doctor,' he said. 'I told her she worked too hard ... she didn't have a sit down until this afternoon, then tonight, when I went upstairs, she was sitting up in bed, reading. Normally she always put my pyjamas out, but today she hadn't. I said "Where are my pyjamas?"'

'She turned to me,' said Ernest, 'and gave a little gasp, and then she was gone. She had been a bit giddy over these past couple of weeks, other than that she had been perfectly well.'

Ernest had a neighbour – Samuel Bell – with him. They had worked together when they were younger. Ernest, with his life shattered in one brief moment, did not want to go to bed, so we three sat up talking. I knew he had spent most of his working life making cricket bats. It was only that night I heard the full story.

'I left school when I was twelve, Doctor. It was during the First World War, when you were allowed to leave school at twelve if you were going to work on the land. When I was thirteen, I got a job with Burroughs, the people who make cricket bats, and I worked for them fulltime until I was sixty-eight, then I went part-time. I think I had just stopped when you first arrived here.

'I used to travel all over England at one time finding willow trees, choosing them, felling them, and bringing them back to be split up for cricket bats. I was very lucky, Doctor; I always had a job, and they looked after me. I had a gold watch when I had been with the firm fifty years, and several international cricketers still used to come and see me after I had retired.

'You were lucky to have work between the wars,' he said. 'If you got a job, you hung on to it. Many of the youngsters were out of work. For those that were in, it was often three days' work a week for married men, two days' work for single.'

I suggested that he came back and spent the night with us. I did not want him left on his own.

'Not to worry, Doctor,' he said. 'Thank you for asking me, but I don't think I'll go to bed tonight. Samuel will sit with me for a while.'

'Yes,' said Samuel, 'Don't you worry, I'll keep an eye on him.'

I called daily for the next few days. Ernest's brother and sister came down from Yorkshire to help with the funeral arrangements. Ernest's health was generally so poor he wasn't able to do a great deal himself. I let him have some tablets to help him sleep, and something to take on the day of the funeral.

Pam and I went to the funeral. There were fifty or sixty villagers there, mostly the older ones. This had been a great shock for all of them as Fay was almost a generation younger than most of Ernest's contemporaries.

The Reverend Wood gave a simple service. He said we would remember Fay for her cheerfulness and busyness around the community, her work as a cleaner in the church, her help with the mobile library. At first it seemed sad that

91

there was no more to say about her. On the other hand, the simplicity and fullness of her life couldn't really be recorded.

I feared for her husband now that she was dead. After all, she had kept him alive, kept him going. He stood erect behind the coffin, breathless as he walked, following it to the graveside. I made sure that I was close to him as we left the churchyard. I had the feeling he could so easily collapse, but he did not. I even had to tell him to walk more slowly.

It was arranged that he would go up to Yorkshire to live with his brother and sister. The funeral was on a Thursday; he was going the following Wednesday. His cottage was owned by the Burroughs Cricket Bat Company so there was no property to sell. He was just going to clear up his possessions and go.

In a way I hoped that he might have died in those intervening few days. Without Fay I was sure he would find it difficult to manage.

But he did not die, and he did go away. I feared for him in strange surroundings in spite of the fact that his brother and sister were going to look after him. There was no alternative; he needed both a nurse and a housekeeper.

One of the local farmer's wives said to Pam as we walked back from the church, 'Isn't it awful? Fay died on Saturday, Ernest is leaving on Wednesday. They have lived practically the whole of their lives round here. In no time at all we shall probably forget both of them.'

I knew I wouldn't.

*   *   *

I found, in general practice, that I depended very much on my senior partners for dealing with problems that went beyond normal medicine and prescribing. So much of medicine has to be learnt after you qualify, and so much of medicine (in fact the major part of medicine in general practice) is the sheer management of people. As the old boy I met in a pub over celebration drinks the day I qualified said, 'So you are a doctor now. Don't forget a doctor's main job is to buck us all up.'

I remembered a time when I was a Bevin Boy at Dinnington Colliery in Yorkshire when we had a new colliery manager. He was straight from university, with an honours degree in mining engineering. He said the first day at his new job his first problem was to deal with two women who had been caught stealing coal from the pit tip. What was he to do with them? They had not included it in his honours degree curriculum.

Similarly, in medical school they did not tell us how to manage a situation where a wife had been beaten up by her husband, where the main causes of ill health were poor housing, poor income or just total unhappiness.

There was no instruction on how to cope with the bereaved. This was a major problem. Although I had the refreshment of delivering on average three babies a fortnight, I had at the same time to cope with three bereavements. It was never possible to forecast how much any particular bereavement would take in terms of my time, patience and energy.

I began to learn some things about people. I found that the people who had been the most happily married often coped better with the death of a partner than did those who had been unhappily married. In marriages that had not been going too well the sudden death of a partner sometimes resulted in the remaining partner reacting violently out of sheer guilt.

Reactions included attacks on doctors and nursing staff with wild allegations of negligence and malpractice. It had to be somebody's fault; there must be somebody to blame, be it the doctor, the employer, the seller of a faulty car, or one of a host of other 'suspects'. There would be a true and heart-rending exhibition of grief about the loss of the love of their life.

It was strange how the effects of bereavement manifested themselves sometimes. Couples who had a complete and happy life in the fullest physical terms, with full physical communication between each other, although they grieved tremendously after losing a partner, usually managed reasonably well. The bereaved who seemed to suffer the most and grieve the most were often those couples where there had been a lack of physical communication even to the point of an almost nonphysical relationship. I had imagined that it would be the physically compatible who would be the ones who had the most trouble in coping, but it was this other group, in my experience, which was more bereft. Perhaps their lack of physical expression was channelled into a higher form of spiritual communication. Whatever it was, this group of people seemed to suffer the most.

It is impossible to generalise. It is unlikely that definitive papers could ever be written about these circumstances. But the longer I stayed in practice, the more aware I became of what was likely to happen in particular circumstances.

In the general management of people's health, so often we treat the symptoms and not the disease. The disease perhaps may be an unhappy home life, unhappy marriage, unhappy work, unhappy day-to-day living situation – all emerging as some sort of medical condition, either real or imaginary, psychiatric or organic.

I wondered sometimes how much impact we really made on the course of people's lives and health, or whether we were just doing a temporary repair job . . . putting a patch on a leaking psyche, which would blow again before very long.

*　　　*　　　*

After ten years in practice I had already seen various groups of drugs go through complete cycles. A drug would start by being the new wonder drug, to be followed by other similar wonder drugs. Their imperfections would become apparent with use. They would be dropped, and then perhaps they would be picked up again because their benefits outweighed their disadvantages. Then there would be some new look at their new situation. It would be decided that a particular therapy, prescribed for many years, was completely ineffective against the condition it was meant to cure and that, in some cases, the symptoms and side effects it created were worse than the original condition. It is quite likely that some of the treatments that we have seen over several decades for, say, high blood pressure, will be found not only to have been useless but actually harmful.

The difficulty in assessing any medical treatment is that you cannot measure the result of a particular doctor giving a particular preparation to a particular patient. Two doctors giving the same preparation to the same patient might have completely different results. It is impossible to measure the effect a doctor has on a patient, particularly one he communicates with. In a way the further we go forward, the further we go back, and we go back realising the imperfections of the things we prescribe. We realise that we have to treat people not conditions, that we must begin to treat people as a whole, and the whole includes their background, their family, their objectives, their aims and ambitions.

They were dangerous times when, because of my accumulating experience, I began to think that I knew about people. I was confident that I could predict how events would take place, how a particular situation would run. The patient, often influenced by my positiveness, would further believe in me and help implement any course I suggested. It was usually just when I thought I had begun to know something as an irrefutable fact that I would be brought down to earth with a bump. And so it was when the Suttons arrived to live in Tadchester . . .

*   *   *

I had been in practice about ten years when I had to look after the Suttons' seven-year-old son. They had recently moved to a large house on the Dratchet Road, two miles outside Tadchester. Their son was ill when they arrived and, from the letters which accompanied his medical records, I saw that he had been seen by the very best people in the country. His medical condition, as far as was known, was incurable. It was a type of degeneration of the nerve fibres in the body.

When I first saw little Charles Sutton he was confined to his room. He crawled about a bit on the floor, talked quite chirpily

95

and was the very-much-loved only son of middle-aged parents.

I used my first couple of visits to get to know him. I knew of no specific treatment that could help him at all. After my second visit, his parents took me on one side and asked, with tears in their eyes, if there was any doctor, anywhere, they could ask for another opinion. They had heard there was a good children's doctor in Taunton – would I make an appointment for him?

I was as kind as I could be to them and said I was happy to make arrangements for him to see anybody they liked, but I thought there was very little that could be done.

As I thought, the child specialist in Taunton gave the same answer as all the other specialists. Nothing could be done, and the child had about six months to live. Charles was seen by specialists from Bath, Bristol, Cardiff, all giving the same answer: there was no hope for this boy.

When I was next called out to Charles, the parents requested that Stephen Maxwell came. I felt badly; you cannot be all things to all men but when patients change to other doctors, for whatever reason, you feel slighted. I had done a tremendous amount for the Suttons and thought we were on the best of terms.

Steve was non-committal about it. 'I am quite happy to see this boy, Bob lad. Apparently they heard somewhere that I had won a paediatric prize when I was a student and they would like my opinion of the situation.'

I saw no more of the Suttons and heard little from Steve about them until, six months later, I saw Charles's death announced in the local paper. This coincided with the arrival at the surgery of a most beautiful silver tea service for Steve, from the Suttons, with a note thanking him for all he had done.

I was extremely puzzled. I had done all that I could. I had sought every opinion that I could, and all of them were the same. As far as I knew, Steve Maxwell had sought no further opinion, and the child had died exactly as everybody had predicted.

I popped into Steve's room at the end of evening surgery. He was sitting at his desk like a wise old owl, smiling at me over the top of his gold, half-rimmed spectacles.

'Come in, Bob, and sit down,' he said. 'What can I do for you?'

'Tell me, Steve,' I replied, 'about the Suttons. I obviously made a big boob somewhere. Where did I go wrong, and what did you do when you got there?'

Steve said, 'I looked through the piles of notes about this poor little lad and through all the reports of the dozen or so specialists he had seen. Then, when I saw the child and the parents asked me what I thought, I said I thought he had every chance of getting over it.'

'Yes,' I said, 'but he didn't get over it. There was no chance of him getting over it. And yet they are obviously very grateful for all you did.'

'Yes,' said Steve, 'they have rather overdone it in terms of the gift. But as they explained to me after little Charles died, they knew all along that there was no chance of him recovering. But they wanted somebody to come to them and give them hope so that the last six months of his life would be a positive struggle – with the prospect of him getting better all the time – rather than six months of sitting down just waiting for him to die. It meant for the parents that the last six months of little Charles's life were lived with some kind of hope and had most of the strain taken from them.'

I realised as I left Steve's room how much I still had to learn about general practice . . . and people in particular.

CHAPTER 9

Down on the Farm

The first Christmas following the death of Pam's mother had been naturally a quiet one. The Christmas after that, when time had helped to abate the grief, was to be just the opposite. Pam's mother, Bill, a great lover of life, would not have had it otherwise.

The jollifications were enhanced by the presence of Ron Dickinson, our junior partner. For two years previously he had spent Christmas with his parents up North, but now he decided to sample the Tadchester festivities.

It was a tradition at the hospital Yuletide party for the doctors to be dressed up by the nurses in outrageous fancy dress costumes. This year, I was to be a Dalek, and was stuffed, protesting, into some sort of outsize dustbin. Even that, though, was preferable to my first year's costume. Then as Batman, I had to dress in a cloak and a pair of sheer – and embarrassingly revealing – black tights. The tights didn't keep out the winter winds, either.

Poor Jane, at that time still a few weeks off her second birthday, was terrified by the whole proceedings at the party and screamed inconsolably when she saw me getting out of my giant tin can. Pam had to take her home, missing the rest of the

junketing and my carving of the turkey on the children's ward.

Paul and Trevor, however, whose appetites could politely be termed healthy – and impolitely gluttonous – loved every minute of it. They spent the whole time happily being stuffed with pop, sweets and biscuits by nurses and patients alike.

Ron Dickinson was dressed up by the casualty nurses as a kangaroo, and it was exactly right for him. He bounced round the hospital to the squeals of the nursing staff and kept on bouncing until New Year's Day. Every party he attended he seemed to finish up in his underpants and covered in beer – the perpetual student.

He was nicknamed Peter Pan by Henry Johnson, and very aptly: in all the many years I eventually knew Ron, he never seemed to age.

Our Tadchester Christmases were very much centred round the hospitals, and each hospital tried to outdo its rival. Ron bounced round each one, was the life and soul of every party and, as he was still a bachelor, made many of the young nurses' hearts flutter.

One New Year's Day, however, he met his Waterloo. Tadchester Rugby Club had chosen this day to have their annual dinner. 'To sort of round off Christmas' was the reason they gave. I was fortunate in being on duty and unable to attend.

The unconscious Ron was carried to my house by four almost equally drunken companions at three in the morning.

They were a sorry sight, shirt-sleeved, clothes soaked through, on a bitter night with no idea of the whereabouts of their jackets, coats, ties – and in one case trousers.

I bedded them down on the lounge floor with a vomit bowl apiece. I turned on the electric fire and levered Ron onto his side, so that if he were sick there would be no danger of his choking.

As I turned him, he stirred. One eye opened.

'Happy New Year boss,' he said. 'Just bacon, eggs and kippers for breakfast, please . . .'

         *   *   *

After the excesses of Christmas and Hogmanay, the first few weeks of the New Year can hardly be anything but an anti-climax. Body, brain and bank balance need time to recover.

John Denton introduced me to a delightful way of easing into the New Year and reminded me that in the midst of what felt like death, we were indeed in life.

'Morning, young Bob! How's your head?' boomed the voice over the phone, in an accent from darkest Manchester. (John had opted for the country life after his army service, but had been born and raised in the industrial north.)

'It's still attached to my body, John,' I said. 'But otherwise it's hard to say.'

'I've got something that should clear it,' said John. 'We start stripping trout tomorrow morning at the fish farm, and it's always a bit of a social event. Plenty of fresh air in the barn and a hair or two of the dog that bit you.

'As it's Saturday tomorrow, I thought you might be free to come over. Bring Pam and the kids, too: they'll enjoy it.'

'Sounds fun, John. What time?'

'About ten. Should have a decent crowd in by then. Oh, and bring a bottle.'

'What kind?' (My muddled brain was trying to connect a bottle with stripping trout of their eggs: I thought perhaps John might be presenting me with some roe.)

'Any kind you like,' said John. 'So long as there's summat in it.'

'Ah. A bottle as in bottle party?'

'By 'eck, lad. You catch on quick. See yer.'

I arrived at the fish farm *en famille* and *avec bouteille*, to find a handwritten sign which read STRIP SHOW THIS WAY, followed by an arrow pointing to a large barn. Inside the barn was a sight neither I nor the family will ever forget.

In the middle of the floorspace stood four large galvanised tanks, filled with water and pulsating with fish, two such tanks on either side of a long bench. Standing on each end of the bench were a couple of smaller tanks and, in the middle, a clutter of large bowls and dishes. Over this, as if it were an altar, John supervised his helpers in the ritual of stripping the fish.

The bench was lit by an electric bulb dangling from the ceiling. What was really amazing was the rest of the barn. It was lit by the warm glow of candles, dozens of them, burning on trestle tables, benches, boxes and tea chests.

Standing around, or sitting on an assortment of stools and chairs – in one case a plush leather armchair – were dozens of people. They were of every age and station, from the youngest ragamuffin of the town to several magistrates and well-to-do members of the county set. Even scruffy old Charlie Sloper, veteran cadger, was there, wandering around the tables and helping himself to other people's food.

Everybody had brought something to eat and drink, from humble cheese sandwiches and cider to smoked salmon and champagne. A portable record player in the corner played the Vaughan Williams *Fantasia on a Theme* by Thomas Tallis. It was as if we had walked into a wooden-walled cathedral where some holy rite was being enacted.

'You could say,' said John, as he stripped away at the trout,

101

first squeezing out the eggs from several hen fish into a bowl, then the milt from a couple of cock fish, 'that this is life, this is. The beginning of life for several million creatures. All happening before your eyes. There's not much that's holier.'

'You old fraud,' I said. 'Going around all year pretending to be a no-nonsense, down-to-earth, practical unbeliever – and now turning into some kind of high priest.'

'Just the other side of the coin,' said John. 'Look at these fish. No creature is more practical, down-to-earth, no-nonsense than a trout. Just an appetite with fins. But they're performing a miracle here, with a little help from their friends.

'And look at them.' He gestured at the assembly, which was growing in numbers by the minute. 'They know they're witnessing a miracle. That's what they've come to see. That's why they're making an occasion of it. And by doing so they're creating the atmosphere that a miracle deserves.'

They were. It was an atmosphere such as might have existed in a medieval church, used as the real focal point for the village and the surrounding countryside, when religion was part of daily life, and not just a burst of once-a-week piety.

'May I help, John?' I asked, wanting to get down to some practicalities before I was carried away on a wave of mystic euphoria.

'Aye,' said John. 'You've got the fingers for it. I daren't let some of these cack-handed buggers anywhere near the fish for fear they'd do some damage.'

Basically, trout-stripping is artificial insemination. To avoid hit-and-miss natural spawning, with its risks of under-fertilisation, of breeding from inferior or unhealthy stock, and of the eggs and fry being eaten by the adult fish – perhaps even the parents – trout farmers take control of the whole breeding process.

First of all, only big and healthy fish of good pedigree are used as 'broodies'. When a hen fish is lifted and her belly sags, swollen with eggs, then she is ready for stripping.

Stripping is simply stroking the belly with a wet thumb and forefinger, towards the vent, squeezing out the eggs into a clean dish. No force is used, and no attempt made to take eggs which do not flow easily, for fear of damage to the fish.

Three or more hens are stripped into the pan. Then a cock fish is stripped, to cover the eggs with milt, or sperm. On John's farm, often two cock fish are stripped into the same dish, in case one should be infertile.

The eggs and the milt are then mixed together gently by hand, covered with water, and left for about a quarter of an hour or until the eggs separate from each other. The eggs are now fertile. They are washed to remove dirt and surplus milt and, as 'green' eggs, are laid down for hatching or sold to other breeders.

Each fish may be stripped two or three times over a period of perhaps a fortnight, and then put back in the stock pond to recover and become 'clean' again.

As I stripped the fish, gaining confidence with each one, I could appreciate John's feelings about the creation of so much life: hundreds of thousands of new lives beginning every quarter of an hour. And I realised why the barn was so crowded and so charged with that indefinable atmosphere.

I was stripping merrily away, enjoying it more and more, when John said, 'Hey up, our Bob. You'll be doing me out of a job in a minute. Would you mind if this young gentleman took over?'

I turned to see a tow-headed, grubby boy of about twelve standing there.

'Hello,' I said. 'It's Tommy Thompson, isn't it?'

'Right,' said John. 'He's taken time off from pinching my trout to see where it all starts, haven't you, Tommy? Right, lad, get stuck in. But gently, mind . . .'

I was out with John on his beat once when he surprised Tommy Thompson in the act of catching trout with a hazel-twig rod and six feet of line. 'The best little poacher for miles' was how John described him, acknowledging an honourable adversary.

Whenever John came across Tommy in the act of poaching, the rules were that John made a lot of noise and Tommy vanished into thin air. Tommy knew the rules and observed them. For his part he never took more than a brace of trout at a time, and treated the river with respect.

Tommy was one of the many local poachers who were of great help to John in reporting the arrival of professional fish-thieves from outside the district, or of outbreaks of disease among John's beloved trout. 'The local villains earn their corn,' said John. 'There's hardly a spot of fungus on my fish that I don't know about within the hour.'

The ceremonial stripping went on to the accompaniment of eating, drinking, quiet conversation and subdued music. The big barn, normally cold and draughty, had warmed fuggily to the heat of the candles and the assembled bodies. The only jarring note in the proceedings came when John discovered Charlie Sloper pocketing (repeat, pocketing – Charlie never was fussy about dress) a large handful of fertilised trout eggs.

He was swiftly and unceremoniously ejected, cursing loudly and protesting innocence at the same time.

'What's the matter, John?' I asked. 'Did Charlie fancy some caviare for his tea?'

'Caviare be buggered,' said John. 'The little tyke was going to use it as bait. It's illegal for a start and deadly for a second. That short-arsed heap of rubbish can do enough damage to my fish stocks, without any free bait from me.'

When Charlie's curses had died away, I suddenly realised that for an hour or so I'd forgotten all about Pam and the children. I needn't have worried: they were so engrossed in everything that they'd forgotten all about me. Even Jane, who was only two, was entranced by it all.

For Trevor, Paul and Jane, that scene has remained one of childhood's beautiful memories. It came in useful to me, too, when it was time to tell each of them the facts of life. I didn't have to waffle on about birds and bees. I said simply, 'Do you remember the time we went down to the trout farm . . . ?'

CHAPTER 10

Love Me, Love My Goat

Animals played a big part in the life of Tadchester and its hinterland. The houses I visited on my rounds were usually within sight or spitting distance of some livestock or other. Not surprisingly, animals were responsible directly or indirectly for a larger proportion of cases than a normal surgery was used to coping with.

My surgeries held too many surprises to allow for complacency, and whenever I lowered my guard, something got through and jolted me.

*   *   *

One of my firmest jolts was given by the Hamlins. The Hamlins were sort of semi-gypsies and divided their time between collecting scrap iron and sheep-farming.

There were about twenty-four in the whole family. Swarthy, dark-looking characters, they were friendly, good natured and well integrated into the town. They lived very much as a clan and their twenty-four included at least two lots of grandparents and various family groupings that were not always easy to determine. There were about fourteen or fifteen young children, but who belonged to whom I was never sure.

I confidently diagnosed impetigo when one of the Hamlin children was brought to see me with a weeping sore on his face. It was only when I had seen the fourth and fifth Hamlin child with this type of impetigo that I began to suspect I had made a wrong diagnosis. The children had sores on their faces, lips and hands. They did not seem to respond to my usual ointments. I thought I had better visit them at home.

Their homestead consisted of a group of disused Nissen huts turned into bungalows, standing next to a huge scrapyard filled with old cars, bits of railway line and all sorts of other metal objects. The heap of scrap seemed steadily to grow in size without anything ever happening to it, but it obviously provided the Hamlins with plenty of money: their run-down Nissen huts were cosily and lavishly furnished inside with clean curtaining, ornaments and pictures, very much in the gypsy tradition. There were also new cars, washing machines and TV sets, which could not have been provided for by the rather mangy flock of sheep they kept.

The flock of sheep were a legacy from the last war, when they were the Hamlins' answer to meat rationing. It was a simple philosophy – if you couldn't buy meat in the shops, then you grew your own, and if there was a bit left over you could always get a good price for it.

I found, in all, that eleven of the twenty-four in the family had these infectious-looking sores. Although I had seen similar conditions before, I had never seen anything quite like this.

I paid my respects to the oldest Hamlin – Gregor Hamlin, a wizened old man in his eighties, with a gold earring in one ear. He was not easy to communicate with. He had had a slight stroke a few years back which made speech difficult and he rambled on in a confused, disjointed way. I tried to talk to him about this epidemic amongst his family but all I could get from him was a shaking of the head and 'They got orf. They got orf'.

What they had got off from, I had no idea. I assumed it was some prison sentence from one of their less scrupulous deals. But this was no help to me in treating this unpleasant skin con-

107

dition that was affecting so many of them.

Eventually I had to put all those contaminated on antibiotic tablets and creams. I agreed to go and visit them again as the numbers infected had now risen to fourteen and they could really justify a surgery on their home ground.

On a sunny evening when I made my next visit they were all outside clustered round Gregor as he talked to Andrew Faber, the vet, who was holding a limp-looking lamb in his arms. As I got near, I saw that most of my patients were very much better, even from a distance the infected areas of skin were hardly visible. As I approached Gregor he nodded excitedly at me, waving his stick.

'They got orf. They got orf!' he shouted.

I wondered again from what crime his family had been reprieved. It must have been something pretty stupendous to take priority over the skin rashes.

'He's right,' said Andrew Faber, holding up the lamb. 'I'm going to engage him as my assistant.'

By now I was completely confused.

Over a cup of tea in Gregor Hamlin's Nissen hut, Andrew patiently explained it all.

The sick lamb and most of the Hamlins were suffering from the same disease. It is primarily a condition of sheep but if bitten by or in close contact with sheep, human beings can pick it up. Its name is ORF!

Happily the treatment I had prescribed was the treatment that it required anyway, and it was one more deposit in my knowledge bank.

I got up to go. Gregor Hamlin looked up: 'You going orf now, Doctor?'

I looked down at my hands; they were spotless.

'No,' I said. 'Not if I can help it.'

*   *   *

Mark Adler was one of several freelance illustrator artists in Tadchester. In his anarchic appearance and attitude to life, he strongly resembled Spike Milligan – and some of the things

which happened to him were straight out of a 'Goon Show' script.

A passionate conservationist, he was one of the first to recognise the danger to toads from the road leading to a new housing estate. The road had been built over what was once a farm track, and passed a pond to which the toads migrated to breed every spring.

The migration route lay across the farm track, and for untold centuries the toads had faced no greater hazard than the occasional cart. But the road changed all that: suddenly they were being crushed in their hundreds beneath the wheels of fast cars and lorries.

The phrase 'Help a Toad Across the Road' had not yet been coined as a campaign slogan, but that was exactly what Mark was doing and it was from his lips that I first heard it. Several times a day, armed with a bucket lined with damp moss, he would patrol the road and gather up the toads which were making their laborious way across.

A motorist brought Mark to the surgery and left only after solemn assurances from Mark that he would be all right. Mark limped into the consulting room, the flattened toe of his right boot beginning to rise again from the swelling of the foot underneath.

I cut the boot and sock away to reveal a badly swollen and bruised foot with at least two bones broken.

'How do you like that, Doc?' said Mark. 'I went to help a toad across the road – and got run over.'

Apparently in his enthusiasm he had leapt out to snatch a toad from the path of an oncoming car. He got the toad all right, but as he turned to leap back, the car went over his foot.

'It was the driver who brought me here,' said Mark. 'Nice bloke, but not into the toad thing. He spent half his time fretting in case he'd done me some permanent damage and the other half calling me a bloody fool. Mind you, he was good enough to tip my bucket of toads into the pond before giving me a lift in.'

The experience gave Mark a respect – I was going to say 'healthy respect' but it didn't quite work out like that – for traffic on the road.

A few weeks later he was in again, the plaster cast still on his foot, this time with a couple of broken ribs and badly pulled muscles in one arm.

'After getting that big flat foot,' he said, 'I became paranoid about crossing the road. I looked right, left and right again, and wouldn't set foot on to the road until there were absolutely no cars, lorries, buses in sight.'

'Good thinking,' I said. 'So what brought this on?'

'I looked right, left, and right again … not a four-wheeled vehicle in sight … So I stepped out into the road … and got run down by a horse.'

That was typical of Mark's enthusiasm, or perhaps obsession would be a better word. When he got a bee in his bonnet he would concentrate on it to the exclusion of everything else. This time he had been looking for motorised traffic in the middle distance, and the galloping horse from the local riding school, which must have been almost upon him, hadn't even entered his consciousness.

*   *   *

The riding school provided me with a steady flow of patients, mostly inexperienced youngsters who after a few lessons had become over-confident and taken a tumble, but Jim Fraser was the only parent I had to treat.

Jim, the son-in-law of the lovely old Mick and Alice, appeared at my front door one Sunday morning, supported by his wife, Philomena. There was no Sunday surgery, of course, and strictly speaking he should have gone to casualty at Tadchester General Hospital. But I was a friend of the family, and this did seem to be rather a delicate matter.

Jim stood there, knock-kneed, watery-eyed, and clutching the source of the pain which was roughly, or precisely, in the area of his masculinity.

'Sorry, Doctor,' said Jim. 'It's my ... phwarh ...'

He broke off, gasping and speechless. So Phil told me the tale as I helped Jim on his painful way indoors.

She and Jim had called at the riding school to collect their two children from their morning lesson. The pupils were still out on a cross-country canter, so the two parents walked across the back field towards the gate where the horses would enter on their return.

As they walked across the field, Jim saw a tethered horse whose rope had become wound tightly several times round its leg. The horse's head was pulled down by the rope and the animal was obviously in danger of struggling and hurting itself.

'I'd better sort this out,' said Jim.

'Are you sure you know what you're doing?' asked Phil. Jim was not exactly built like John Wayne and his love of horses far exceeded his experience.

'No problem,' said Jim. 'You just show 'em who's boss.'

With encouraging words of 'Whoah, boy' 'Steady, lad' etc. Jim tried to unwind the rope. The horse stood still, not that it was able to move anyway, and Jim decided there was nothing for it but to pull up the tethering stake and unwind the rope from the free end.

Soon the rope was untangled and the horse was able to lift its head. Jim patted it professionally on the neck.

'Told you,' he said. 'All you've got to do is show 'em who's...'

At that very moment the returning horses and riders appeared at the bottom of the steeply sloping field. Jim's horse whinnied in recognition, reared, and shot off like a bullet.

Jim hung on to the rope and was towed at top speed down the field, leaping through the air in giant strides and landing each time with a jolt on the tussocky grass.

'He looked like the first moonwalker on earth,' said Phil. 'Apart from the screams it was very impressive.'

When the horse reached its old mates it stopped suddenly. Jim, who was in mid-bound, crashed sickeningly into its hind-quarters and collapsed spark-out on the grass ... still clutching the rope.

'I say, who's that?' demanded the haughty-looking riding mistress.

'It's my *father*,' said young Laura, in a tone of disgust. 'He's being silly again.'

Phil went to the aid of the stricken Jim and busily patted his face to bring him round.

'Is he all right?' asked their son Richard. 'Only I've not had my pocket-money yet.'

Jim opened his eyes.

'All you've got to do,' he groaned, 'is show 'em who's boss...'

Examination of Jim showed some pulled muscles in his arms, shoulders and inner thighs, the last were the ones which were causing the pain. But apart from that there was no real harm done.

'I don't like to ask this,' said Phil, blushing. 'But has he done himself any mischief? I mean, will it have any permanent...? Will it affect his...?'

112

I cut Phil short to spare her embarrassment.

'Don't worry, Phil,' I said. 'It's very painful at the moment. But I can assure you that Jim will definitely play the violin again...'

* * *

Dogs figured in a number of cases; two in particular come to mind, along with the Tadchester Arms and the annual fair.

The fair brought lots of trade to the town, and the local pubs would hire casual bar-staff for the week it was on. It also brought lots of pocket-picking, petty pilfering and break-ins.

During one fair the Tadchester Arms was broken into. A locked and full till had been carried out bodily, the subsequent loss representing a big part of the profits of fair week. The following year the landlord, Geoff Emsworth, bought a surprise for would-be intruders in the shape of a trained, but very vicious, alsatian guard dog.

The night before the fair, Geoff hired a young student to work in the saloon bar.

'Start tomorrow lunchtime,' he said. 'See you here at eleven o'clock.'

Geoff was outside, dealing with draymen, when the student arrived.

'Just in time, son,' he said. 'Go behind the bar and through the flap into the cellar, and lift out the crates of light ale to make some space at the bottom of the steps. I'll see you down there.'

The boy went into the pub. Within seconds there were sounds of savage barking and screams of pain.

'My God!' said Geoff. 'I forgot!'

He ran into the pub, charged behind the bar and dragged the dog off the student, whose jacket had been ripped to shreds and whose arms were a bloody mess.

Geoff rushed him round to surgery. I stitched the boy up and gave him an anti-tetanus injection. He certainly was in a mess: it took thirteen stitches to repair the damage to his arms.

Geoff was beside himself with remorse.

113

'How could I be so stupid?' he said. 'I forgot he hadn't been introduced.'

That sounded crazy, but it was all that was needed to make the dog accept a stranger. It had been trained to accept people introduced by its owner, but to make life very unpleasant for anyone else.

The student was a brave lad. He reported for duty at the pub that same evening and was properly introduced. By the end of the night he was scratching the dog behind the ears – and the thing was looking at him with something very much like soppy love in its eyes.

I heard some strange reasons for unexpected pregnancies during my time at Tadchester. The heaviest crop – both of unexpected pregnancies and strange reasons – regularly came to light a month or two after the fair. There were always girls silly enough to believe the stories of sudden but undying devotion spun by the wandering fairground lads. And there were always girls mercenary enough to bestow their favours for a few free rides on the dodgems or a couple of illicit trophies from the coconut shies.

They would usually turn up at the surgery convinced that they were afflicted by anything but pregnancy. On hearing the news, their reaction was almost always the same: they just couldn't understand how it had happened.

However, one girl – Julie – understood exactly how it had happened.

'That damned dog!' she said.

'Pardon?'

This was one of the moments when my guard was down and a jolt came through.

'That dog and his cold nose!'

'I think you'd better explain, Julie,' I said. 'Either I'm a bit dim this morning or you've made medical history.'

Julie explained. She had met this lad who took the tickets for the Big Wheel. Name of Carlo (unlikely, but more romantic-sounding than his probable real name of Charlie). Carlo had dark wavy hair and ever such white teeth and had a way of looking at you which made you go funny all over. (I managed to stifle a yawn at this bit.) Carlo had said he could not do without Julie and that next time the fair came near Tadchester he would bring her something special, such as an engagement ring.

On the strength of this, Julie went with him after the fair had closed one night to the barn behind the Tadchester Arms, which Geoff allowed the fair people to use to store spares and odds and ends.

Among Carlo's odds and ends was a single bed mattress, and it was on this that they plighted their troth.

At a crucial moment during their plighting, when it was dependent on Carlo's restraint to prevent it being fruitful, the cold nose of a wandering dog alighting upon Carlo's naked posterior meant he lost his concentration and resulted in Julie's visit to the surgery.

Julie was unlucky all right, but Carlo would never know how lucky he was – that the damned dog wasn't the flaming alsatian . . .

*   *   *

One of the saddest animal tragedies I witnessed was not a goring by a bull, or a savaging by some huge dog, but the conflict between two schoolteachers and their pets.

Miss Geraldine Smith and Miss Marigold Bendle first came to Tadchester on holiday when they were student teachers at a training college in London. They fell in love with the place, and each year always managed to have two or three weeks together in the town.

After qualifying, Miss Bendle took a teaching post up in Cumbria, and Miss Smith stayed on in London on a postgraduate course, but their correspondence and the Tadchester holidays kept them in touch.

Miss Bendle finally finished up as head of the English Department at a girls' school in Chester, and Miss Smith finally made a headship at a small girls' school in Kent.

I once read a book on planning retirement. The author advocated that you should start looking for a place to retire in your early forties, buy a cottage there if possible, and over the years slowly build yourself into the community.

The author would have loved the Misses Bendle and Smith: they started planning their retirement at the age of nineteen.

Miss Bendle was a short, plump, good-natured lady, with long dark curly hair. Miss Smith was tall, slim with short cropped hair and an abrupt manner. In her mid-forties she took to wearing steel-rimmed spectacles, which increased her rather severe aspect. She was the sort of person you would imagine to be for capital punishment, against promiscuity and who would stand up whenever she heard the national anthem.

Over the years the two women became well-known and well-liked figures in the Tadchester area. Neither ever showed any desire to be married, and they were rarely seen in male company.

In their early fifties, actually on Miss Smith's fifty-first birthday, they bought their dream house: an end-of-terrace cottage overlooking the harbour at Peargate.

From now on, all of their holiday time was spent in Tadchester, pottering about and tinkering with their cottage, preparing for the time when they could eventually pack up work, and live together happily in retirement.

The time got closer and closer, until there was just one summer term before they could come and live in Tadchester for ever.

During this term, the pupils of both teachers must have suffered. Miss Smith and Miss Bendle were almost already living together in the house of their dreams. They wrote every day, full of excited plans and each hinting to the other that she was planning a surprise that would make their future days together even richer.

Miss Bendle's surprise was a big fluffy Persian cat, intended to give softness and warmth to their new home. Miss Smith's surprise was a strong and energetic bull terrier which they

116

could take for walks along the cliffs and watch chasing rabbits across the common.

I was called to the house about two hours after they had got together at their new cottage.

Miss Bendle's school broke up a day before Miss Smith's and she had arrived with her precious fluffy Persian cat twenty-four hours before Miss Smith.

I reckoned that I was called about an hour after two vets had been called independently. When I arrived one vet was stitching back some fur on a very nasty and bloody-looking area of the cat. The other vet was dealing with some very nasty scratches around the eyes of the bull terrier.

The two women, whom I am sure had not spoken a cross word in years, were screaming abuse at each other and at each other's pets.

I had to put five stitches and an anti-tetanus injection in Miss Smith's arm where her dog had bitten her when she tried to pull him off the cat.

I had to swab Miss Bendle almost all over with antiseptic as well as give her a shot of anti-tetanus: her cat's claws had ripped into her as it sought shelter from the attacking dog.

It was the end of the relationship. Miss Bendle moved out that night, stayed overnight at a guest house, then moved north to look after an old aunt in York.

Miss Smith stayed on at the cottage on her own for two or three months, and most afternoons could be seen walking her dog on the cliff. The dog was kept on a very tight lead, as if he was the last living thing in the world. Miss Smith was giving him no chance to get away.

Suddenly one morning, she too was gone. A 'For Sale' notice went up on the cottage and Miss Smith was never seen or heard of again.

*   *   *

The story of Miss Smith and Miss Bendle became almost overnight folklore in Tadchester. I was talking to Bob Barker about it one day.

'Definitely a case of love me, love my dog,' said Bob. 'But did you ever hear of love me, love my goat?'

'No,' I said, 'but I'm sure you'll tell me.'

'Some years ago,' said Bob, 'a church deacon bought the malthouse on the edge of the River Tad. Although it had river frontage it went quite cheaply: there was almost a sheer drop of sixty feet from the house to the river's edge. You could manage to get down the bank to the river side with a struggle, but what you could not do was keep the undergrowth in any sort of order. It had plenty of water and grew profusely.

'The deacon had spent some years of his ministry in Africa, and had observed the habits of the indigenous goats, that would eat anything and strip foliage to soil level. So he bought some goats. In no time at all his bank was cleared of foliage and he had the bonus of free goats' milk.

'The one snag to the whole scheme was the goats' affection for the deacon's wife. They followed her everywhere, and she was the only person they would allow to lay a hand on them, particularly at milking time. There was almost always one of the goats in milk all the time and needing to be milked every day. The deacon and his wife were never able to get away on holiday as a couple, or even have a full day out.

'The crisis came when the wife was taken ill. After only one day the goats' painful bleating could be heard clear across the river.

'Several people tried to relieve their feelings, without success. Then there was an imperious demand from the sick-room. The gardener led two of the goats upstairs, and the deacon's wife milked them from her bed.

'The deacon wisely said nothing, but after two days of having goats milked in his bedroom, he set off on a mysterious mission to the town. The next morning the goats had gone – 'stolen'.

'The deacon made a great show of getting in touch with the police, but the culprit was never found.

'However, for a few weeks one of the Tadchester butchers had goat's meat for sale, and Charlie Sloper had a rare spell of

affluence. 'A right toff, that deacon,' he was heard to say.

The deacon's wife, though grieving for the goats, did recover from her illness, and she and her husband lived happily ever after, or as happily as any couple could after such an experience.'

'Is that a true story?' I asked Bob.

'Yes,' said Bob. 'Quite true. I was a young church organist at the time, always willing to help – and I acted as link-man between the deacon and Charlie Sloper. And goat's meat isn't at all bad once you get used to it...'

CHAPTER 11

Deserving Cases

The National Health Service, comprehensive as it is, can never fully take the place of each looking after his own.

Two of my favourite patients were Mick and Alice, married fifty years and ... (the usual phrase here is 'never a cross word', but I've yet to come across a marriage of even fifty days to which that applies).

'A bloody good row at least twice a week,' was how Mick described their formula for married bliss. 'Clears the air something lovely.'

Mick was retired now, and his breathing and eyesight were such that he had had to give up his part-time job as lollipop man outside the local school. Alice worked on full-time in the Tadchester Hospital canteen.

It was Mick's health I had always watched, but it was Alice who suddenly fell very ill. They were an independent old pair, and by the time I was called Alice's condition had degenerated into pneumonia.

'How is she, Doctor?'

Little Mick stood blinking moistly, his hands still working through some rosary beads. (Mick and Alice were staunch Roman Catholics and much-loved members of St. Malachy's

Church. Only a few months before, a special mass had been said for their Golden Wedding and a surprise slap-up reception laid on by the congregation.)

'I didn't want to bother you at first,' said Mick. 'Alice was dead against calling you out, and she's always been so fit. But I knew she was badly when she stopped arguing. I know we're getting on a bit, but I can't lose her, Doctor, I can't.'

'She *is* poorly, Mick,' I said. 'But I've put her on antibiotics and she should improve within a few days. Now I want you to give her one of these tablets every four hours and two of *these* tablets every six hours. And make sure you . . .'

I broke off. Mick wasn't listening. Behind the tears, his eyes were filled with pain and fear. Fifty years is a long time.

'Tell you what, Mick,' I said. 'You'll have enough to do with the housework and things.' (I knew full well that Mick was in no state even for that.) 'I'll call on your daughter Phil on my way back and ask her to keep an eye on Alice.'

'No, no, Doctor. You can't do that,' said Mick. 'They're off up north tonight for a few days with their cousins up there. They've not had a break for a long time and their kids are really looking forward to it.'

'All right, Mick,' I said. 'Don't worry. I'll fix something.'

I fixed it very quickly. Mick needed looking after almost as much as Alice. Capable as the district nurse was, this was a job for family.

Mick and Alice had brought up seven children. Six of them were those of Alice's sister, who had died not long after her husband. Their own child was Phil – Philomena – now married to Jim. Together, Phil and Jim ran a little hairdressing business down in the town. Mick was right: they worked hard and needed the break. But this was a matter of priorities.

I called in at the salon, where Phil was taking the rollers out of a customer's hair.

'Right,' she said, after I had explained. 'Thanks, Doctor. Leave it to me. Jim, Mum's poorly. Could you finish off Mrs. Wainwright while I get things organised?'

Phil picked up the phone and rang the relatives up north, postponing the visit. Then she rang those of her 'sisters' who were on the phone and living close enough to be of help. That done, off she sped in her car, leaving Jim to attend to the remaining customers and to look after their two children that evening.

Within a couple of hours, Alice had been made more comfortable, Mick had been fed, the accumulation of pots in the sink had been washed, and the house had been tidied.

For the next week, Phil and the sisters kept up a rota of calls all through the days and into the nights. Phil had issued each sister with a list of the times and types of Alice's medicaments. Each got in whatever shopping was necessary, made a hot meal for Mick and prepared whatever nourishment Alice was able to take.

Then Alice started to mend. Phil called one morning to find her mother lying uncomfortably between two armchairs in the living room; Mick had been sleeping in these chairs to allow Alice to rest undisturbed.

'What the heck are *you* doing here?' demanded Phil. 'You're supposed to be upstairs in bed. And where's Dad?'

'Oh, poor lad,' said Alice. 'I could hear him in the night, tossing and turning on these chairs. With his bad back he wasn't getting a minute's peace. I was feeling better, so I came

122

down and made him swap. He's upstairs now, getting some decent sleep.'

Two days later, Phil knew her mother was over the worst. She called in on her way to work. Alice and Mick – Alice in her nightgown – were in the kitchen, arguing hammer and tongs.

'What's the matter?' asked Phil.

'What's the matter?' said Alice. Then, pointing an accusing finger at Mick, 'He's the matter!'

Mick shuffled uncomfortably, trying to look defiant and innocent at the same time. A difficult feat.

Apparently Alice had woken up feeling much better, and hungry for the first time since the illness. Mick had tottered upstairs, and was delighted to find her sitting up.

'Don't worry, love,' he said. 'I'm going to look after you. How do you fancy poached eggs on toast and a cup of tea?'

'I'd love some,' said Alice. 'But don't burn the toast.'

'Have no fear,' said Mick. 'I know just how you like it.' (He did: very lightly browned. But every time he had made toast in their fifty years together he had burned it to a cinder.)

Mick went downstairs and Alice sat on the edge of the bed expectantly. Twenty minutes passed, half an hour, forty minutes ... Alice was beginning to feel chilled. And there was still no tea and toast. Not even a smell of burning.

Finally she went downstairs into the kitchen. At the kitchen table sat Mick, supping from a pint mug of steaming tea, and reading the sports section of the morning paper.

'Where's mine?' demanded Alice.

'Where's what?' said Mick. Then, as it all came back to him, 'Oh, 'eck ... I forgot.'

I realised when I heard the story how right I had been to overrule Mick and call in Phil. I realised also that Alice was back to her old fighting self – thanks to a bloody good row – and that the long and loving marriage was safe for some years yet.

*   *   *

Nowhere in the dictionaries of saints or heroes does the name of

123

Mick Mitchell appear. This is some small attempt to rectify the omission.

I was making my last call on Alice, now fully recovered, just to make sure that there was nothing else I need do for her.

'How's Mick coping now?' I asked.

'Same as usual,' she said. 'Always under my feet. But I'll tell you something, Doctor: that little feller downstairs is a saint and a hero.'

I must admit it hadn't occurred to me to endow him with these qualities, fond as I was of the old lad. And certainly his recent performance hadn't been over impressive.

'I'll tell you about him,' said Alice. 'We'd arranged to be married, all those years ago. The banns had been called, date set, church booked and everything. It wasn't to be a posh do: times were bad and Mick was out of work, but we were going ahead with it.

'I was one of eleven kids. My dad was dead and my mother was having a real struggle to make ends meet. She'd got behind with the rent and the landlord was threatening to throw the whole family into the street.

'So Mick went and pawned his best suit, his best boots and his watch and chain, and paid the money to the landlord. That left him with no decent clothes to be married in, and with no job he had no hope of getting them back in time for the wedding. So he postponed it: he wasn't going to show me up by standing at the altar with patches on his pants. It was another six months before we got wed.

'Later on, my eldest sister, a widow, died and left six kids. All my other brothers and sisters had more children than they could cope with, so we took them in. For years Mick worked all hours God sent to bring them up, and somehow we managed it. Thank God for his best suit: it was in and out of pawn like a yo-yo.'

I said goodbye to Mick in the kitchen.

Shuffling nervously, obviously trying to remember if there was something else he'd forgotten to do for Alice, he didn't look at all saintly or heroic. But I knew better, and against Mick's

124

five-foot-and-a-bit I felt quite small.

There's another name I'd like to add to the list of saints and heroes (or heroines) – Alice.

Mick had taken on enormous burdens for her sake, but she had made sure he didn't carry them alone. And in these later years, with her love and attention – not to mention the bloody good rows – she never failed to let him know how much he was appreciated.

Thank God, I thought, that out of everything in this world they'd found what they both most loved, cherished and deserved. Each other.

*   *   *

A couple who could not, in the widest terms, be said to deserve each other were Major Hawkins and Charlie Sloper. They had been described as one of the funniest double acts since Laurel and Hardy.

Major Hawkins was tall, erect, brisk and immaculately groomed, the epitome of an officer and a gentleman. Charlie Sloper was the exact opposite: the local poacher and ne'er-do-well, pint-sized, dirty and unbelievably smelly.

As a lieutenant, Major Hawkins had been Charlie's platoon officer in France in World War One, and he used to say that for that alone he deserved a medal. Charlie was hardly an exemplary soldier: in fact he was the most scruffy, idle, scrounging, malingering excuse for a soldier in the whole of the Somerset Regiment.

Major Hawkins would groan every time Charlie's unshaven and grimy face appeared among the morning's defaulters. After listening to Charlie's wild excuses he would pass the appropriate sentence and mutter under his breath, 'Desert, you squalid little man. For God's sake, *desert!*'

But one day, during an attack on the German lines, Hawkins was blown badly wounded into a flooded shell hole. He owed his life to Charlie, who leapt in after him and kept his head above water until help arrived – no mean achievement for a man whose own stubbly head scarcely topped five feet.

Back in civilian life, Major Hawkins married and settled down to a safe but dull job in an estate-agent's office. Charlie resumed his old trade of poaching and odd-jobbing. He contracted liaisons with several women, one after the other, all of whom had the good sense to clear off when their reforming zeal had exhausted itself against the immovable object of Charlie's life style.

The two old soldiers avoided each other for twenty years, but in World War Two, Major Hawkins was appointed commander of the local Home Guard. And who should appear in the ranks but Charlie.

'Oh, no,' muttered the Major as he faced another war saddled with Sloper.

This time it wasn't so bad. At least the Major saw Charlie only three or four times a week, and Charlie's nocturnal activities kept the Home Guard platoon supplied with wild game to supplement their domestic meat rations. The Major's patriotism would not allow him to buy anything on the black market – he even refused the odd bits of extra meat offered by the butcher – but he could see nothing wrong in the occasional rabbit, hare or pheasant, so long as it was legitimately come by. And for that he had Charlie's solemn oath.

(Charlie's solemn oath lost a little of its credibility over the Christmas of 1943. The goose he supplied was delicious, and Major and Mrs. Hawkins enjoyed it enormously. But after the discovery of a chronic shortage of ornamental geese on the lake of the local manor house, Charlie got a severe talking-to.)

After the war, Major Hawkins found life lacking in savour. His job was dull and not too well paid. His social-ladder-climbing wife, who had hoped for better things from him, chose their friends. So he started going into the public bar of the Tadchester Arms to renew his association with Charlie.

It had to be the public bar: Charlie was not allowed in the saloon for a dozen good reasons. Although the Major looked distinctly out of place, he quickly became very popular with the regulars as a fount of knowledge, arbiter of bets and arguments, but most of all because of the repartee between him and Charlie.

The Major played up to his officer image, greeting Charlie with 'Good morning, Sloper, you squalid little man. Gad, if the Germans had only known.'

Charlie would respond with a few bars of *Colonel Bogey*, a raspberry and a sophisticated 'Piss orf!' Then the real fun would start. For an hour they would insult each other until the air was blue.

Sometimes they would have arguments in earnest, usually after Charlie had done something anti-social such as scrumping from the Major's fruit trees, or been caught green-handed with a cabbage from Mrs. Hawkins' kitchen garden. Mostly, however, it was purely in fun. Their bonds grew even stronger after the Major's six-month illness, during which Charlie walked his dog twice a day, even though Mrs. Hawkins would allow him no nearer the house than the garden gate.

It wasn't possible to blame Mrs. Hawkins entirely: she had let him in once and he and the very sick Major had got roaring drunk on a bottle of scotch which Charlie had smuggled in. Mind you, it probably did him more good than a whole arsenal of antibiotics.

*   *   *

So the strange friendship went on: fun for everybody and especially for the two old Contemptibles. But eventually the years began to tell.

Charlie grew progressively scruffier, dirtier, smellier. His clothes, which he filched from dustbins and whatever was thrown out at the end of jumble sales, became tattier and more bizarre. A worn but well-made leather brogue on one foot, a teenager's training shoe on the other; on one hand a fur-lined gauntlet, on the other a perforated lightweight driving glove: this was nothing unusual. And in between was a collection of faded, dirty, greasy tatters which would have disgraced a scarecrow.

127

He seemed to have given up washing altogether. Round about Christmas time he would appear with his face a few shades lighter, but his beard remained untouched. The public bar regulars gave him plenty of room, especially when the bar warmed up.

For years bets had been laid about what colour Charlie would be underneath if he ever really washed. The nearest anybody came to knowing was when he spilled some brown ale on his hand and rubbed it against his coat. The man nearest to him swore that he had glimpsed a flash of white, but it needed corroboration before the bets could be paid ... and by the time another witness was called, Charlie had rubbed his hand again and smeared it back to its original off-black colour.

Charlie's home, an old unsanitary cottage, was apparently very much like Charlie himself, and you entered at your peril. Fine if you didn't mind fleas, lice and bubonic plague, but not so good if you had any reservations about such things. I had no opportunity to find out: Charlie never ailed, never had done in the whole of his life, and seemingly wasn't going to start now.

As Charlie became scruffier over the years, so the Major became more fastidious. And both men became less patient with each other, each prone to fly off the handle and turn the ritual banter into something approaching the nasty.

Things came to a head one warm evening. Charlie sat in the public bar, steadily ripening. One by one the regulars shifted their seats. Finally, the corner was occupied only by Charlie and Major Hawkins.

Suddenly the Major peered intently at Charlie's beard, through the tangle of which he had spied something crawling.

'You dirty, unspeakable little man!' he bellowed. 'You've got cooties!'

'No I ain't,' protested Charlie, hurriedly wiping his beard. 'That's a drop of brown ale.'

'It's the only gravity-defying brown ale I've ever seen!' roared the Major. 'The bloody thing was walking upwards. My God, I should have had you shot when I had the chance!'

128

'And I should have left you in that bloody shell hole!' screeched Charlie.

That was the only mention of the shell hole either of them had ever made in public. And those were the last words they spoke to each other.

Major Hawkins stalked out of the bar, followed by raspberries and shouts of 'Piss orf!' from Charlie, and never came back to the Tadchester Arms.

A few months later the Major died. Quite suddenly, quite painlessly, and with no warning at all.

Mrs. Hawkins dealt with his death in the same brisk way she had dealt with his long illness of several years before. As soon as the death certificate was signed, she had the Major's old dog put to sleep. The funeral notices announced, 'Private ceremony. No flowers.'

Outside the lichgate of the church, as the hearse arrived, stood a little man whom nobody recognised: spruce, trim, silver-bearded, wearing a neatly pressed suit, on the breast of which hung a set of old campaign medals.

As the coffin was lifted onto the shoulders of the pallbearers, the little man sprang to attention and, ramrod straight, threw a perfectly timed and precise army salute.

'Who is that chap?' asked the manager of the estate agents', who was escorting Mrs. Hawkins at the head of the small band of mourners.

'I've really no idea,' she said.

And no more she had, until the coffin was lowered onto the trestles in front of the altar. There on the lid was a small bunch of flowers which that morning had been growing in the window box of the Tadchester Arms.

Charlie always had a way of getting round regulations. And, for once, Major Hawkins would have approved . . .

CHAPTER 12

Age and Dignity

After Alice had fully recovered from her pneumonia, I made an appointment for her to see Mr. O'Malley, specialist at Tadchester Hospital.

'O'Malley,' said Alice to her daughter Phil as she prepared for the trip. 'He sounds like a good little Catholic to me. Do you reckon he's a little Catholic, Philomena?'

'Look here, mother,' said Phil. 'It doesn't matter if he's a Bush Methodist or sitting on a bed of nails. You're going there for an examination, not Communion. Now don't you dare mention anything about religion.'

'I won't, I won't,' said Alice. 'Not a word. But it would be nice if he turned out to be a little Catholic.'

Mr. O'Malley broke the news.

'You have gallstones, Mrs. Mitchell, and a stomach ulcer. Normally I would operate, but because of your age and your breathing, I think it would be too much of a risk. Don't worry at all: just take things a bit steadier from now on.'

'Oh, thank you, Mr. O'Malley,' said Alice. 'I knew you'd find out what was wrong with me. With a name like that you had to be good.

'Tell me,' she said, before the horrified Phil could stop her,

131

'are you by any chance a little Catholic?'

'Little' hardly described Mr. O'Malley's sixteen stone weight and prop-forward build, but he replied, 'Yes. As a matter of fact I am.'

'Saints be praised!' Alice exclaimed. 'I knew it all along. Didn't I tell you, Philomena?'

As Phil blushed and spluttered, Alice grabbed Mr. O'Malley's hand.

'I'd just like to thank you ever so much for sorting me out. It must be a terrible job you've got, telling people what's wrong with them all day. I don't know how you stand it. The strain must be something cruel. You just make sure that you relax now and again and get plenty of sleep. And don't brood over things. You could make yourself poorly like that, you know.'

Alice left, almost frogmarched out by the embarrassed Phil. She left behind her a specialist who suddenly felt very tired, very worried and very, very sorry for himself – good little Catholic though he was.

*   *   *

Philomena Fraser visited Tadchester Hospital every week on early closing day to do the hair of the old ladies in the geriatric ward. All she charged was the cost of the materials: her own time and skills she gave for nothing.

Even though in many cases the hair was down to a few white and wispy strands, the fact that it was still worth the attention of a hairdresser raised the morale and self-respect of the old dears no end.

Phil's hairdressing sessions were the social highspot of the week. The old ladies gathered in the little room used as the salon, and sat around as if they were at Vidal Sassoon's. They read magazines as they waited, and chatted away to each other as if they had met for the first time that week.

The sessions were always full of laughter. Phil called all the 'customers' by their first names, and joked incessantly with them.

132

'Come on, Edie, love,' she'd say as an old dear tottered slowly to the chair. 'The rollers will be cold by the time you get here.' And, 'What do you fancy this time, darling? Something a bit more sexy? Be careful, though: you don't want to get that young doctor going, do you? You know what he's like when he sees you . . . especially with your teeth in.'

The good humour of the afternoon lasted all evening, long after Phil had packed her gear and gone home. The old ladies would be admiring each others' coiffures, recalling all the jokes and laughing at the sauciness until well after lights out.

The sessions were threatened though, after the matron dropped in on one of them. She stood in the doorway of the room, coldly observed the scene, listened to the banter for a few minutes, then left.

As Phil walked down the corridor after the session, lugging the drier and a suitcase full of equipment, she was hailed from the matron's office: 'I say, Hairdressah!'

'Yes, matron?' said Phil cheerily, dropping her gear and poking her head round the office door.

'Come in and close the door behind you, Hairdressah,' said matron. 'There's something I have to say.'

'What's up?' asked Phil, her smile fading at the look on matron's face.

'You must remember that this is a hospital, Hairdressah, not a social club or a beauty parlour. We expect certain standards of behaviour and have certain rules for the benefit of all which must be observed. I'm sure you understand.'

'No, I don't,' said Phil. 'Not a word. What are you on about?'

'Your conduct of the hairdressing sessions,' said matron. 'It puts the wrong ideas into the patients' heads. They are old ladies, not silly bits of girls. Your visits leave them chattering and giggling like flibbertigibbets and totally unamenable to discipline.

'Furthermore, I notice that you are in the habit of addressing them by their first names. This must cease. It has always been a firm rule that patients are to be addressed by their correct

133

titles: Miss or Mrs. followed by their surnames. Is that clear, Hairdressah?'

Phil stood there for a second, shocked and disbelieving, then came suddenly to the boil.

'It's perfectly clear, matron. Now I'd like to make a few things clear to you. Firstly, my name is not Hairdressah. It is Mrs. Philomena Fraser. Everybody calls me Phil, but to you, it's Mrs. Fraser.

SCISSORS! COMB!

'Secondly, I am perfectly aware that they are old ladies. And so are they; only too aware. The one thing they crave is to be young and attractive again. I can't give them back their youth and I can't make them pretty. But I can make them feel good, if it's only for one afternoon a week. You look after their bodies. The consultant geriatrician looks after their poor old minds. But I make them feel *feminine*. And at eighty-odd that must be a good thing for a woman to feel.'

'Now look here!' snapped matron.

'I've not finished yet,' said Phil. 'Thirdly, they like being

134

called by their first names: even by the nicknames they had when they were young. Miss Victoria Patience Bassington loves nothing more than to be called Buster, the name she had when she was captain of her school hockey team all those years ago. Mrs. Sarah Elizabeth Holmes was Sally as a girl; inside that old body she's still Sally.'

'I shall report your conduct and your attitude to the proper authorities,' said matron.

'Report away,' said Phil. 'Fourthly, the old loves I have sitting around the hairdressing sessions are completely different from the apathetic souls who sit around the ward all week. They relate to each other, they come alive, they're having an adventure. Above all, they're having some laughs. That may be against the rules, but in my book it's the finest tonic in the world.'

'I think it's high time . . .' said matron.

'You're right,' said Phil. 'It's high time I left. But I shall be back for next week's session and conduct it exactly as I have been doing, and shall continue until such time as I'm told to go. But remember: I'm not doing this for money, and I'm certainly not doing it for practice. I'm doing it because I love these old dears and I might just be making their last days a little more bearable.

'You must excuse me now, I have a family to look after and they'll be wanting their tea. And you have to make your report.'

The matron's report went in to the next meeting of the hospital committee. It didn't stay before them long: the committee members visited the hospital frequently and were well aware how much the old ladies enjoyed Phil's visits. They went further than just dismissing the report: they asked the consultant geriatrician to have a quiet word with the matron, pointing out the psychological benefits of the hairdressing sessions. He was glad to do it, and from then on Phil had no more trouble.

Matron never addressed her as 'Hairdressah!' again. In fact

she never addressed her at all if she could avoid it, but when she did it was, 'Mess-ezz Fraysah!'

'Really funny, that,' said Phil. 'She sounds just like Charles Laughton in *Mutiny on the Bounty*. And perhaps it's not entirely coincidence.'

*   *   *

What matron couldn't accomplish, old Nellie Raines almost did.

Nellie was within a couple of days of her ninetieth birthday, and Phil gave her a really special hairdo.

'There you are, love,' said Phil, after she had combed the last curl into place and put Nellie's spectacles on her nose so that she could see into the mirror. 'How does the birthday girl like that?'

Nellie peered into the mirror and her wrinkled old face lit up.

'It's beautiful, Phil,' she said. 'Beautiful.'

'Right, then,' said Phil, turning away to pick up a towel. 'We'll have you out of there, me old love, and get to work on the next young lady.'

When Phil turned back, Nellie was still sitting there, looking into the mirror with a blissful smile on her face.

'Come on, Nellie,' said Phil. 'We know you're beautiful, but you can't sit there all day admiring yourself. Who's next for shaving?'

Another old lady got up and hobbled towards the chair. Still Nellie didn't move.

'Nellie, darling,' said Phil. 'You'll have somebody sitting on your knee if you don't shift yourself. Let's be having you, Nellie? Oh, my God . . .'

Her eyes still open, and smiling rapturously, Nellie was stone dead.

'I nearly gave it up there and then,' Phil said to me afterwards. 'But I told myself that in a geriatric ward, this was always on the cards and it didn't seem to upset the others too much. The next old dear hobbled up, looked at Nellie, and said, "She's dead, you know. But doesn't she look lovely? So happy."

'After Nellie had been taken away, I carried on. The others were expecting it, and I knew that if I broke off then I'd never go back. Poor Nellie, missing her birthday. But the other old dear was right. She did look lovely . . . and so happy.'

CHAPTER 13

Growing Up

My children were growing up, as all children do, too quickly. Trevor had passed his eleven-plus and would be leaving the junior school that Paul still attended. It was the only school he had ever known.

The boys were quite different in temperament. Trevor was an avid reader, studious, and not athletically inclined. Paul was the extrovert, the all-round gamesman, always kitted out with the latest games equipment. Even by himself, he would not dream of knocking a cricket ball about in the garden without wearing white flannels, pads, cricket boots, batsman's gloves, a white sweater and a club cap.

Games at the junior school were limited. The school had few facilities and the curriculum allowed little time to play. The pupils, however, nearly all got through the eleven-plus.

The school did produce one outstanding sporting personality: the only truly consistent team manager that I have ever come across. She was the boys' games mistress: one Miss Polonsky. Polish, in her sixties, she wore ankle-length skirts and gym shoes, and ruled her team with a rod of iron.

She was straight 5:3:2:1 on formation. When she gave you your position on the field, this was your position for life. Each

position had its own strict geographical limitation. The goal-keeper could not cross the goal-lines; neither back could leave the penalty area; the half-backs could not cross the halfway line and had to stick to their respective parts of the field, either left, right, or centre. The forwards could not cross the halfway line, backwards, that is. They had to keep pressing ahead. If the left wing should wander over to the right, it could mean fifty lines and an hour's detention. If the centre-forward deviated anywhere from the midfield he was likely to get a rap across his kneecap with a heavy whistle.

The system resulted in Trevor, who had as much athletic grace as a young hippo, getting his only good report for sport. In the space for games were the words 'Football. Good positional player'. He was the right-back and it suited him to stand happily on one spot for the hour-and-a-half of his games afternoon. Wild horses could have dragged him out of the area – but only after a struggle.

His companion in the penalty area, the left-back, was a boy

of great ability and the star of the team. It was easy to imagine his frustration at being confined to the few yards of the penalty box. One day, with a rebellious outburst, he neatly took the ball from the foot of one of the opposing forwards in his own penalty area. As if the ball were glued to his boots, he twinkled magically through the field, beat the ten men in front of him with yards to spare, and scored a thundering goal.

The games mistress immediately ruled him offside, and his subsequent gesture (which he claimed was a victory sign but was really something very rude) resulted in his being sent off and barred from football for a fortnight.

While Trevor was at the school the football side never won a game. Nor were there records anywhere registering a win under this particular management.

Miss Polonsky had been games mistress for twenty years when the boys arrived. The school's continuing lack of goals under her leadership would qualify her as material for the *Guinness Book of Records*. As she always explained, it is taking part, not winning, that is the essence of sport. And at least her teams were consistent.

*   *   *

Having children brought us a new range of friends. The children were always going to parties, and there were picnics, and all the other usual comings and goings. This additional travelling presented new problems. It was fine when we lived Up-the-Hill as we were near public transport and walking to the town was no trouble. Since we had built our house near the river, we were a good mile-and-a-half away from the main centres of activities.

Pam longed to have a vehicle of her own, shortage of money being the only thing stopping her. One of the first things we did after building our house was to buy a boat. You could not live near the river's edge without a boat, and money spent on the boat meant no money for a car.

Kevin Bird, who had a finger in everything, solved the problem. 'A second vehicle is no problem,' he said. 'Come over to Winchcombe with me one Wednesday afternoon. I can get you something for about £30.'

I didn't believe it, but two weeks later he took me to a park behind one of the Winchcombe garages, full of derelict and rotting cars. The best and most presentable of them were a battered old Ford and a 10 cwt van. The van had a box-shaped body and a long battered bonnet, but looked in reasonable condition compared with the rest of the vehicles in the yard.

'That's the one,' said Kevin.

Knowing nothing about cars or engines, I could not contradict him and left him to do the haggling. He bought the van for £25.

We had been given a lift to the garage by one of Kevin's associates, confident that we would have something to drive back in. The journey in the old van was surprisingly uneventful. The hand brake was difficult to get off, the steering wheel did swing about a bit, and the traffic flipper indicators worked only spasmodically. But the thing did go.

We drove home to Millstone. This was the name we had given to our new house after I had finally paid all the bills, fixed up the mortgage and shuddered at the hidden extras.

I was so looking forward to seeing Pam on wheels of her own at last. I called to her from the drive, full of confidence.

'Surprise, surprise, darling. A cherished ambition is about to be fulfilled.'

'Oh, a car!' cried Pam, as she rushed outside to be confronted by the grey 10 cwt van. Her face dropped. Whatever she had been expecting to see, it certainly wasn't this.

'It will be useful,' she said, with a hint of sarcasm, 'for when you go net fishing.'

I couldn't deny that the thought had crossed my mind that it would be easy to stow all the fishing gear in the back.

'Anyway, providing it goes,' she said, 'I'll settle for it.'

The van was named Emily by the children and became part of the family folklore. As well as the minor defects so far encountered we found that unless you held the gear lever in place it tended to slip out of gear. Turning off roads often proved difficult. Changing down, you had to keep one hand on the gear lever. Not being able to rely on the traffic indicator, you had to stick one arm out of the window to indicate which way you were going. This left no free hand for the steering wheel, but steering with the knees isn't too difficult when you get used to it.

Emily's golden moment came when Pam was driving the children home from school. She was taking Zara's son Nicholas back home, up the steep hill to their house. As she changed gear, the lever came right out of the box on the floor. Pam stabbed at the gearbox, managed to hit a bull's eye first time, somehow changed gear, and continued on up the hill.

The interior of the van had been whitewashed by some previous owner and there was always enough residual colour to mark your clothes if you sat at the back. For seats, we had five or six sections of sawn-off logs. They were not fastened down, so whenever the van tackled too steep a gradient Emily's passengers would slide towards the back doors.

But Emily was marvellous. Pam used to cart round Jane's pram in her. She could pack a dozen children in the back for a picnic or to go swimming. With our seine nets on board, we explored beaches for twenty miles along the coast.

Frank Squires and Eric found if they sat by the back doors of the van, facing each other, locked arms and swung to and fro as if they were rowing in opposite directions, they could make Emily's tail swing from side to side. This gave nightmares to the driver (usually me) but it was always good for a few laughs at the back.

Several friends borrowed Emily to move house. She could carry all but the largest furniture and never, mechanically, let us down. She was part of the family for five years, when with great reluctance she was used in part exchange for an elderly Ford Zephyr. We saw her intermittently for several years after this, always with a pang of nostalgia.

*   *   *

Our boat, a fourteen-foot, clinker-built dinghy with an outboard motor, did not give us quite the same fun as our dear van Emily. The river estuary was tidal and our front gate was about a hundred yards up the road from the water's edge. The heavy outboard had to be carried down to the boat whenever we used it, plus oars, rowlocks, a baler. There was also a square lug sail and mast that I had had made, convinced that one day I could sail the boat. As it had no keel, however, we were never able to manage it. We could only follow the direction of the wind, and that was usually in the opposite direction to wherever we wanted to go. To go boating at all, the tide had to be right, the weather had to be right, and I had to be off duty. For the first year we used it a lot, but as the years went by we used it less and less. It became whatever the nautical term is for a white elephant. After a while, for all the use it got, it could have been renamed the *Marie Celeste*.

Syd Boon, a boatman who had a boatshed on the river's edge just below our house, used to paint and caulk it for me every year and Horace Jewell, an old sailor patient, always made sure it was shipshape.

You had two options when you took out the boat: you could go either upstream or downstream. The important thing was to come back in with the water high, otherwise you had to drag the boat and yourself over two hundred yards of instant adhesive mud. I had two pairs of wellingtons sucked from my feet at various times when I had mistimed my journey home.

I only once ever went out to sea in her. It meant a three-mile journey down river. Kevin and Frank, both experienced sailors, came with me. At the mouth of the river we were exposed to the elements and the boat bobbed up and down like a cork. The others laughed at me as I pulled on a lifejacket and took my wellingtons off. The sea was not in my blood and I didn't intend to let it get in. I was only too pleased to get home, and after that confined myself to pottering about on the river, close to home.

The highlight of the boat's life was a picnic outing arranged for one summer Saturday. We were to go in convoy with Horace Jewell's boat. He had lent us his services and his boat for the day. I was to go on ahead by car and prepare the picnic.

In my boat were Pam, Jane, Paul, Trevor, Zara, Eric and Nicholas, and a little friend of Nicholas called Teresa. In Horace's boat were Kevin and Janice Bird, Frank and Primrose Squires, Philip and Joan Gammon and their two daughters, with Horace at the helm. The weight took the boats right down to their gunwales. I saw them safely off, then jumped in my car and drove up through the town to Wally Turner's farm. Wally and his wife Molly had prepared mountains of food, including cold roast and half-cooked chickens. We drove together across the fields down to the edge of the River Tad, which wound its way through Wally's land.

I put up a tent, set out the food, and lit a fire with a barbecue roasting spit over it. As soon as the boats came into view I hastily skewered the chickens and put them on the spit over the fire as if it was I who had given them this rich golden colour rather than Molly's gas stove.

The boats arrived with all passengers safe. They had met no particular hazards on the way up; in fact they were extremely encouraged at one point when an angler rose to his feet as my boat, skippered by Eric, passed him. The angler ran along the bank, waving at the boat, with all the children waving back at him. It was only when the boat veered near to the bank that they could hear the offensive language that accompanied the waving. The angler's line was caught on the boat's rudder. He was not at all pleased.

The river voyage had sharpened everybody's appetite, and the piles of food soon started to disappear. Wally and Molly were always marvellous hosts and whatever they produced always had a high cream content. Eight-year-old Teresa was found being sick behind a bush. On close questioning she admitted to having eaten eight paper cupsful of trifle and six cream cakes.

The climax of the afternoon was the illegal use of the seine net in the river. You had to have a special licence to use a net in this part of the river. But we were amateurs and thought that it would be fun just to see if we could catch anything.

Our seine net was about eight feet wide and thirty yards long. It had a row of cork floats on the top, and lead weights keeping the bottom rope down.

We managed to straddle it across the two boats and started to row upstream. As soon as the net was fully in the water, the current in this narrower part of the river caused the boats to be dragged downstream however hard we rowed. We got to the bank with a struggle. We had kept the two ends of the net upright and somehow we all got on to the bank and began to draw the ends in.

There was tremendous excitement on the bank. The children had never seen us net fishing before – we had always done it at night on the coast.

As the net came in something startlingly white could be seen at the far end. The excitement among the kids rose to fever pitch. With one last heave the whole net was on the bank and Frank rushed forward with a stick to stun the great white fish at the end of the net.

The children crowded round. Suddenly the most hysterical laughter came from Philip, who was unfolding the net. He stood in front of it, pushing back the children who were crowding round to see our catch. I shoved past him to see what was causing his merriment. Then I fell about in hysterics and helped him block the view. Our gleaming white object, our magic fish, had turned out to be a male contraceptive device whose other name is given to the correspondence you use if you have a pen pal in France.

The children were disappointed that they didn't see the catch and could not understand the hysterical laughter from the adults. But later they all voted it their best day ever.

Since then the kids have grown old enough to be told the story of the catch and to understand the adults' embarrassment.

'Full marks, dad,' said Paul several years later, stretching his six-foot-odd length on the settee. 'That's one true fishing story that's not boring. Something I'll be able to tell my grandchildren. Memories are made of this ...'

CHAPTER 14

Schooldays

Just before I came to Tadchester, George Tonbridge had arrived with ambitions to run his own school. A teacher and educationalist with very definite ideas of his own, George started off with fifteen boys. In eleven years he had built up a boys' public school with 300 pupils.

George was a man of tremendous energy and enthusiasms. As it was his school, his money, he reckoned that he had the right to make changes of any kind at any time. As the school grew in size he would wander round, making instant, erratic and empirical decisions – that a new classroom should be built, or an old one pulled down or moved. He changed the site of the swimming pool three times altogether, twice after excavations had started, and would wander into a class and intervene with his own brand of instruction, regardless of the subject or who was teaching it.

He nearly drove his staff mad and, indeed, there was a steady turnover on the fringes. The majority, however, stayed with him. He had an infectious magic which almost always won through, and which could fill the most hesitant or timid teacher full of confidence.

It must have been this infectious magic which persuaded me

to take on the job of school medical officer: I can't think of anything else which would have made me do it. It was rewarding in many ways, but added an extra dimension of worry I could well have done without.

Many of the boys' parents were based overseas. In trying to do their best for their children from great distances, they would send demands for all sorts of unnecessary medical treatment. There would be a telegram from Brazil saying, 'UNDERSTAND JAMES BUMPED HEAD THREE WEEKS AGO stop IMPERATIVE HEAD IS X-RAYED.' Other parents were of homoeopathic bent and would leave instructions that their son must never have antibiotics or other such medicines, and that at any hint of illness he should be whipped up to London to see some chosen homoeopath or chiropractor.

I sometimes forgot, and gave James or whoever the normal treatment, earning myself virulent letters from Hong Kong or the Philippines saying I would be reported to the British Medical Association, struck off, or at the very least sorted out in some way the next time the parents were in England.

With so many boys going to so many different places at holiday times, the last month of term was always a nightmare. I had to see that each boy had the vaccinations and immunisations required for his particular destination. However many notices the school matron put on the board there would always be one or two boys turning up the day before they were about to leave school saying, 'I'm off to Chile tomorrow.' (Or Morocco or Bombay or Djakarta) 'Do I need any injections?'

I found that being school medical officer took up a disproportionate amount of my time. Not only did the job entail dealing with sick boys and anxious parents, it also meant routine medical examinations, attendance at boxing and rugby matches, sports days and speech days. Not only that, some of the teachers would regard me as their own private doctor and accost me in the common room with all sorts of real and imaginary afflictions. Being highly educated, teachers not only required medical treatment but also a detailed explanation of exactly what was going on and what effect the treatment would have. It was all rather tedious.

I tried, patiently, to explain that to understand fully what I was saying, they ought really to have had two years' anatomy and physiology and three years' clinical medicine, and a pharmacy degree on the side.

Once or twice I marched into George's study to resign. Inevitably I came out cheerful, resolute and brimming over with confidence. What George had said had really inspired me. The strange thing was that I could never remember what he *did* say.

One day I asked, 'George, how do you cope with all this – the boys, the staff, the parents, the organising, the expansion? Don't you ever feel like packing it all in?'

(This time I did remember his answer.)

'I taught maladjusted children for several years,' said George. 'It cost me my fiancée and almost my sanity before I finally quit. Compared to that, this is easy. A piece of cake.'

George's story of his time at the school for maladjusted children had me convinced that coping with this present school really *was* a piece of cake, and I felt guilty about complaining. The maladjusted children he had taught were very bright. In many cases their superior intelligence was a factor in the maladjustment.

The policy of the school was to make information on their maladjustment available to the boys, to help them come to terms with it. Naturally, they talked among themselves with the consequence that every boy in the school knew what the others' symptoms were. Sometimes they would taunt each other with their conditions: 'Yah! Soppy old Turner! Enuretic, aren't you, Turner? Old pee-the-bed! Old soggy pants.'

The boys called all the teachers, including the headmaster, by their first names. Their conversation was as frank and open as their language was colourful. And this led to the split between George and his fiancée, Hilda.

Hilda still lived in George's home town, Cheltenham, so George's appointment to the school had meant a separation. She came down in the summer for Open Day. A good-looking girl, and a natural blonde, she immediately attracted the attention of the boys.

'Hey, George!' they called. 'Nice bit of stuff you've got there. Bet she's a right goer! What's her name?'

George introduced Hilda, who was blushing madly.

'Are you and George having it away then, Hilda?' asked one of the boys.

'What's he like in bed, Hilda?' asked another.

'Never mind about George, Hilda darling,' said another, all of twelve years old. 'I can give you a much better time. See you behind the pavilion in ten minutes. Any way you like it...' And here he launched into a list of sexual techniques which would have made a sailor blush.

'George!' commanded Hilda. 'Stop this boy's filthy mouth!'

'All right, Geoff,' said George. 'Do me a favour.'

The boy stopped.

'And make him apologise!' said Hilda.

'Certainly not,' said George.

The school encouraged the boys to talk freely as part of their therapy. While they were talking they were getting things out of their systems and unconsciously providing clues about their maladjustments.

After another demand for an apology and another refusal, Hilda stormed off. That was the last George saw of her. A couple of days later she returned the engagement ring in the post.

'I was very cut up at the time,' said George. 'But it was all for the best. She'd have made a dreadful teacher's wife, even in a school where the kids were normal.'

'And was that what made you give up maladjusted teaching?' I asked.

'I'd rather you rephrased that,' George chuckled. 'God, no. It took more than Hilda. It was young Simpson. And the longest ten seconds of my life.'

He paused and gazed absently out of the window.

'Go on, for God's sake, George,' I said. 'Don't leave it there.'

'Sorry. Yes, young Simpson. About fourteen he was. Sickly,

151

asthmatic. Parents at daggers drawn. Bullying father, director of a big merchant bank, despised his son because he was physically weak. Over-protective mother. Just about all you need for a maladjustment.

'He was bright, that boy. Wipe me off the chess board in ten minutes and run rings round me at bridge. But disturbed . . . he was possibly the worst case the school had had to handle.

'It was the usual things at first: breaking windows, odd bits of sabotage, provocative behaviour. All really appeals for attention; cries for help. I spent a lot of time, and so did the other staff, trying to make him see that people did care for him, did worry about him.

'But it's difficult for outsiders to replace the love which ought to come from inside the family, and his behaviour grew worse. One night he set fire to the dormitory curtains. Another time he picked up the school cat, which had wandered into the dorm, and its fur brought on an attack of asthma. The little sod did no more than throw the cat through the window, straight through the glass. The dorm was on the second floor and the poor cat broke its back.

'It was in that dorm we had the confrontation which made me realise I was not God. If I were, I think I'd resign: being God is no fun.

'I was doing the rounds at lights out when some boys came running from the top dorm. It was Simpson, they said. Out on the window ledge. Threatening to jump.

'I ran up to the dorm and there he was; out on the ledge. In his pyjamas on a bitter winter's night. I made the boys stay clear and I went to the window to try to talk him back in. The proper drill, I suppose, would have been to have called the police and fire brigade. But by the time they arrived – remember this was way out in the sticks – he would either have jumped, fallen or frozen to death.

'With every attempt I made to make him see reason, he became more and more bitter. "You're like all the rest of them," he kept saying. "No better than my bloody father. Nobody in this world gives a damn about me and I'm better off

152

out of it!''

'Finally, after no argument had had the slightest effect on him, I decided on the most awful gamble. "All right," I said. "Jump, you little bastard. Jump!"

'He looked at me in total disbelief and I was able to hold his eyes in a battle of wills. Suddenly he burst into tears, crumpled on the ledge, and held out his arms to me. I grabbed him, yanked him in, and held him like a baby while he sobbed his heart out.

'From my challenging him to his collapsing seemed like ten years. I found out later it was exactly ten seconds.

'From that night on Simpson began to improve. Even his asthma attacks became less frequent. He realised that he had cried wolf once too often and that his bluff had been called, and better then than later in life. We became great friends, but that was the end of my work with maladjusted kids. I couldn't go through another trauma like that. At the end of the year I left to start the school here with some money from a legacy.

'So you can understand now, Bob, why this place really is a piece of cake. Now then, what was it you wanted to see me about. . .?'

*　　*　　*

A few weeks after my conversation with George, he began to have problems which confirmed very much the old saying that you can't have your cake and eat it.

The first problem was related to the screening of a television series on escapes from a prisoner-of-war camp. Boys started disappearing during the night and reappearing a hundred miles away three days later, having been living on turnips and making forced marches by night.

As most of the parents of the 'escapees' lived on the other side of the world, the Post Office made a huge profit from long-distance telephone calls and telegrams until the TV series ended and the boys gave up the habit.

Although this first problem seemed to have been solved, there were shorter-lived and inexplicable disappearances.

153

George was beginning to wonder if he was losing his reason.

The science block was a prefabricated, single-storey building, and out of bounds after school hours. George noticed an increasing number of boys hanging round the block outside lesson times, and on three occasions actually saw boys enter.

He rushed to the building to nail the culprits, but inside there was no trace of anyone. He looked in cupboards, under desks, but there was just no one. George even went to the optician to have his eyes checked. He had heard of people having floating bodies in their eyes: he wondered whether it was these bodies that were floating into the science block.

He admitted his fears to the head of the science department who, to George's relief, had noticed exactly the same phenomena but had not liked to say anything for fear of looking foolish.

They decided to lay a trap. The science block had two rooms and two entrances. So on a Wednesday half-day George and the science master kept watch and saw six boys go into the science block, one by one.

'We've got them this time!' said George. He rushed to cover one entrance, while the science master covered the other.

Both rooms of the building were completely empty. They had noted the names of the six boys going in, but all were present at an immediate roll call in the grounds. Definitely nobody had left the block.

One afternoon the science master smelled cigarette smoke in class. He was convinced that some boy was smoking behind his desk. No boy would admit to it so the master paraded round the room, determined to solve this crime at least.

There was no sign of any cigarette behind any desk. But over a trap door leading to the floor space below the room, he thought the smoke hung a bit more heavily than it did anywhere else. He pulled open the trap door and was met by a blaze of electric light and a dense cloud of cigarette smoke. He peered through the trap ... and saw a sheet-lined, underground cavern, lit with a string of electric light bulbs.

Lying on cushions, smoking cigarettes, with a bottle of beer each to hand, were three sixth-formers.

The guilty parties were hauled out and the whole story eventually extracted.

It was a hangover from the escaping days. The boys had found the floor space that lay under the two classrooms, with a trap door to each. A few enterprising ones had dug a connecting tunnel, perfectly shored up, to the groundsman's store shed. The mains had been tapped to produce electric light, sheets stolen to line the walls, and blankets to carpet the floor. What had started off as a hidey-hole for two or three was gradually extended. Boys who found out about it had to join the underground organisation, and in all thirty-six boys admitted belonging to it.

George laughed when he told me about it. 'The awful thing is,' he said, 'I have to punish them. I really ought to give them marks for initiative.'

The ringleaders were suspended for two weeks and the

participants were made to fill in the underground cavities and all do an extra term's work on the allotments. As George said, they were so fond of the earth he would let them have a proper go at it – in daylight.

It was reassuring to know that, if ever (God forbid) there was a future war our school had produced, among the many fine scholars and athletes, a goodly number of highly trained escapees and tunnellers,

CHAPTER 15

Writers' Summer School

Bob Barker, my bookseller friend at Sanford-on-Sea, was always encouraging me to have a go at writing. So, too, was Herbert Hodge, local taxi-driver-cum-author, who had been an extremely successful writer and broadcaster. I procrastinated. Life was very full with medicine, Round-Table activities, fishing, friends, family and the children. I was always making the excuse that I would get round to writing when I had time.

We had living in Tadchester one well-known author, Joan Courage. She had written well over thirty books and had contributed to a number of radio and television programmes. I asked her advice about writing.

'You don't go round asking people whether you should start writing or not, Bob,' she said. 'You just get down and do it. Lack of time is no excuse. I know you are a busy doctor, but what time do you get up in the morning?'

'About 7.30,' I said.

'Get up at six' said Joan. 'And write until 7.30.'

She paused just long enough to allow this to sink in, then continued, 'If you are really interested in becoming a writer I suggest that you come with Connie White and myself to the

writers' summer school in Derbyshire. You will have a week under the same roof with 350 other aspiring writers. There are courses on different aspects of writing, such as the short story, writing for radio and television, as well as celebrity lectures and a hectic social life. It lasts a week and it's inexpensive.

'Meanwhile, don't ask me again whether you should start writing. Either get on with it or be quiet about it.'

Considerably chastened I came home and discussed it with Pam. She thought that I had been working too hard and that a writers' school would provide a welcome break.

The longer I lived in Tadchester, the greater my work load had become. The number of people who depended on me for support rather than for actual straightforward medical treatment steadily increased. So many people had such horrendous lives for a whole variety of reasons. I found I was advising them to cope with situations that I felt certain I could not have coped with myself.

I knew that Steve Maxwell carried an even greater work load than I did, and I just didn't know how he managed. I sometimes felt like the man in the variety act who spins plates on the top of canes. He increases the number of plates until in the end he has about thirty spinning, and has to rush from one to the other, giving them a twist to keep them going, trying to stop any of them falling to the ground.

I told Steve and the others that I was going to a writing school, and from then on they all pulled my leg. There would be notes reading, 'Would Somerset Maugham please go and see Mrs. Brown up the hill', or 'Could Mr. Cronin spare a minute after the evening surgery.'

I felt I had to make a start by writing something before I went to the school, if only to justify my attendance there. I followed Joan's advice and got up early in the mornings, and as Bob Barker had suggested I started to write down some of my own experiences.

A patient I greatly admired was Miss Gill, a delightful elderly lady, who had made a great success of living although she had been bedridden for forty-seven years, looked after by her friend Miss Booth. She once said, 'People come to see me because I have time to listen.'

I built up a little story about her and Miss Booth and a robin that used to visit them, and how they were affected by a television set they were given. After forty-seven years the television set freed Miss Gill from her bed. For four months she was able to watch things such as a Royal wedding, church services, cricket matches and tennis matches before she quietly died.

It was when I tried to put my thoughts down on paper that I realised the depth and strength of character of these two delightful ladies. What a wonderful couple, what a marvellous story.

The other story I tried to write was about Ben Fellowes, an upholsterer with cancer of the lung who kept on asking for the date when he was going to die. He tidied up his affairs and died on the exact day that he was told he was going to.

Ben was very brave and had great natural dignity. I wrote of him: 'I only knew him in this last phase of his life, but I always felt that he was one of those few men who, spurning hope, have the rare courage to see things as they are. When he saw the problem without adornments he said to himself, "The only thing that I have left to do is to die. I will make the best job of it I can."'

159

Joan encouraged me to submit my stories to the Talks Department of the BBC. She showed me how to present the manuscripts, and I had them typed and sent them off. Joan warned me that it would be months before I heard anything from them and added that I should not be too hopeful as the chances of having one's first scripts accepted were pretty slim.

Nothing ventured, nothing gained ... and at least I had actually written something.

Eventually it was time for the writers' summer school. Connie White came down to stay for a couple of days. She was a children's writer, and one of the wisest, nicest ladies I have ever met, a sort of female Bob Barker. I was to drive Connie, Joan and myself up to the school at Swanwick in Derbyshire.

Joan was a great talker. I don't think Tadchester could offer the intellectual stimulation that she really needed. Having Connie to talk to in the car allowed her to let rip. Joan was supposed to navigate but all three of us were so engrossed in conversation that we none of us took much notice of our direction. Eventually we found that we had missed the M1. We wandered round, finding our way and losing it again as Joan got off on some other subject. Our journey to Derby took us nine hours.

The conference centre where the school was held, The Hayes, was a large old country house that had been a prisoner-of-war camp during the war. It was said that the ghosts of some of the prisoners could be seen wandering the grounds at night. It was also said, however, that one had never been seen until after the bar had closed.

The Hayes was used mainly by religious bodies for holding their annual conferences. The writers' summer school was so different from all the rest of the conferences that the staff looked forward to it. Writers were less restrained than religious delegates: certainly there is nothing on record about church elders doing an impromptu strip on the last night of conference.

The main building was a seventeenth-century mansion containing offices, various libraries and recreation rooms, with corridors leading off to numbered individual cubicles. About two hundred yards away up a hill was the main residential block, The Garden House.

The first thing that struck me when I arrived at Swanwick was the noise. Everybody was talking nineteen to the dozen. It was worse than Connie and Joan in the car. Everybody had saved up fifty-one weeks of conversation and was determined to get rid of it in this one week.

To my surprise instead of being put into one of the cubicles I was given a room near the section of the house where the celebrities, lecturers and administrators were put up. A room with my own sink and toilet next door. Much better than the cubicles I had peeped into as I walked round the building. I popped in and thanked Marjorie Harris, the secretary of the school.

'Why have I been singled out for such favour?' I asked.

'Well,' said Marjorie (and I thought she blushed), 'Joan did mention that you were a doctor. We do have the occasional accident and we hoped you wouldn't mind our calling on you.'

'Not a bit,' I said. 'Only too pleased.'

Joan had said on the way up, 'Don't tell anybody you are a doctor.' She must have forgotten that she had already told Marjorie.

Having unpacked and wandered round the grounds I went into the lecture theatre for the Chairman's welcome. As the Chairman greeted us he named various celebrities, household names in the world of writing and publishing, each of whom stood up and took a bow.

I looked on them with great awe and couldn't believe that I would be able to rub shoulders with them and talk to them. Then, to my surprise and horror, my name was called. Dr. Robert Clifford, covered with embarrassment, was introduced to the assembly. It wasn't because of any potential writing ability.

The Chairman said, 'We have with us for the first time Dr.

161

Robert Clifford, a budding writer. He has kindly consented to cope with any medical emergencies while he is here. Have a good look at him; he is the man you want if you are ill.'

Suddenly I began to have doubts about being a doctor amongst writers.

The meal which followed the Chairman's introduction was incredibly noisy. Everyone was shouting to be heard. I was almost hoarse by the time it had finished. Afterwards I started back to my room to sort my things out.

There were seven or eight people standing in a line on the landing where my room was situated. I walked past them, wondering what the queue was for, and went into my room. When I got inside there was a knock on the door. I opened it to meet the head of the queue.

'Are you the doctor?' he asked.

'Yes.'

'May I see you? I have a problem.'

It seemed just like home. My heart sank.

'Come in,' I said.

'Well,' said the man, 'for the past seven or eight years I have had terrible indigestion after meals and have never had the time to see a doctor. Could you give me something for it?'

I wrote a prescription for a simple antacid, and suggested as kindly as I could that coming to see a doctor on holiday wasn't perhaps the best time or place. I let him out of the door. The line of people now numbered nine or ten. I realised that I was holding an evening surgery.

The queue for evening surgery grew each day. On the evening before we left there were twenty-four people waiting for me.

After the first lecture in the evening, given by a novelist who spoke extremely well, I wandered around drinking and talking. There was no chance of getting away from medicine. Everywhere I went, people greeted me with 'Hullo, Doc.'

I found myself with a group of about half a dozen people of roughly my own age, all experienced writers. I was fascinated to hear about their writing, and they were all wanting to hear

162

WRITER'S CRAMP! ...NEXT!

about medicine, happily from a writing point of view. Time flew. The first time I looked at my watch I discovered that it was four a.m.

I had just got back to my room when there was a knock on the door. Marjorie Harris said, 'Could you help us please? We have a lady at the school whose husband has just died of a coronary at home. Could you come and break the news to her.'

I had to go along and see this poor lady, who the day before had left her husband for the first time ever to come to the school. He had been perfectly all right on the railway platform when she waved him goodbye, and now, less than twenty-four hours later, he was dead.

She was a highly intelligent woman and took it all extremely bravely, but she was so shattered I offered to drive her back to Canterbury the next day. She was too numb to make any decision. I gave her a sedative and said I would see her in the morning. By the morning she had come to some sort of terms with her grief, was composed and had arranged for a friend to come up from home to fetch her.

163

Later that morning, I attended what the curriculum described as a writers' workshop. The man conducting the proceedings suddenly stopped in the middle of his talk, and started to pull things out of his pocket and look at them intently. He seemed unaware that we were all listening to him, and I realised something was wrong. I and another delegate managed to get the meeting closed and took him to his room.

'Where am I?' he said. '*Who* am I?'

I sat in his room with him and he went on continually: 'Who am I?... Where am I?... Who am I?' He had become completely disorientated.

There was one other doctor in residence, one of the celebrity writers, who was also a vet and a host of other things. He came over and relieved me at mealtimes.

As the day wore on there was no improvement. I rang the local health authorities and they sent a man over who agreed to admit the lecturer to hospital. I then had to escort the poor chap over to the hospital in Derby, not getting back until all the day's lectures and other functions were over. I did find my group of friends from the night before tucked away in one corner of the lounge. Somehow I didn't feel tired and once again our conversation went on and on. We explored themes and ideas, and this time it was five a.m. before I got to bed.

This became the pattern of the week. The following morning in the celebrity lecture an elderly lady collapsed and I had to help carry her out to her room and resuscitate her. The days and evenings became progressively filled with medicine and the nights with my special group of friends became longer. In the end we abandoned bed altogether and would set off in a convoy of cars to have breakfast at a transport cafe a few miles outside Derby. As well as my now established evening surgery I was consulting medically most of the day. One girl who was obviously miscarrying, I sent to hospital. Two other girls thought they were pregnant. One had five or six months' obvious evidence bulking out her skirt, so I was able to give her pretty definite confirmation.

The hospital rang to say that the lecturer I had taken in two

164

days before, was now fit. Would I collect him, and thereafterwards keep an eye on him? I was delayed in setting off: one of the elderly ladies fell and broke a hip and I had to give first aid and arrange for an ambulance.

I really was enjoying my week, in spite of it all. Sitting with my new friends at night, I had a freedom of mind that I hadn't had for many a long year. There was a highly charged and contagious atmosphere about the whole place.

I noticed the noise in the dining room was even louder than ever. We all seemed to be heading for some tremendous climax. On the last night I don't think anyone could have got any sleep at all. Nobody seemed tired and on the last morning, the Friday morning, emotions exploded. It was as if some huge and caring family were breaking up. A lot of the writers were returning to London in a fleet of hired buses and here were the most dramatic scenes of the week. Stony faced men and weeping women were watching friends and acquaintances depart. It must have been like this in the First World War when men were going back to the trenches.

I understood why. The week seemed to have been a year. My late-night group were now almost family and, in fact, I was to know them and their families for the rest of my life.

Our journey home was quiet; I think Joan and Connie had been able to get rid of every surplus word they had saved up for the last ten years. Without interruptions I was able to find all the right roads and we got home in seven hours. My eyes seemed to be glued to the windscreen. The lack of sleep, which I hadn't noticed at Swanwick, started to catch up with me.

Pam hugged me when I got back.

'What was it like having a week away from medicine?' she asked.

I smiled. 'Oh,' I said, 'there was just enough medicine to keep me going.'

I went to bed and slept solidly for forty-eight hours. I never ever tried to get completely away from medicine again.

*　　　*　　　*

Many years later, in fact, I had completely the opposite sort of experience to that at Swanwick. I opted to go on a trans-Saharan safari, and hoped desperately to be involved in medicine in foreign climes.

In the party of ten, three of us were doctors: a consultant lady gynaecologist, an American anaesthetist, and myself.

It had been my responsibility to collect the medical supplies for this venture. To be on the safe side I had got in enough to equip a medium-sized hospital. This included miniature operating sets, local and topical anaesthetics, several hundred antibiotic capsules, tablets, diarrhoea specifics, bandages, inflatable splints, suturing materials, water purifiers, antihistamines, steroids, insulin and the usual run of dangerous drugs.

My two colleagues, not trusting anyone else to take the right stuff, had come similarly equipped, thus tripling the quantity. If we hadn't discarded some of these supplies before we left base there wouldn't have been room for us to carry petrol and water, which the other members of the party seemed to think were more important.

We three colleagues were all geared up for medical drama, although the individual objects of our expedition were quite different. Our gynaecologist was all set to do a Caesar under local; the American anaesthetist was hoping to anaesthetise for her; and I was sure I could prove myself as an expert in resuscitation of babies in desert conditions.

We had taken a brief look into the medical histories of our companions. Of the seven, four still had appendices that had not yet been removed. There was a pretty good chance that at least one would be bad.

We were due to cover about 4,000 miles of the Sahara starting from the oasis of El Golea, that marked the end of the tarmacadam road, crossing the Tadémait Plateau to Ain Salah then on to the oasis of Tamanrasset in the Hoggar Mountains; travelling south to cross the border at In Guezzam into Niger. On to stay a few days at the native market town of Agadés; then east across the dreaded Ténéré Desert to the Bilma oasis. A few days there then north back into Algeria again to the oasis of Djanet. From Djanet an expedition across the Tasilli Plateau with pack donkeys to see and photograph the rock drawings (Tasilli frescoes). Then north through Fort Polignac and the Ouargla oasis back through the oil country to El Golea, then home.

Whatever the achievements of other trans-Saharan safaris, our claim must be that we were the healthiest. In the whole six-week journey, under a merciless sun, nobody was ill. We didn't even have a case of diarrhoea. Undismayed, we sought all the time to practise our skill on the local populace.

In the Hoggar Mountains at Assekrem near the hermitage of the famous French priest Charles Foucould, my two colleagues each pulled a tooth from the mouth of a wandering Arab woman when I wasn't looking. I inspected their handiwork later. The extractions couldn't have been too difficult – I'm certain that if the patient had sneezed she would have lost her complete set without any outside help.

We were getting depressed that nobody wanted us, desperate to be needed, and the three of us used to sit in one corner of the encampment speculating on the hopefully deteriorating health of our companions.

In Agadés in Niger the anaesthetist had an asthma attack which I managed to treat before the gynaecologist got to him. In Djanet in Southern Algeria the gynaecologist had to powder my athlete's foot. In the middle of the Ténéré Desert I had to remove a foreign body from her eye and wash it out afterwards. She wasn't so pleased when I said I would be claiming to be the first general practitioner ever to irrigate a lady gynaecologist in the middle of the desert.

At the Bilma oasis we saw a mosquito and made our presence felt by insisting that the camp site be moved thirty yards from the water and that everybody took anti-malarial drugs. I was the only person to be bitten and was so full of anti-everything that any mosquito sampling me would never make it home to base.

Climbing up to the Tasilli Plateau, the anaesthetist insisted on giving the guide two aspirins for a pain in the leg, when in fact he was only trying to tell us to go in a different direction.

We continued to look hopefully for signs of illness amongst the natives, but like members of the expedition they all looked disgustingly healthy. Before we realised it six weeks had slipped by and we were back at our base ready to fly home to England with our stores intact.

When I commiserated with my colleagues about our lack of opportunities for practising our skills, the gynaecologist told us in a snooty tone that for the last three or four evenings she had been paring the corns of the expedition leader. This was the meanest betrayal of medical ethics: knowing that he would require more than one treatment, she could have at least shared the duties.

The final ignominy was on returning to England, where I was summonsed by the Customs people for taking dangerous drugs out of the country without an export licence.

Long before the Saharan trip I had realised that you could never really get completely away from medicine. Once a doctor always a doctor. But it seemed that whenever you were trying to make an impression, you usually had to do it in competition with several of your colleagues.

A friend of mine, a doctor of philosophy, was once on a coach tour of the Nile Valley. One of the passengers was a beautiful and well-known actress. Getting off the coach one day she stumbled and hurt her ankle. She sat at the side of the road, clutching her ankle and sobbing with pain. The courier rushed back to the bus.

'Is there a doctor on board?' he asked.

My friend the doctor of philosophy rushed to help, but was beaten to the patient by a doctor of theology.

CHAPTER 16

More Things in Heaven and Earth

I do not believe in ghosts. I dare not and must not.

As a physician my function is to care for the body and, as an optional extra, the mind. As a matter of routine I am called upon to issue a death certificate, to confirm the obvious – that this body is a dead one – and to give my opinion on the cause of death.

In other and more harrowing cases, I am called in as part of a team to decide whether life, real life, is extinct. A young motorcyclist in collision with a lorry, for instance, may have a heart which is still beating, but his brain, which controls and governs the working of the rest of the body, perhaps damaged beyond repair.

The end of life is the point at which I have to set my limits as an adjudicator. Were I to worry about whether there is life after death, the whole of my own working life could very soon become insupportable.

I think about it, of course, and perhaps make one or two private admissions to myself; but if I am to do my job, it must be here ... on earth ... with the living. Once someone has crossed the border between life and death, then he or she is out of my care and hopefully in better hands.

* * *

Having got that off my chest, I can feel free to talk about the Tadchester ghosts. There were a lot of them about, as there are in every town and village in Britain with any kind of character or history. The manor house at Altriston was reputedly haunted by two ghosts; the statutory White Lady, said to be an ancestor of the Tyster family, and a priest to whom something nasty had happened during the Reformation.

Almost every old pub in the town had a ghost, though their credibility was more than open to question. The pub ghosts tended to be seen around closing time by customers whose objectivity and accuracy of observation – not to say ability to focus – were not at their best. Whenever a pub changed hands it was almost routine for the new landlord or his wife to claim to have seen the resident ghost.

'Great for business,' said Geoff Emsworth, landlord of the

Tadchester Arms, whenever another sighting was made in a local pub.

The Tadchester Arms itself had the most famous ghost; that of Henry VIII himself, who was supposed to have slept there during a peasant-bashing expedition in the West Country. And one night after hours he was seen in a dark corridor near the dining room above the pub by two new and subsequently terrified Chinese waiters.

The story received front-page treatment in the *Tadchester Echo*. It was accompanied by a photograph of the waiters, who were by now looking far from inscrutable, under the portrait of Bluff King Hal which hung in the dining room. For weeks afterwards the pub was thronged with people hoping to see the ghost.

It wasn't until much later that I discovered the truth. I was fishing with John Denton one evening. As he walked towards me along the bank, his back to the setting sun, I was looking at the silhouette of a big man wearing a rounded hat and a short cape, arms akimbo and with a straddle-legged walk: John in his pork-pie hat, open tweed jacket and wellington boots, with his thumbs tucked into his belt. The living image of the portrait in the pub. At least, to misquote W.S. Gilbert, 'In the dark with the light behind him.'

'My God, John,' I said. 'Anybody would take you for Henry VIII in that get-up.'

'Aye, lad,' he said. 'What do you think those Chinese lads saw? I'd been having one for the road with Geoff in his rooms after hours and I was letting myself out by the back stairs. You've never seen two blokes shift so fast in all your life. Not a word to anybody mind.'

'Naturally,' I said. 'But surely Geoff knew?'

'Of course he knew,' said John. 'I went back and told him. But he'd be daft to pass up a chance like that, wouldn't he? It's what he'd always said about the ghosts in other pubs – great for business . . .'

*   *   *

172

The Tadchester Arms' 'ghost' was all too solid. But a few weeks later I had a case which called for a less prosaic explanation.

Four-year-old Emma was brought to the surgery by her mother because of what she saw, or thought she saw, in her bedroom at night.

'Tell the nice doctor what you see, Emma,' said her mother.

'A kind grandma,' said Emma. 'She smiles at me and looks after me in the dark.'

She stopped. There was a faraway look in her eyes as if she were enjoying some very pleasant and private memory.

'I shouldn't worry,' I said to the mother. 'Children of this age often invent imaginary companions.'

'I don't think she invented this one,' said the mother. Then, to Emma, 'Tell us more about the kind grandma, love'.

'Well,' said Emma, 'she's ever so kind and ever so nice. Her dress has lovely ruffles around her neck. She wears a big badge in the middle of the ruffles. And she has these funny glasses on a stick.'

173

Emma went off into her trance again, a look of complete contentment on her face.

'Now, Doctor,' whispered the mother, 'both Emma's grandmothers are alive. Neither of them is as old as this lady sounds, and certainly neither of them dresses like she does.

'But an old lady – Miss Lingard – used to live in our house before us. I've asked neighbours who knew her and they all come up with the description of a kindly but eccentric spinster, who loved children, and who always dressed in Edwardian-style clothes.

'See what I'm getting at, Doctor? Every neighbour described her in the same way: wearing a high-necked dress with a lace ruff around the neck, a big cameo brooch pinned to the ruff, and using a lorgnette instead of conventional spectacles. It's Miss Lingard, Doctor, I'm sure!'

This really was a new one on me. At medical school they had mentioned nothing about spectral spinsters in out-of-date costumes. But the mother needed something to set her mind at rest.

'Emma is not distressed by the appearances?' I asked.

'On the contrary,' said her mother. 'She enjoys them, even looks forward to them. I'm sure she feels the old lady is protecting her in some way. It's just that, to me, it's so eerie.'

'The wisest course,' I said in my most convincing tone, 'would be to treat these appearances, whether they are actual appearances or just in Emma's imagination, as completely normal. When Emma mentions the old lady, show the same interest you would in an imaginary playmate.

'Make sure that she really is tired when she goes to bed, and give her a hot milk drink to help her sleep. I think you'll find that with time, as Emma develops more and more interests, these appearances will become fewer and in the end cease altogether. But please come back if there are any other developments.'

Not bad, I thought, for a piece of off-the-cuff, top-of-the-head prognosis and reassurance. But it seemed the right thing to say. I only hoped it would work.

It did. Twelve months later, the mother was in my surgery again and I asked about Emma.

'Goodness,' said the mother. 'I'd almost forgotten. Yes, it worked out just as you said it would, Doctor. The appearances did become fewer. And there hasn't been a single one since Emma started play school, nearly three months ago. It was obviously all her imagination.'

'Of course,' I said. And meant it. I had to.

*   *   *

After Emma, I began asking friends if they had had any first-hand metaphysical experiences. I was surprised by the answers. A good half seemed to have had a weird experience of some kind or other. And a good half of them, like myself, didn't believe at all in ghosts.

A similar story to Emma's was that of a younger child, again a girl, daughter of friends and just coming up to three years old.

Tracy told her parents, Les and Dolly, about the 'big genkelum' who used to sit on a chair by the bed at nights. He had 'shiny white hair', was a 'happy genkelum' and had 'one toof gone'.

'I went cold when I heard,' Les told me. 'Tracy's bedroom used to be my father's when he lived with us. He died four years before Tracy was born. He was a big jolly chap, about eighteen stone, with silver hair. He died early in the New Year. Not long before, at Christmas, he'd bitten hard on a piece of pork crackling and lost a front tooth from his top set.'

*   *   *

Harry Walters, a sceptic if ever there was one, told of his mother living with them before she died.

'She had an obsession about the drain at the back of the garage,' he said. 'She was convinced there was something wrong with it and was forever pouring bleach and disinfectant down. To keep her happy, I had men in to look at it, but they could find nothing wrong.

'Six months after her death I was planing some wood in the

175

garage, late on in the evening, when I sensed something outside. Through the window I could see my mother, peering at the drain and looking very worried. As it grew darker, she faded. I ran back into the house, telling myself it was nothing but imagination.

'But a few weeks later the drain cracked. A root from a large tree next door had forced its way into a joint and smashed a complete length of pipe from end to end. From the size of the root, it must have been in there for years. The ground subsided and the whole back wall of the garage fell down. I've felt ever since that my mother had come back to try to warn me.'

*   *   *

Lucy Parker told me about the birth of her son in St. Mary's Maternity Home. It was to be a breech birth – the baby was presented backside-first instead of head-first – and such births are never easy. Several attempts were made in the last few weeks of pregnancy to turn the baby in the womb, but the baby always turned back again.

'That must have been worrying for you,' I said.

'It was,' said Lucy. 'Until I woke up after falling asleep between pains. Standing by my bed was my cousin Eric, in his RAF uniform. Eric was ten years older than me, orphaned, and my mother had brought him up. He always looked upon me as his kid sister. I looked upon him as my wise, protective, big brother.

'Anyway, there he was, standing by the bed. "Don't worry, kid," he said. "Everything's going to be all right."

'I felt so peaceful then, and went straight back to sleep. The next time I woke the contractions were coming really strong, and my son was born within the hour perfectly healthy.'

'That must have been a great relief,' I said. 'I bet Eric was pleased for you too.'

'I'm sure he was,' said Lucy. 'But I've no way of knowing. He was killed during the war, flying with Bomber Command, when I was only ten.'

*   *   *

176

After all these stories I was beginning to feel a bit punch-drunk. (Can you get ghost-drunk?) So I was very pleased to bump into John Denton in the High Street.

'It's nice to meet somebody who doesn't believe in ghosts,' I said. 'Even though he does do a very good imitation of one.'

'Ghosts?' said John. 'A lot of it's in the mind. I get half a dozen reports a year of the Phantom Angler, seen at dusk by the river and vanishes when anybody gets near him. That's no more of a ghost than I am: it's that tatty little villain Charlie Sloper, knocking off my trout again.

'No, I don't believe in ghosts. But then I don't believe in total abstinence and that doesn't stop it existing in some quarters. Have I ever told you about the goings-on at my cottage?'

'No,' I said. 'But I've a feeling you're about to.'

'Dead right,' said John. 'Well, you know the place. Used to be a gamekeeper's cottage-cum-lodge. Bigger than average and with a cellar, which is unusual for cottages in these parts, but the cellar was for the keeper to hang the game in away from the gentry's sensitive nostrils, and to keep his traps and gear in.

'In the middle of the night, about three weeks after I'd moved in, I heard a dog padding up the stairs. It nosed the door open, jumped onto the bottom of my bed, and curled itself round to sleep.

'I shouted, "Our Biddy! Get back down there!" and kicked out. My foot connected with nothing: the weight at the bottom of the bed just disappeared. I switched on the light and there was no sign of any dog.

'Biddy, my collie, always sleeps in the kitchen with the door on the catch, and I was puzzled about how she'd got upstairs. So I went down. There was the kitchen door, still on the catch. I opened it, and Biddy was in her basket, inside.

'This happened several times after that. It was always the same: the sound of a dog padding upstairs, the bedroom door being nosed open, and the weight at the bottom of the bed.

'I thought, "Bloody hell! It comes to something when you're being haunted by a flaming dog. Other people get Anne

177

Boleyn." And after that I just took no notice of it.'·

'Is it still happening?' I asked.

'No,' said John. 'Not the dog. That's stopped. Now I'm getting the Phantom Burglar.'

'Go on,' I said.

'Try and stop me,' said John. 'Keep all this to yourself, mind. I don't want folk round here thinking I'm barmy.'

'Scout's honour,' I said.

'Right,' said John. 'Shortly after the dog stopped coming, I was sitting in the living room having a quiet read and a glass of scotch. About eleven o'clock at night, it'd be.

'All of a sudden there was a hell of a crash from the cellar as if the window had been kicked in. There were quiet footsteps across the cellar floor. And then they started coming slowly up the steps.

'I picked up the poker and went into the kitchen to the cellar door. The amazing thing was Biddy. She's a gentle old bitch, or rather a gentle young bitch, but she's normally frightened of nothing.

'This time she was terrified. She crouched on the floor, staring at the cellar door. All the hairs on her back were up, she was trembling all over and whimpering with fright. And the footsteps kept on coming until they stopped at the top of the stairs.

'"Right, yer bugger," I thought. "I'll have you now and no messing."

'You know the light to the cellar is on the kitchen wall by the door, to stop you going arse-over-tip down the steps in the dark? Well, I switched that on with one hand, knocked up the door sneck with the poker, and charged through the door and down the steps.

'I finished up at the bottom, swinging the poker like a lunatic – and there was not a soul in sight. Not a sausage. The window was as it always is: bolted on the inside. Biddy was still whimpering at the top of the stairs. I called her down, but she wouldn't budge.

'Well, at that, I started shaking. I went back upstairs, locked

178

the cellar door, and knocked hell out of the scotch. I'm getting used to the footsteps now. It's happened three times since, all to the same pattern and all with the same results. But I've felt a bit better about it since I found out the likely cause.'

'And what's that, John?' I asked. By now we were approaching the Tadchester Arms.

'Told you I didn't believe in total abstinence, didn't I?' said John. 'With all this talking it's beginning to feel as if I'm suffering from it. And in case you think I'm completely round the bend, I'd like you to hear a bit of local history from one of our local relics. We'll find him in the public bar, I shouldn't wonder ... After you.'

I preceded John into the public bar and ordered two pints of bitter.

'Make it three, if you wouldn't mind, Bob,' said John. 'I've found what we're looking for and it's usually thirsty. I'll see to the next round.'

John lumbered over to a corner table.

'Ah, Charlie!' boomed John.

Charlie it was. Charlie Sloper.

'Word in your ear, if I may!'

'T'warn't me,!' shouted Charlie, with a sudden appearance of panic. 'I was nowhere near your stockponds last Wednesday!'

'So that's where they went ...' muttered John to himself. Then, 'No, Charlie. This is more of a social call. This is Dr. Clifford, who's dying to meet you and who has just bought you this pint.'

'Don't want no truck wi' doctors!' snapped Charlie. 'Never use 'em! Don't know what they're up to, most of 'em!'

'Dr. Clifford is interested in local history,' John continued, patiently. 'I'd like you to tell him about Keeper Brand.'

'Keeper Brand!' spat Charlie. 'Bastard! Shot the arse out o' my britches many a time when I was a lad. And he killed my mate! You ought to know, anyway, Bailie. You lives in his old cottage. And I told you all about him a few months back.'

'So you did,' said John. 'But you tell it much better. Go on.'

179

'Brand,' said Charlie, a fierce hatred in his eyes, 'was gamekeeper when all that land by the river belonged to the big estate. This is going back some. Before the Great War.

'Brand was a holy terror. Black Jack Brand we used to call him. Got so nobody could come by a pheasant or a hare or a brace of trout without getting two barrels of shot up his arse. Sit up all night by those bleeding pheasants, he would. Shotgun across his knees. And still be awake all next day. Wasn't human, if you ask me.

'He used to live in your cottage. And that's how my mate Stokie got killed. Only eighteen he were, and a good-hearted lad. Anyway, one night he sees the cottage all in darkness and he reckoned Brand was out sitting shotgun somewhere. So he got into the cellar, just to have a look around like, in case there was any game hanging up and going begging.

'The cellar was empty, so he decided to go upstairs and see what was in the kitchen. When he got to the top of the stairs, Brand was waiting for him. He must have been sitting in the cottage without lights.

'The old bastard slammed the cellar door open and knocked Stokie from top to bottom of the stairs. Smashed his skull, it did. Killed him stone dead.

'When Brand seen Stokie was dead, did he feel sorry for him? Did he buggery. First thing he did was look round for his old dog, which should have been in the kitchen. He found the dog upstairs, sleeping on his bed.

'He did no more than pick up the big ash stick he kept by his bed and beat the old dog's head in. That was Brand for you. In temper he was a madman.

'He got away with it, of course. Death by misadventure, the coroner said about Stokie. In the course of a felony, or some such rubbish. Nobody knew about the dog until Brand was in his cups here one night and let it slip.

'The old bastard was found drowned about six months after in a flash flood. Accidental death, that was. But some of Stokie's relatives could have told you different...'

'Thank you, Charlie,' said John. 'That deserves another

pint. But would you excuse the doctor and myself if we stood at the bar? We have some medical business to discuss.'

'Stand where you like,' said Charlie. 'So long as you don't forget that there pint.'

'That's better,' said John at the bar. 'I don't like sitting near Charlie too long. Apart from the pong, you're liable to pick up a few unidentified flying objects.

'Now then. See what I mean? What happened at the cottage way back could explain the dog on the bed and the footsteps in the cellar. *And* the state that Biddy gets in.'

'What about Brand?' I asked. 'Hasn't he turned up yet?'

'No,' said John. 'But I think he'd know that the cottage isn't big enough for both of us.'

'Hey,' I said. 'You're the one that doesn't believe in all this stuff.'

'Right,' said John, grinning. 'I'm an atheist, thank God. And I've never had need of superstition, touch wood.'

He winked.

'A bit like yourself, I reckon.'

*   *   *

My mother's brother, Uncle Bertie, told me of the time he heard ghosts talking in the downstairs sitting room, one winter's night in 1932.

'I was terrified,' he said. 'I was in bed and was tempted to put my head under the clothes. But I said to myself, "No I must go down and face them." It was the bravest thing I ever did.'

'I slipped on my trousers and crept silently across the landing, then started to come slowly down the stairs.

'Suddenly I heard soft footsteps behind me. Each stair I moved down, I was followed by two soft footsteps. If I stood still, they stood still. They started again as soon as I moved. These weren't the footsteps of people – they were the soft light sounds of someone from another world. The house was obviously full of ghosts, upstairs and downstairs.

'I got down the stairs at last and started to walk towards the sitting room. The footsteps stopped. Whatever it was behind

181

me had decided to stay on the stairs to cut off my retreat.

'I was in a cold sweat but still determined. I took a lunge at the sitting-room door, pushed it open and burst in the room shouting, "Go away ghosts!"

'But there was nothing there, nothing other than the wireless that had been left switched on.'

'Oh, come on,' I said. 'Whyever didn't you think it was the wireless in the first place?'

'Well,' said Uncle Bertie, 'in those days the radio programmes closed down at 10.30 at night. What I had heard was a test transmission that they sometimes did during the night when all programmes had finished, and all radios presumably had been turned off.'

'What about the footsteps?' I asked. 'Were they just imagination?'

'No,' said Uncle Bertie. 'When I pulled my trousers on, I had forgotten to do up my braces – and the soft footsteps I heard were my braces dropping down the stairs behind me.'

CHAPTER 17

But Once a Year

Tadchester's Christmas festivities always brought with them such a crop of bizarre accidents that I dreaded being on call over the holiday period.

Some of the accidents were caused by practical jokes.

One Christmas Eve a gang of navvies were working on a hole in a quiet road on the outskirts of Tadchester. Their lunchtime break was long and convivial.

When they got back to the hole, the largest of them – name of O'Reilly, would you believe? – was in no mood for work. He was in no state for it, come to that, and sat on an upturned barrow swigging heartily from a bottle of Bushmill's and singing lugubriously of his homeland.

When the gang were within half an hour of finishing, O'Reilly passed out. His mates decided on a jolly Christmas jape. They propped him up so he was sitting on the shallow trench in the road, put his feet in the trench and poured quick-setting cement around his wellingtons. They covered him with a tarpaulin, set the red warning lamps around the trench, and went happily home.

A policeman, attracted by muffled snores from under the tarpaulin, found O'Reilly at ten o'clock that night. Set solid. It wouldn't have been so bad if just the wellingtons had been encased: O'Reilly could have been hauled free, leaving his footwear behind. But his weight had caused his legs to sink deeper and deeper into the concrete until eventually it had oozed over the top and filled his wellingtons. When I got there his lower legs were trapped immovably.

A telephone call to the home of the contractor resulted in a scratch squad of navvies being rounded up. With the help of drills, sledgehammers, spades and picks, they eventually hacked O'Reilly free of the trench, but still with his legs in a block of concrete. The more delicate job of chipping through to the wellingtons, the socks, and the final painful prising off of the hairs on the legs, was done in the fire station where the light was better.

O'Reilly, shocked, chilled, bruised and horribly hung-over, had to spend the night under observation in Tadchester Hospital. He discharged himself on Christmas morning, lurching off in a pair of borrowed wellies and swearing every kind of slow and painful revenge on his mates. Whatever mayhem he caused must have happened outside the hospital catchment area, otherwise the Tadchester casualty ward would have been very crowded over Christmas.

'I suppose,' I said, when the hospital reported no repercussions, 'that we must be thankful for small murphies.'

*   *   *

Practical jokes like the one played on O'Reilly may sound funny, but they do have a habit of misfiring. Something similar had happened just before Christmas the previous year, when a party of lunchtime revellers had left one of their number unconscious, his arms folded across his chest, on top of a catafalque in Tadchester cemetery.

He might very well have died of exposure if he had not been discovered towards dusk by a little old lady who had gone to place some flowers on her husband's grave. As it was, he recovered quickly, but the old lady had to be sedated for shock at the discovery of what she thought was a disinterred body. After that she visited the cemetery only in broad daylight.

*   *   *

Even cosy family gatherings can end in catastrophe. I was called out at two o'clock one Boxing Day morning to a really big case, big because the casualty weighed twenty stone.

After shifting three bottles of scotch during Christmas night and the early hours of Boxing Day, he had lurched upstairs to bed. Halfway up he had collapsed and become wedged between the wall and the banisters. Moreover, he had started a severe nosebleed: what seemed to be pints of blood were running stickily down the stairs when I arrived.

I was greeted by four female relatives.

'We tried to shift him, Doctor,' they said agitatedly. 'But he was much too heavy.'

'Pity,' I said as I tugged at the giant frame to attempt emergency treatment, 'that there weren't any other men in the house.'

'Oh, there were,' said one of the women. 'And there still are: four of them.' She opened the door to the sitting room to reveal four comatose forms. 'All unconscious.'

The scotch really had gone the rounds that night.

*   *   *

Even the best-run festive occasions can go awry. In my younger days as a House Surgeon in a London hospital I used to dread hospital Christmas parties. To avoid giving offence, I would have to take a drink with every head of department, every matron and every ward sister. Apart from that there was usually some embarrassing moment for somebody. Towards the end of the jollifications, pent-up passions among the nurses would suddenly become un-pent, and some of the younger doctors were lucky to escape with their lives, let alone their trousers. The young doctors, too, were not always models of decorum. More than one would demonstrate during the evening that his interest in female anatomy was not purely professional.

185

Most of the embarrassment one Christmas came from the managing director of the firm next door to the hospital. He had got himself invited on the strength of being the friendly chap next door and on the promise of bringing vast amounts of booze.

He kept that promise all right: there were bottles and bottles of spirits and wine, and crates and cans of beer, stout and lager.

My premonition that something would go wrong became stronger as the evening wore on. The captain of industry became more and more under the influence, dancing about madly and holding the nurses in places never recommended by any school of dancing.

Finally, after a nurse's pretty dimpled knee had caught him in a sensitive spot and left him with a pained expression, it was tactfully suggested that perhaps it was time he went home to his ever-loving.

'Certainly,' he said, through clenched teeth, his eyes still watering. 'Don't bother. I can find my own way out.'

Next morning, one of the cleaners tried to use the back service lift to take the rubbish away, and found it jammed between floors. Maintenance men were called, the lift winched up and the doors opened.

There, on the floor of the lift, in a crumpled and unconscious heap, lay the captain of industry. As it turned out later, he'd got into the wrong lift, pressed several wrong buttons and then, in an attempt to hit the one for the ground floor, had connected with the emergency stop and then passed out.

The maintenance men picked him up, brought him round, and set him on his woozy way home.

'My God,' he muttered, as realisation dawned that it was now well into the next day. 'How am I going to explain *this* to the wife?'

*   *   *

'Soon be Christmas,' said Pam cheerily, as she made out lists for cards and presents.

Really, I love Christmas and always have done, and I loved

186

it especially at this time when the children took so much delight in the magic of it all. Jane would be nearly three this Christmas, and for the first time would be able to join in all the fun.

However, I could not share Pam's enthusiasm, I had the distinct feeling that this was going to be one of *those* Christmases. There was an omen.

The Tadchester Drama Society had been hard at rehearsals for its panto. This year it was to be *Dick Whittington*, with Pam in the title role.

To advertise it, a gigantic banner had been strung across the High Street, between the upper floors of the bank and the Co-op. It read:

Tadchester Drama Society proudly present
DICK WHITTINGTON
A spectacular pantomime for all the family
with
PAM CLIFFORD   KEVIN BIRD   ZARA MARTIN
The Tadchester Orpheus Choir

I was in the bank one windy morning about a week before the panto's opening, when from outside came a screech of brakes and an ominous *crump*! I ran outside to find a car with its bonnet concertina'd against a lamp post. Draped over the windscreen was the banner: the wind must have loosened the fastenings and brought it down.

The driver was dazed, had a few scratches about the head, but otherwise was intact. I helped him out and guided him into the bank, where I sat him down and checked over his cuts and bruises.

'What the hell was it?' he asked. 'All of a sudden some damn great thing flopped down onto the windscreen and I was blinded.'

'Not to worry,' I said. 'No harm done ... er ... except to yourself and the car.'

'Thanks,' he said. 'But what *was* it?'

'A banner,' I said, 'advertising the Tadchester Drama

187

Society's panto. It should be very good: my wife's playing the lead.

'I don't suppose,' I said hesitantly, 'that I could interest you in any tickets...'

My visit to the bank had not been a very happy one. The manager had called me in informally to point out the poor health of my bank account. He suggested that I should try and find some way to resuscitate it.

The outlook was bleak.

From the bank I went to see a patient who was extremely rude to me. Normally I can take rudeness especially from old or anxious patients. But this patient was neither, and the rudeness got right to me.

It was turning into a disastrous day; nothing was going right. When I got back to the surgery there was a message from Gladys, 'Will you please ring home, Dr Bob. Mrs Clifford wants you.'

Gladys looked anxious.

I rang, more than a bit apprehensive. Pam answered.

'Could you come home as soon as possible? I've some news for you that I don't want to tell you in the surgery.'

My heart sank. This was the last straw of this awful day. I had to sit through surgery, my mind racing through all the dreadful possibilities. Was my mother ill? Had some disaster befallen the children? No, if it had been a medical disaster I would have heard of it. I got out of the surgery as soon as I could.

'You got through them like greased lightning tonight,' said Grace. 'What's up with you, Dr. Bob? Have you got hot pants or something?'

'Possibly,' I said, in an attempt to keep up the banter I was in no mood for.

By the time I got home my heart was sinking lower and lower. I put the car away and dragged my feet up the steps to the front door. Pam was waiting inside.

'Look!' she called, excitedly, waving an envelope with a bit of red in one corner. 'It's from the BBC!'

'This is all I need,' I thought. 'A rejection slip.'

The BBC had had my two scripts. One about Miss Gill and Miss Booth, and one about Ben Fellowes, the man who knew he was going to die, for more than three months now. And now they were being turned down.

I unfolded the letter and read:

Dear Dr Clifford,

Many thanks for your manuscripts which we have been considering. I am happy to say that we like both these short stories and would like you to come and record them at some mutually convenient date. We are at present looking for a doctor to do some other pieces for us, and may be able to offer you a regular monthly spot if you are interested. Please ring me on extension 725.

Great! Who said it was a lousy day? This was the best day of the year. The first two things I had ever written had been

189

accepted by the BBC. The story of Miss Gill and Miss Booth would be heard in thousands and possibly millions of homes. The courage of Ben Fellowes would get the recognition it deserved. On top of that it looked as if I was going to be able to do something creative outside medicine; something that could enlarge my medical experience, yet not interfere with my home life, the practice, or my patients in Tadchester.

I was going to be able to set off in a different direction.

Life was going to be different from now on.

As I put the letter down, my mind racing with the excitement of all the possibilities stretching ahead of me, there was a knock on the door.

I answered it. Outside stood a man in overalls, blood pouring from his hand.

'Are you the doctor?' he asked.

'Yes,' I replied.

'Sorry to bother you, sir. I was just down the road when my windscreen shattered. I punched it out and I think I got some glass in my hand.'

'Come in,' I said. 'I'll see what I can do.'

I smiled to myself.

No, life was not going to be different from now on. It was really always going to continue in very much the same way.

Postscript

There is the fable of the old man sitting outside a town, being approached by a stranger.

'What are they like in this town?' asked the stranger.

'What were they like in your last town?' replied the old man.

'They were delightful people. I was very happy there. They were kind, generous and would always help you in trouble.'

'You will find them very much like that in this town.'

The old man was approached by another stranger.

'What are the people like in this town?' asked the second stranger.

'What were they like in your last town?' replied the old man.

'It was an awful place. They were mean, unkind and nobody would ever help anybody.'

'I am afraid you will find it very much the same here,' said the old man.

If it should be your lot to ever visit Tadchester, this is how you will find us.

Look Out, Doctor!

For Steve, Hewie, Fred, Stan, Joan and Pam,
who put up with me, for so many happy years

Contents

Prologue

Life is a tragedy, for we are all born eventually to die. We survive our tragedies by laughing at them.

A friend once told me that when he was under the influence of ether he dreamed he was turning over the pages of a great book, in which he knew he would find, on the last page, the meaning of life.

The pages of the book were alternately tragic and comic, and he turned page after page, his excitement growing, not only because he was approaching the answer, but because he couldn't know, until he arrived, on which side of the book the final page would be. At last it came: the universe opened up to him in a hundred words: and they were uproariously funny.

He came back to consciousness crying with laughter, remembering everything. He opened his lips to speak. It was then that the great and comic answer plunged back out of his reach.

Christopher Fry

CHAPTER 1

It's Not Cricket

My first patient in the surgery was Benny Talbot, a tall, gangly youth with a prime crop of acne pustules and mini-boils scattered at random over his body.

Excess sugar in the blood could have been one reason for the spots and boils, so I asked if he suffered from thirst (a positive symptom in recognising sugar diabetes). He told me that he was often so thirsty on a Saturday night that he had been known to down ten pints of beer at the Tadchester Arms. Not quite what I meant: a symptom like that would mean that half the young men of Tadchester were diabetic.

An undiagnosed diabetic can be so thirsty that he will drink the contents of his hot water bottle in the middle of the night. My spotty patient did not admit to ever having been so tempted. He did, however, remember that he sometimes had to get up in the night to pass water, and on close questioning, he did think this was probably Saturday nights.

Still on the trail of sugar, I gave him a blood sample bottle with an envelope to take to the hospital, for a blood test, and a bottle to take to the surgery toilet to fill with a specimen of urine.

He returned in a few minutes, announcing his return by banging on the door with his knees. When I opened the door, I

11

found him precariously supporting a urine-filled envelope in both hands. The blood and urine sample bottles were both in his top pocket.

It was going to be one of those days.

My second patient was John Haggard, a well-groomed, nicely spoken man of about thirty-five. His hair was neat, his shoes shining, and he had sharp creases to his trousers. He was wearing a good, but rather old, grey-striped city suit. He looked immaculate, and it was only on closer inspection that minor blemishes of dress became apparent. His shirt, though clean and starched, had started to fray at the collar. His tie, which was a club or regimental tie, was slightly worn at the knot.

He was a little apprehensive and had an air of gentleness about him that warmed me to him.

12

He was not a patient I knew — he had filled in a temporary resident's card — and I noted that his parents came from an unpretentious home in Stowin. His home address was that of a Midlands hospital whose name was familiar but which I couldn't place immediately. My guess was that he was a hospital administrator, in Tadchester on holiday at his parents'.

He began hesitantly: 'I would be so grateful if you could help me, Doctor. A few years ago I had a nervous breakdown and was admitted to hospital. Happily I made a good recovery and for the last ten years I have run the clerical side of the hospital.' (I was pleased with my spot prognosis of a hospital administrator.)

'This has suited me so far, but I have now been offered a better post in London. I am in the ridiculous situation of never having been officially discharged as a patient. To do so I have to get my next of kin to vouch for me. I popped down here to get my parents to sign the appropriate forms, and I can't persuade them to sign. They are simple folk and don't trust forms. Could you possibly speak to them, and reassure them on my behalf?'

His story was odd but quite plausible. Many patients in mental hospitals rehabilitated themselves by helping out in various administrative tasks, and this chap was obviously quite all right.

I vaguely knew his parents. His father ran the secondhand furniture auctions for Hope's Stores and his mother worked as a cleaner at one of the hotels. They were from the Midlands and had moved down to Tadchester about ten years previously, but they had kept very much to themselves, never really integrating into Tadchester's way of life.

There was an air of quiet desperation about the young man and I impulsively agreed to speak on his behalf.

'Today, Doctor?'

'Yes,' I said, slightly intimidated by his persistence. 'I will pop in and see your parents this evening.'

'Thank you, Doctor. Thank you, Doctor,' he replied, almost fawningly. I began to go off him.

The rest of the day continued in its uneasy and unsatisfactory

13

pattern. At home the children were all beginning to go down with colds, and even the nose of Susie, our Cairn terrier, was disturbingly warm.

My wife Pam was her usual patient, unruffable self. So I cheered up a bit during supper and set off for the Haggards' to intercede on their son's behalf.

The Haggards lived in a bungalow perched in the middle of a two-acre orchard near the riverside village of Stowin. The property was surrounded by a high wooden fence and in the dark of a March evening I could make out trimmed lawns and neatly clipped trees.

The door was opened by Mr Haggard.

'Hello, Doctor. This is a surprise,' he said. 'What can I do for you?'

'I've called to talk to you about your son,' I replied.

'Oh, God! What has he done now?' wailed Mrs Haggard in the background.

'You'd better come in,' said Mr Haggard darkly.

I was shown into the front room: settee in the corner, aspidistra in shining copper bowl in the window, and tall, hard-backed chairs arranged round a shiny pedestal table. In the middle of the table lay a fat family Bible with a huge metal clasp on its side.

I was summoned to sit down at one end of the table while Mr Haggard sat at the other. It was like being called to a board meeting.

Mr Haggard lowered his head as if to start our meeting with a prayer. Suddenly he looked up and shouted, 'Look out, Doctor!'

I shot out of my chair just in time to miss a cricket bat smashing down on the top of the back of it.

Standing wild-eyed, brandishing the bat, was my well-groomed and nicely spoken patient of the morning.

I acted instinctively. I turned and hurled myself at him head-down, as if I were going into a rugby scrum. The whole weight of my body was behind my head, which slammed into his solar plexus and pinned him to the wall.

I stood back and he fell into a breathless heap on the floor. I

14

was taking no chances: I jumped on him and held his head in a lock. He had unleashed some primitive force in me, and if I'd carried on I could have killed him.

I was conscious of Mr Haggard pulling on my sleeve.

'It's all right, Doctor,' he said. 'You can leave him alone. He won't hurt anyone now.'

As soon as I let go, the son curled himself up in a ball and lay weeping at the foot of the wall. Several hours, several policemen and two duly authorised officers later, Master Haggard was on his way back to the Midlands hospital, which I now remembered was a hospital for the criminally insane.

The sad story was that the Haggard son, who was normal most of the time, had occasional brain storms during which he became physically violent.

He had an intense grudge against doctors. It was after he had cracked the skull of a doctor in the Midlands that he was incarcerated in hospital and his parents moved to Tadchester.

Things were not sorted out until the early hours of the morning. As I drove back along the Winchcombe Road the car started to lurch.

I stopped and got out. The back tyre was flat.

It had definitely been one of those days.

* * *

I was the fourth partner in a group of five in a little Somerset town called Tadchester. Tadchester (population 6,500) stands on the estuary of the River Tad, in one of the most beautiful parts of the Somerset coast. It is a market town, with some fishing, some light industry, and a great deal of farming.

The town is split in two by the River Tad, and further split by the large hill which dominates one side of the river. The other side of the river is flat pastureland, stretching off to marshes and the sea coast. You are not just a Tadchester resident — you are strictly Up-the-Hill or Down-the-Hill. It has important social distinction: the population Up-the-Hill tends to be the Havenots.

We were the only general practice in the town, and also took care of the local hospital. The five partners each had his own area of responsibility at the hospital: Steve Maxwell, the senior partner, had a special interest in medicine; Henry Johnson, the second senior, was the surgeon; Jack Hart, the third partner, was the anaesthetist; I, as the fourth partner, was reckoned to be the expert on midwifery and was pretty good at piercing ears; and Ron Dickinson, the fifth and junior partner — an accomplished athlete who spent a great deal of his time running, jumping, swimming, sailing, water ski-ing, etc. — was our ENT specialist and removed the local tonsils. We were a happy and well-balanced team.

One of the delights of Tadchester was that it was one of the few British ports where the quay was clean and fresh, where unloading ships were not surrounded by dirt and railway tracks. The coasters that came from Scandinavia, France and Belgium with loads of coal, timber and clay would always unload tidily onto a string of lorries on the quay.

You could while away a pleasant afternoon sitting on a bench by the quay, watching the ships unloading and the salmon fishermen shooting their seine nets. Two or three fishing boats still went out of Tadchester, and landing craft, from the school of amphibious warfare at the mouth of the Tad, would often appear on exercises. These squat grey boxes would come charging up the river followed by men in tiny boats, all in camouflage green. Even these seemed to blend in with the surroundings.

Work prevented me from taking frequent strolls around the town, but three or four times a year on a Saturday morning, I would make a point of doing what almost amounted to a grand tour.

I would start at the top of the High Street, parking my car behind the black and white chip shop, by the grace and favour of Jack and Lesley Morris, the owners. I would then walk down the High Street, passing a few small shops before branching off right to the pannier market, where dozens of individual stalls sold vegetables, cream, eggs, chickens, potatoes and bric-à-brac. I knew most of the stallholders and it was very much like

16

doing a ward round. My mind had to race to connect every condition with every recognisable face and not confuse the ailments with the names. A complete circuit of the market, then down to the bottom of the High Street, passing the new Woolworth, Hope's Stores, a mini department store that had been there since 1699, round The Globe pub on the corner, then a cup of coffee at the Copper Inn, which was directly on the quay just downstream of the bridge.

From the Copper Inn one could see most things that were going on in the town and on a Saturday morning everybody who was anybody met for coffee. There would be JPs, councillors, doctors, solicitors — all representatives of the hierarchy which ran the town. This was where business deals were done and had been done for 500 years.

Running parallel to the quay were Milk Lane and Rope Lane, narrow streets honeycombed with shops, like primitive shopping precincts. In years gone by there had been a rope factory off Rope Lane and the bollards on which the ropes were stretched still stood at either end of this narrow street. I expect at one time there had been a dairy in Milk Lane, but it was all gift shops now.

On my tours I would wander down Rope Lane, which linked the High Street with Bridge Street, and pop into the electrical shop owned by my very good friend Eric Martin, for a yarn. Then onto the quay again to meander round the park, the children's putting green, Humber Memorial Art Gallery and Museum and back along the broad street that swept off the quay, along the eastern edge of the town, passing the Hambrose Garage and the Regal Cinema, then up Pitt Lane to the top of the High Street.

Everyone I passed was always very friendly, and I would sometimes be offered jobs like cleaning fish or washing dishes.

'Come on, Doctor Bob,' someone would shout. 'Give up doctoring and have a go at this for a change.'

I think I made these trips to reassure myself. I knew most of the people in the town but usually saw them from the other side of the surgery desk, when they were not feeling at their best. It was very refreshing to see them in different circumstances, and it certainly helped when I was feeling a bit down.

All in all, we had a good town.

*   *   *

Every summer, invading holidaymakers strained the local medical services to the limit, and Tadchester people much resented sharing their medical facilities with foreigners.

Illness on holiday is much worse than illness at home. Not only is the holiday ruined for the patients — lying staring at a ward ceiling instead of enjoying the sea air and scenery — but also for their relatives and friends who spend much of their time in waiting rooms hoping for news.

Death on holiday — though obviously no happy event for the patient — is extra harrowing for the relatives or friends who have to make complicated arrangements to have the body transported back home.

Only a very small proportion of the visitors fell ill, of course, but as they took up so much of our working day we forgot that the other 99·5 per cent were healthy and thoroughly enjoying themselves.

Ironically, the seriously ill were the least trouble: they went straight into hospital. The biggest problems were the patients who were not well enough to cope in their holiday accommodation and therefore had to be looked after.

My partner Henry used to come into his own with cases like these. Although principally a surgeon, Henry, aided by Jack Hart, also had under his charge the Fever Hospital that perched on top of the hill in Tadchester.

The hospital had four large wards, which in the days when tuberculosis and other infectious diseases were very serious, were always full. As antibiotics dealt with these problems, so the hospital gradually emptied.

Only a skeleton staff was kept on, and just two of the wards were open. I think there was some vague scheme to use the hospital fully in the event of an atomic war, but to all intents and purposes this was now Henry's private hospital.

He would take in convalescent patients, or elderly people whose children needed a rest from caring for them, and in the summer he took in most of the semi-hospital cases needing care and attention. Henry was the final arbiter on admissions. I could never assume that I might admit patients in my own right and, though I could visit them, could play no part in their treatment.

One such patient was Herbert Bagley. He had come down with a group of lads from Bath to stay at the local holiday camp at Sanford-on-Sea, and was taken ill with a very sore throat. The sore throat didn't settle down and didn't respond to antibiotics. A blood test showed that he had glandular fever.

Herbert had an awful time. He had glandular fever at its worst with every possible complication: high fever, jaundice, inability to eat, vomiting and excruciating soreness of the throat. He was in hospital just over a month and I used to visit him every couple of days and try to cheer him up.

He was a handsome, likeable lad with a great big frame. His strong arms were tattooed with 'I Love Hazel' on the left and a crown and anchor on the right. Perched on his locker was a large photograph of a scowling girl with short hair and big thighs, sitting astride a dropped-handlebar racing bike.

'That's what keeps me going,' he said. 'That's my Hazel. We're getting married next spring.'

Though I would never have said it, I thought that he could have done better than the baleful Amazon in the photo.

Within a week of Herbert's being discharged, I was called to Sanford-on-Sea again to see another lad, Sid Parker. He had an exact replica of Herbert's symptoms and glandular fever was diagnosed again. He passed Henry's scrutiny and was admitted to the Fever Hospital. Again, I used to visit him every other day.

On my second visit I noticed propped up on his locker a large photograph of a glowering, short-haired girl with large thighs, sitting astride a dropped-handlebar racing bike.

I was about to say 'Oh, I'm afraid the last patient must have left this behind,' when some instinct stopped me.

'Who's the lady?' I asked.

'That's my Hazel,' said Sid. 'We're getting married in the spring.'

I made no comment. There wasn't a lot I could say, anyway.

Glandular fever is sometimes called the kissing disease. It is thought that one of the ways it spreads is by mouth-to-mouth contact. If both these lads had pursued Hazel and were contemplating marrying her next spring, then it was likely that they had been kissing her. So it was likely that Hazel was the cause of Herbert and Sid finishing up in hospital.

Sid came from Clevedon, south of Bristol. He was quite different from Herbert: small and neat, had some good 'A' levels and was waiting for a university place. Again, a likeable lad. And again, I thought he could have done better than Hazel.

The nurses were completely loyal and, apart from an occasional quiet snigger, didn't give the secret away.

Sid got better in three weeks and went home. We were left with the mystery of one boy from Bath and one boy from Clevedon, both sublimely confident that they were going to marry this cross-looking, hefty cyclist in the following spring.

We had a busier year than usual with holidaymakers. Two outbreaks of gastro-enteritis at the holiday camp absolutely packed the Fever Hospital, and the memory of Sid and Herbert was submerged in the avalanche of work.

The family and I took our holiday late that year. We hired a villa on the western coast of France below the Sable de Lonne, took a ferry to Cherbourg and then motored leisurely down over two or three days.

We spent our first night in the most beautiful town of Vitre where, it seemed, every other building was a church, and booked in at a quaint old hotel. Both the proprietor and his wife were charming and we were immediately adopted by their twenty-year-old son, Ernst, who was anxious to use his English and learn about England.

Ernst had an English fiancée whom he was going to marry next spring. We congratulated him and invited him to call on us in England.

'I will get you a photograph of her,' he said. He rushed up to his room and came down with the now familiar photograph of a scowling, short-haired, thick-thighed girl straddling a dropped-handlebar racing bike.

'This is 'Azel,' said Ernst. 'I look forward to bringing her to you after we are married.'

I still wonder about the power of this girl with the thick thighs, unprepossessing face and dropped handlebars. Three men were proposing to marry her in the spring — and those were only the ones I'd met. Were they just the tip of the iceberg? Were there dozens of men all over Europe who were confidently planning to settle down with Hazel (or 'Azel)? What was the secret of her attraction? What was her special magic? Certainly, if she could bottle it, she'd make a fortune.

I tried to find out whether Ernst had had glandular fever, but neither his English nor my French were up to it.

'Have you had a fever?' I asked.

'Yes,' he replied. 'I love her very much. Always I am in fever.'

It was stalemate.

Ernst never arrived with his blushing (or scowling) bride, nor did we even hear from him afterwards.

For Pam and myself, Hazel joined the Mona Lisa as one of the world's most enigmatic women — though she, poor girl, was definitely no oil painting.

CHAPTER 2

The Kiss of Life

For some reason I could never understand, the number of people who wished to visit the surgery steadily increased in number year by year, although the population of Tadchester was almost static. The number of residents had even fallen a little bit after the closure of the coal mine but then picked up as the plastics and electronics factories got underway.

As we had an appointments system we were actually able to count how many people attended. If we weren't careful we could easily be overrun.

I don't think that people came unnecessarily: just being worried is reason enough to go and see your doctor, however stupid the worry. Worry is a debilitating, exhausting business. If you think that spot on your face is cancer and you've made your will and visualised your funeral, you will go on worrying until someone has reassured you.

We were fortunate in our surgery staff. Practice manager was the fierce Gladys who had been our senior receptionist for so long that she thought of it as *her* practice. When I first came to Tadchester I remember overhearing her telling some friends that she now had another doctor to train. But she had a heart of gold. Under her stern exterior there was, in fact, a very human

person, highly capable of distinguishing the wheat from the chaff. She had to screen people coming in, otherwise we would have been overwhelmed.

Our other watchdog was the inimitable Grace, much more newly arrived than Gladys.

Grace got away with everything with sheer audacity. She had the art of saying the most outrageous things without being offensive.

An over-weight businessman trying to make a surgery appointment with Grace would be met with, 'What is it you want, love? The maternity clinic?'.

Although other staff came and went, Gladys and Grace were permanent fixtures. As well as this they were great buddies. Completely different personalities, they somehow gelled as a pair, and at weekends you would see them together walking their dogs along the beach at Sanford-on-Sea.

Grace was irrepressible. She could have made her living as a stand-up comic. The only time I have ever known the wind taken out of her sails was when a patient fell in love with her.

She was happily married to Jack, a mechanic who worked at one of the Tadchester garages.

Her admirer was a tiny gentleman, a Mr Wood who had a photographic shop down on the quay. His courtship started with a number of small presents he brought with him when he came to the surgery.

His visits were frequent. He came to see me with a whole lot of bizarre complaints, none of which was important, but he was prepared to sit discussing them for hours.

Each time he came he brought Grace some little offering: chocolates, a bottle of wine, or flowers.

'Just a small expression of my appreciation,' he would say, looking earnestly at Grace. 'You're so kind to me and you are so good to us all here.'

At first Grace was flattered. She called Jack Wood 'Tom Thumb'. As he was only about five foot three, I don't think he would have liked that. As the weeks went by it became steadily embarrassing. He would arrive at the surgery an hour early for his appointment and sit in the chair facing the reception desk, glancing devotedly at Grace. The normally boisterous Grace became quieter and quieter.

'Blimey,' she said when he had gone, 'I feel I can go and get dressed again now.'

He used to hang about outside the surgery offering to take her home, but Grace usually found some excuse.

It came to a head one day when Grace set off for home in the most appalling driving wind and rain.

A car pulled up with a *whoosh*! and the door was flung open. Grace would have accepted a lift from anyone that day.

'I had only just got in the bloody car,' she said, 'when I felt a hand on my knee. "You can put that back on the wheel," I said. "It's no good trying to steer with my knees."'

'I'm sorry, Grace,' said Mr Wood. 'I wouldn't offend you for the world, I just wanted to be friendly. It's my mission in life to try and make people happy. Are you happy, Grace? Could I make you happier?'

'Didn't know what to say,' said Grace, 'I was sweating all over.'

At this stage she was so furious she hadn't realised that instead of driving home he had drawn up outside his photographic shop.

'I said to him, "What are we doing here?"'

'Well,' said Mr Wood, 'you must know how much I admire you. I want to take you to my room above the shop where we could physically and mentally commune. I think making love is one of the best medicines in life. I think it's helpful for people and I do like to help people.'

The hand reached again for her knee.

'By this time,' said Grace, 'I was really fighting mad. I hit him under the chin with my right elbow and his head went back and hit the side of the door.

'"You can just bugger off," I told him. "After you've got hold of that steering wheel and driven me home."'

'I could cope with that little bugger,' she said. 'I wasn't going to walk back in the storm.'

They drove home in silence. When they reached her gate the crestfallen Mr Wood said, 'Is there no hope?'

'You go back to your shop and jump into your developing tank,' said Grace. 'When you've grown another foot come back and ask me again.'

The next day in the surgery Grace was back to her old rip-roaring self.

Miraculously Mr Wood recovered from all the numerous minor ailments that he had been consulting me about. And Grace, though she made us all laugh about the story of her admirer, was secretly quite pleased that a man had found her so desirable.

Our nickname for Grace had always been Amazing Grace, but from then on we got into the habit of calling her Sexy Grace. And it stuck.

*   *   *

Gladys was the commandant of the local Red Cross society. When I first came to Tadchester, she enrolled me as medical officer to the Tadchester Forward Medical Aid Unit. We used to race round the country taking part in competitions dealing with mass 'casualties', in the sort of numbers you'd expect if there was a nuclear war. The Government decided that these competitions were too expensive to run and after achieving great heights — we reached the national finals at the Albert Hall in front of the Minister of Health — the Tadchester Forward Medical Aid Unit was disbanded.

I had by now, though, earned a reputation as a first aider and spent a great deal of my time teaching the methods involved, writing instructional pamphlets, examining first-aid test candidates, and taking part in demonstrations. I was chatting about this one morning at coffee with Henry, Steve, Jack and Ron. Coffee time was when we got our worries off our chests, and it really was a very important part of the practice. If we had anxieties we would share them with our partners, and I was indeed fortunate with my colleagues.

'God,' I said, 'I'm so fed up with first aid. Pam says I'm even waking her in the night trying to give her mouth-to-mouth resuscitation.'

'I've heard it called worse,' said Jack.

Steve Maxwell looked over his half-rimmed glasses.

'You haven't been in the practice long enough, Bob, to remember Miss Polly Fulton,' he said.

'For twenty years I gave the first-aid lectures to Tadchester Red Cross and for twenty years Polly Fulton came and attended — and she was a good seventy when she started. She sat at the back of the class, always asked a question on shock and to my knowledge never ever participated in any practical first aid. She was never seen wearing her uniform at football matches, fetes or cinemas. I thought all my tuition had been wasted until one day I met her in Bridge Street. She came up excitedly and said "Dr Maxwell! Dr Maxwell! At last my first aid has been useful. There was a terrible accident on the Hovery Road yesterday. Three cars piled up, there were fractured arms and fractured legs, amputated limbs. It was absolutely terrible!"

"'I'm glad you were there," I said. "What did you do? Put on splints and tourniquets, dial 999?"

"'Oh no, nothing like that," said Miss Polly Fulton. "But if I hadn't known to put my head between my knees I would have fainted..."'

* * *

Henry was never lost for words. Not to be out-done, he went on to tell his first story.

'I was examining these young farmer chaps in their first aid,' he said. 'They don't know very much, so I kept the questions fairly basic. I said to this young lad, "If you saw a pretty girl lying face downwards in a stream what would you do?"

"'Well," said the young farmer, "I'd jump into the stream."

"'Good," I said.

"'Pull her to the bank."

"'Good," I said.

"'Loosen her clothing."

"'Good," I said.

"'And then," said the farmer, "I'd start giving her artificial insemination."'

Steve roared.

'I pass,' said Jack Hart.

'The only thing I can think of,' said Ron Dickinson, 'was that I once had trouble teaching a man mouth-to-mouth resuscitation. I knew it was going to be tricky when I had to make him take his cigarette out of his mouth before I started...'

* * *

As the years went by we had to make additions to the surgery. We were now no longer just a general practice, we had grown into a health centre, with health visitors, district nurses, social workers, even psychiatric social workers. There seemed an unending stream of extra staff.

Rooms accumulated, were turned into such things as

chiropody clinics and eye clinics, and much of the intimate atmosphere of the surgery was lost.

I found the work of district nurses and health visitors invaluable. They were dedicated women, often doing the most menial of jobs, and were able to reduce our workload quite a bit.

Social workers tended to remain aloof from us. They did their own thing and there was never enough cooperation. A tremendous amount of time seemed to be spent in case conferences and writing reports. We reckoned that one doctor working hard for a full day would cover the work of all the social workers in the Tadchester area for a week.

I don't think it was their fault. They didn't really have too many powers and they couldn't allocate beds of their own. Among the auxiliary helpers, they really were the odd men out, and we felt that the whole social work position ought to be re-appraised.

One addition that proved especially useful to the care of patients at home was the increasing scope of the occupational therapist. I had always thought of occupational therapists as ladies who taught you how to do tapestry, solve jigsaws, knit and crochet rugs, but this new breed of determined young women were like engineers. They could have bungalows built or adapted for the handicapped, they would fix up all sorts of home aids, and to two of my patients particularly they gave a completely new lease of life.

Dr Jacqueline Dean, a medical colleague, was a walking museum of pathology. She had liver trouble, bone trouble, blood trouble, bowel trouble, and had been bedridden or almost bedridden for a couple of years. With the help of her sister and the physiotherapist she could just about get downstairs once a week.

Jackie had been a great horsewoman in the past and had a long-standing love affair with John Wayne — only, alas, via the silver screen.

The occupational therapy people fitted her with a chair lift, very similar to a ski-lift, to go up and down the stairs. Jackie could just make it from the bed to the lift on her own, but once

there she enjoyed herself. Often she would spend the morning whizzing up and down the stairs chasing the cat.

'It's the nearest I'll ever get to riding to hounds again,' she said.

Reg Dawkins, my chair-bound patient with an obscure disease, was delighted with the occupational therapists' gadgets and aids.

They gave him a new chair that he could sit up in properly, a new wheelchair that had many advancements on previous ones and, best of all, an electric hoist to get him into the bath.

He insisted that I went to watch his first immersion and ceremoniously we gave his wife, Mary, a crane-driver's certificate. He would swing off his wheelchair into a cradle which lifted him at the press of a button, an arm would then swing down and he could be lowered straight into the bath.

'Bloody marvellous,' said Reg. 'I think this entitles us both to join the Transport and General Workers' Union now.'

Previously Mary had had to wind him up manually on some antiquated contraption to get him into the water.

'The thing that worries me,' I said to Reg, whose lack of mobility had made him put on weight, and who was now hovering around the eighteen stone mark, 'what happens if there is a power cut and you're stuck in the bath?'

'There is only one thing for it,' said Reg, 'I'll get my Mary to light a fire under the bath and then I'll simmer gently until the electricity comes back on.'

CHAPTER 3

Going Off with a Bang

One of the natural wonders of Tadchester was the great annual elver run up the River Tad.

Tiny elvers — transparent baby eels no more than three inches long — swarmed upriver in countless millions every spring, migrating from their birthplace in the mid-Atlantic Sargasso Sea, back to the fresh waters their parents came from.

When the run was on, the town went into a kind of frenzy. Everyone who could, dropped what he or she was doing and ran down to the river with nets, sieves, bowls, buckets — anything with which to scoop up the tiny creatures.

The run was signalled at the mouth of the estuary by the shrieking and wheeling of gulls, and by the appearance of dive-bombing cormorants. This was the sign for the salmon-net fishermen to put away their seine nets and set out their fine-meshed elver nets, to haul catches sometimes weighing hundreds of pounds in a couple of hours or so.

These commercially caught fish would be sold to Pascoes' processing factory at Stowin, who would pack them in ice and send them out all over the country and to the Continent, canning any surplus.

All the way from the Sargasso, the endless streams of elvers had been harried by predatory fish and birds. It was a wonder that any reached the estuary at all, let alone survived the concentrated onslaught of the net fishermen, to carry on upriver into and beyond the town.

Yet there they were, solid silver streams of them, the vanguard now well clear of the commercial nets and swimming straight into the makeshift equipment of the locals in the middle of town. They were scooped out in their thousands and dumped into buckets to be eaten as 'delicacies in the Tadchester restaurants, as an annual treat in hundreds of ordinary homes, and gulped down by the pound in the elver-eating contests held in almost every local pub.

I was standing on Tadchester Bridge, gazing downstream at the frantic activity, when there was a hooting and a shout from a Land-Rover which had pulled up behind me.

'Jump in, Bob, if you're free. We'll get away from these mad buggers and get our own elvers.'

It was John Denton, the local river bailiff. It was strange to hear a broad Manchester accent from a Tadchester local, but John had been raised in the industrial North and had settled in Tadchester after his army service.

'Fresh air and peace and quiet; that's what I came to

Tadchester for,' he said as I climbed into the Land-Rover. 'There won't be much peace and quiet in this place today.'

John bombed through the traffic and within minutes we were at his cottage a few miles outside the town. He darted down into the cellar, rummaged about and emerged with two enormous fine-meshed nets on the end of long poles.

'I always carry a spare, Bob,' he said, dumping them in the back of the Land-Rover. 'Give us a lift with this bath, will you? There's a good lad.'

On the wall of the cellar hung a large zinc bath. John lifted it down and loaded it with four large buckets.

'Right, then. Grab yourself that pair of wellies in the corner and we're off.'

We raced down to where the river curved in a smooth, incoming bow to form a long and gentle bay. The bank dropped steeply to a flat sand bar four or five feet below.

'This is the best place, Bob,' said John. 'The elvers swing in with the current, almost to the bank. Now let's get the stall set out before they arrive.'

He left the bath just behind us at the top of the bank, tipped in two or three inches of river water, then laid out the buckets on the sand bar in pairs part filled with water and with about ten yards between them.

'When the elvers arrive, Bob, just scoop 'em out, then tip the lot into the buckets. When the buckets are full, climb up the bank and tip the lot into the bath. Then get back down here quick for another go.

'Oh, Rule One with the net: don't slosh it in. Just dip it in smoothly, then a straight sweep downstream into the run.'

'Why the buckets?' I asked. 'Why not just have the bath down here?'

'You ever lifted a tin bath half full of elvers and water up a five-foot bank?' said John. 'You can try it if you like but I'd put your truss on first.'

Ask a silly question...

Ten minutes ticked by and there was no sign of any activity. 'How will we know they're coming?' I asked.

33

'You'll know,' said John. 'You won't have to be told. Just keep your eyes downstream.'

As I watched, two figures appeared at the end of the bay, carrying nets and buckets just as we were. Was this the sign I was looking for?

'Hey! You two!' shouted John. 'Hop it! Down the town or I'll book you! Go on — bugger off!'

John was an excellent bailiff, but diplomacy had never been his forte. And the pair was obviously not the sign I was looking for.

'What's the problem, John?' I asked. 'Won't there be enough for them as well?'

'Not the point, Bob. Fishing in the town is free by ancient charter. Anyone's welcome to have a go there. But this stretch is ticket water. No ticket, no fishing. Let one get away with it and you'd be trampled to death by half of Tadchester.'

'But they might have tickets.'

'Those two? No chance. Two of the biggest deadlegs in town.

'One of my stockponds was thinned out the other week by a person or persons unknown. Couple of hundred table-sized trout went absent without leave. The person or persons unknown are those two buggers, so my sources tell me. Apart from applying the toe of my wellie, there's not a lot I can do about it now.

'But don't worry. I'm being tipped off in advance the next time they propose to call. And Geoff Emsworth from the Tadchester Arms is going to lend me his guard dog. Hound of the "Bastardvilles" is that one. By the time those two get to court they won't have a leg to stand on, not after that dog's finished with them, anyway.'

The two figures had disappeared. John climbed the bank to be sure they were heading for the road, and made one or two abusive gestures to speed them on their way.

A strange quiet had fallen over the river. Ten minutes passed. Fifteen. Then the water at our feet started to ripple with a silver sheen, and then to boil as dozens of fish cut the surface with their fins and dived down again.

From the downstream end of the bay came the raucous cries of gulls. They appeared in a whirling cloud, swooping down again and again onto the water. They were joined by a sudden iridescent flash of colour as a kingfisher shot like a bullet from a branch. And a great grey heron glided down and took up station in the shallows. Within seconds its wicked beak was stabbing down.

'Here they are,' said John. 'Little beauties.'

'What are those fish breaking the surface?'

'Perch, most likely. They hunt in packs, just like wolves. They round up the elvers then dive straight into the middle of them. There'll be trout and chub having a go as well, and perhaps the odd little jack pike. The bigger pike will probably wait until the other fish have had their fill and then pick off some of them while they're digesting their dinner.'

The splashing fish moved past us and the water settled down. Now I could see the massed ranks of tiny silver eels moving steadily past us.

'Right,' said John. 'Eyes down, looking.'

I followed his example and stuck the net in the water, scooping it back downstream in a long, steady sweep. Resistance on the handle increased as the elvers filled the net. A steady lift, and up it came, sagging with a glistening ball of solid silver.

A quick shake and the ball was in the bucket, where it broke up in the water into hundreds of frantic, matchstick-like fish.

'Wonderful,' I said.

'Plenty more where they came from,' called John, shaking his net into one of his own buckets. 'Don't waste time looking at 'em.'

In about fifteen minutes both my buckets were full. As I lurched to the top of the steep bank, I realised the wisdom of leaving the bath where it was. John and I were scooping for an hour, and then the run petered out. For some minutes our nets came up containing just a few stragglers. The gulls had disappeared upstream, pursuing the main run of survivors.

'That's it,' said John. 'For the time being, anyway. There's a break in the run, possibly because the estuary netsmen cut it up, but probably because the tide's begun to turn. There's plenty for what we want, anyway. And there'll be more tonight and tomorrow, if need be.'

Between us, in just over an hour, we must have scooped out about forty pounds of the tiny eels. The bath was alive with their frenetic wriggling. It seemed impossible that such frail and vulnerable creatures could have made their way across the Atlantic in such incredible numbers. But they had done, and had been doing so since before the first man walked the earth.

John and I lurched back to the Land-Rover, lugging the bath between us.

'What are you going to do with all this lot, John?'

'Drop about half of them off at the Tadchester Arms — Geoff's missis makes a lovely elver pie. Then we'll call on some old dears who otherwise might not get any. Then we'll go back and have a fry-up, and what's left we'll split. I'm sure Pam will fancy having a go at some of these.'

We did the rounds, calling first at the back door of the Tadchester Arms, where Geoff Emsworth treated us both to a couple of pints of his best.

'OK, boy. Friends!' Geoff said to the huge, snarling Alsatian which had come up behind him. This was the dog John proposed to borrow to deal with the thefts from his stock pond. I felt sorry for the poachers: 'not a leg to stand on' would be just about right.

Then we called at the houses of eight or ten frail old people to whom John apparently slipped presents of the occasional fish. Their eyes lit up when they saw the elvers. The eels were an annual treat they'd known from childhood, and without John they might have been left out of the town's celebrations.

Back to John's cottage, where he fried some of the elvers and topped two helpings off with an egg apiece. They were really delicious. I was a bit worried about the fact that they were too small to clean, and had to be eaten heads, eyes, innards and all, but John reassured me.

'Nobody in this town has ever died from eating elvers, Bob. At least nobbut the out-and-out gluttons. Oh, and tell Pam the secret is not to over-fry them. If you let them get crispy you've lost half the flavour.'

John drove me back home, a bucket holding about five pounds of elvers sloshing between my knees. Naturally, we had elvers that night.

'Delicious,' said Pam.

'Yummy!' said the kids. 'More, please...'

I just had one helping, including the egg on top. It is possible to have too much of even as good a thing as an elver fry-up. And I could still hear John saying, 'Nobbut the out-and-out gluttons.'

* * *

I saw John the next day. I was fighting off a condition known as Elver Bends, which is a sort of abdominal colic, caused by over-elver consumption.

'Touch of the bends, eh, Bob lad?' said the grinning John. 'A large port and brandy and you'll be as fit as a flea in a couple of hours.'

This was a typical John Denton remedy.

'Eel slaughter,' I replied. 'All those little elvers that will never grow up into eels.'

'Slaughter, nothing,' said John. 'You ought to have been with me when I worked on the Kiltern Estate.'

Five miles to the north of Tadchester lay the Kiltern Estate: 20,000 acres of farm and woodland, several large lakes and a large Elizabethan manor house which even in post-war austerity maintained a massive retinue of servants, maids and grooms.

It was one of the few titled estates that flourished economically. There was money to maintain this grandiose building and there was money for anything young Lord Kiltern desired.

The source of the money was nothing very romantic. It wasn't oil or inherited wealth: it was simply gravel. Many acres of the estate contained highest quality gravel under a very thin layer of top soil and Kiltern gravel appeared on most of the main roads and motorways throughout the country.

The holes left by the excavation of gravel had formed large lakes, some of which had been taken over for sailing, water-skiing and fishing. It was said that one of the qualifications to be taken on the Kiltern staff was to be web-footed.

The estate was run not by the young Lord Kiltern, who would not let anything distract him from his main hobby, but by a

38

board of trustees. They gave Lord Kiltern such a large monthly allowance that it was difficult for him to spend it all however extravagant he tried to be.

His father had been killed during the war and his mother, tottering and prematurely aged, had gone to live in Switzerland in a sort of alcoholics' commune.

Lord Kiltern was able to do exactly as he wanted, and he did. He experimented with every facet of life: drink, drugs, girls, boys, men, women, the lot. In his twenties he travelled around the world as a sort of well-breeched layabout with a retinue of hangers-on who, numerous though they were, still never made any real dent in the Kiltern fortunes.

Having done all that there was to do, and having done it two or three times, at the ripe old age of twenty-eight Lord Kiltern came back to his ancestral home to settle down and indulge in his only real love, shooting.

Some men take great pride in their proficiency as marksmen and enter shooting competitions such as Bisley. Others' prowess is in the number of clay pigeons they can shoot in a certain period of time.

But Lord Kiltern's motivation was much simpler: he was a killer.

He shot everything that moved.

Vast numbers of birds — pheasants and ducks — were raised on his estate, and he would even go and shoot turkeys and geese when they were needed for the table. His appetite for slaughter was insatiable. Everything shootable was shot.

He went up to Scotland for the Glorious Twelfth for his grouse and part of the year was always spent stag-shooting in the Highlands.

Until he was thirty he still made the odd trip to go off and shoot wild boar or big game, but his health, because of the ravages he had imposed upon himself, declined and he became less and less mobile. He had a gun in his hand all day and when he wasn't firing it he was oiling it or cleaning it, and most of his days, when he wasn't out killing something, were spent in his gun room.

Lord Kiltern tried to shoot something every day. When he had run out of all legitimate game he would wander round the stables attached to the great house firing at rats and causing considerable damage to stable doors.

The area round the estate gradually became denuded of wild-life and there had to be imports of even such fast breeders as rabbits. The surviving animals on his estate had adapted to their environment. There was one huge rabbit burrow about a half a mile from the main house, and it had so many holes that there was always a way for the rabbits to escape. It was a thorn in Lord Kiltern's side.

He was determined to beat this impregnable rabbit warren and planned an attack with as much attention to detail as if it were the D-Day landing.

An organ in the main chapel of Kiltern Manor was dis-mantled and the larger organ pipes were taken out to the rabbit warren and stuck in the various rabbit holes. Keepers, dogs, and beaters were organised and with the stage set, the organ pipes sticking out of the ground like the guns of a great battleship, Lord Kiltern was pushed to the scene of the action in a wheel-chair. His abuse of drink and drugs had progressively damaged his kidneys and he had become no longer fit enough to get round the estate under his own steam.

Thirty or so men and dogs were put to work to blockade all the holes not covered by organ pipes, servants were posted by each pipe and ferrets were sent down. The excitement was tremendous. As the pipes were long the servant by each pipe would hear when a rabbit was about to exit. There would be a shout of 'High G, m'Lord,' and a rabbit would pop out of the end of the appropriate organ pipe to be blasted into extinction. 'Low C, m'lord!' and bang! — another rabbit bit the dust. Nearly forty rabbits were collected that day, most of them too smashed to be edible, and the young Lord Kiltern finished up beaming with satisfaction.

His health worsened. He was confined permanently to a chair and his shooting — now from the dining-room window — became more and more bizarre.

On the day he died of renal failure at the age of thirty-five, he had ordered the roof of his conservatory to be removed. Nearly every worker on his estate was dragooned into attempting to drive pheasants across this empty air space. It often meant carrying a pheasant to just outside the door and throwing it up into the air, while the noble lord blazed away. He had a tremendous bag and died, as they say, with a smile on his face.

'I expect that's what they mean when they say "He went in a blaze of glory,"' said John Denton.

'We won't see the likes of him again, thank God.'

'I'll stick to my elvers.'

CHAPTER 4

Normally Abnormal

When I first came to Tadchester I was amazed at the variety of conditions that patients produced: conditions that I had never dreamt possible, things that I hadn't been taught about at medical school.

I was always rushing off to my partners with tales of new and incredible discoveries such as the Irish girl who thought she could suffocate an unwanted pregnancy by sticking Elastoplast over her navel, and the man who took his cat's worming pills by mistake for his arthritis and found they improved him. It was almost as if the normal was the abnormal.

My successes weren't in brilliant diagnoses, but in catching diseases in time and referring them to expert help. And a lot of my work consisted of seeing people through difficult situations.

It was just as important to see that Mrs Jones got going under her own steam again after the loss of her husband, as it was to prove that Mrs Smith had sub-acute bacterial endocarditis.

I considered my greatest medical achievement was the handling of the case of seven-year-old John Turpin.

Before he reached me, he had been seen by all my four partners, two paediatric specialists, one child psychiatrist and

had nearly driven them and his father and mother literally and metaphorically potty.

Johnny Turpin wouldn't open his bowels. He would scream whenever he was taken to the toilet, and every seven days had to be knelt on while suppositories were inserted.

His bowels dominated the whole household. Other members of the family were all nervous wrecks. Both his mother and father were on tranquillisers. His elder brother and sister were very edgy and their schoolwork was falling off.

Medical investigation excluded any organic causes for Johnny's trouble. It was a battle of wills.

It was always a fight to get any medicine down Johnny. He

would never go to the toilet, but would either have an accident in his pants or in the bath. He could honestly be called a 'little stinker'.

His parents were neat, tidy and fastidious. His father had a senior position at the town hall. Their house was spotless and this little smelly son of theirs was really upsetting them.

I'd heard about Johnny from my partners, all of whom had reached an impasse in their attempts to treat him.

He was sent away to a special boarding school where they dealt with this type of problem, but he refused to eat and drink and screamed all the time until they brought him home, just as bad as ever.

The Turpin parents came to my surgery one day, extremely apologetic and in no way wanting to criticise my partners for all the kind work they and the specialists had done. But they were in despair. Was there anything I could suggest?

I told them that Johnny had been seen by the best opinions available, and I didn't know of anything that I could offer. As a last resort, however, I was very happy to see him, and we could take it from there.

They brought in the glowering little Turpin the next day.

He sat on a chair looking at me suspiciously. He had been through all this before. I was one of that group who, given a chance, would stick a finger up his bottom and cause him to scream the place down.

I tried to ask him about why he didn't go to the toilet but made no progress: there was no communication at all. Suddenly I had an idea.

'Johnny,' I said.

He hung his head.

'Johnny,' I said, 'look at me.'

Reluctantly he looked at me.

I said, 'If, for four weeks, you go to the toilet regularly, without a fuss, I will give you five shillings which you can spend on anything you like.'

'Oh, Doctor, you shouldn't,' said Mrs Turpin.

'No, that's all right,' I said. 'It's between Johnny and myself.'

45

'All right, Johnny?'

There was a half nod of assent.

I made a note on his record card: 'Give five shillings if opens bowels regularly for four weeks.'

Four weeks later he came back. Instead of having to be dragged into the surgery, Johnny came bounding in, followed by a flushed and beaming mother.

'How's he done?' I asked.

'Marvellous, Doctor. We've had no trouble at all. It's been like a miracle.'

I put my hand in my pocket — no change. Generosity had to be the order of the day.

'Here you are, Johnny,' I said. 'Ten shillings — well done.'

His face lit up.

'Five shillings to go in the post office and five shillings to be spent on sweets.'

'Oh, Doctor,' said Mrs Turpin, 'you are marvellous.'

A month later he came in beaming again and collected another ten shillings which his mother insisted on paying back. For my trouble she left a bottle of five-star brandy with a note that I was the best doctor in the world.

They must have worked out a system of rewards of their own, as I never saw Johnny again. I only hope I hadn't completely corrupted him.

Occasionally from then on, new patients came to register with me, saying that Mr and Mrs Turpin had recommended me.

Thus are reputations made.

* * *

I imagine that my patients and their idiosyncrasies were unique, but expect that most general practices could provide a cross-section of the sort of people I had to deal with.

After some years nothing really surprised me.

Charlie Hutt was actually one of Henry's patients. I used to see him coming to the surgery in his little three-wheeler. He lived on his own in a terraced house near the surgery.

He'd been a forester in the past and was under retiring age but not working, obviously crippled by either arthritis or some accident. He went everywhere with elbow crutches, limping along, swinging one leg after the other, grimacing with pain.

He always wore a brown leather bomber jacket and brown corduroy trousers. He had shoulder-length untidy hair, thinning in the front and was one of the Tadchester characters. He was not a pub man but would be seen on the quay resting on his crutches, yarning with the fishermen, or in the pannier market, chatting. He was a great talker, and would always pass the time of day with me.

I don't know what he did apart from look after himself and go out chatting. I admired his courage and the way he struggled along with his elbow crutches.

They say everybody has a double and one day I saw Charlie's.

About ten miles outside Tadchester the Forestry Commission had some estates of pines. My friend Eric was delivering a television set to a remote farm near there and as I had the afternoon off I went along for the ride.

Driving along the roadway through the pines we came across the exact double of Charlie Hutt. A man with shoulder-length hair, thinning at the front, brown bomber jacket, brown corduroy trousers, striding along with a chain-link saw in one hand and a log of wood over his shoulder.

I don't ever remember seeing two people looking so absolutely alike, and wondered if Charlie had had a twin.

The next day in surgery I was telling Henry about this amazing Charlie lookalike.

'Good Lord, Bob lad,' guffawed Henry. 'That was Charlie.'

'But,' I said, 'he was walking upright carrying a chain-link saw. He looked perfectly fit.'

'I know,' said Henry. 'About seven years ago Charlie's missus left him. He immediately started to walk with a limp and decided that he was going to use a pair of arm crutches. We've had him X-rayed, examined him, turned him upsidedown — there's nothing wrong with him.

'From time to time he gets fed up with being an invalid and

goes off and spends a day doing forestry work. They pay him a few quid; he's a very good tree surgeon.

'He's just made up his mind he wants to walk with crutches and there's nothing we can do to stop him. But don't you tell him you've seen him in the forests — he'll put a gipsy's curse on you.'

I didn't tell Charlie. A gipsy's curse was about all I needed.

Charlie was just one of a large group of patients who confirmed that, for Tadchester anyway, it was the abnormal that was really the normal.

* * *

Ray Short was our plumber. He had first come on the scene as a plumber's apprentice with one of the established firms in the town. We were so impressed with his tidiness, general application and modest bills that when he set up on his own, we signed up with him as our regular. He was a neat, compact, rather nervous little chap and his slender little wife, Joan, was a patient of mine. Neither of them was above 5 foot 6 inches.

Some people are more married than others, and Ray and Joan were much more than most. Their family was their life.

In days when most people had two children, Ray and Joan earnestly planned four at the right intervals and every eighteen months along came a child, right on time with no complications or fuss. Joan was a marvellous mum to her bonny children, whom she clothed in hand-knitted jumpers and tights. To complete the planning, six weeks after the birth of the fourth baby Joan was sterilised.

Ray was an industrious fellow. Their home, a large detached house near the park, was always immaculate and the garden looked as if it had come straight from a seed catalogue. They were very busy being man, wife and family, devoting all their time to the home and garden, budgie, cat, two dogs and a rabbit. Joan was a member of the Women's Institute and the young mothers' club, and they were as solid and respectable and pleasant as you could wish: a couple who were the absolute pillar not only of any community but of society itself.

48

All seemed to be well with them. The children came to the surgery for their various injections and checks but they were rarely ill. They were extremely well looked after. When the youngest came for his measles injection I did notice that Joan was rather plumper than I had remembered.

The next time I saw her she was a bit plumper still. I made some comment and the normally unflappable, motherly Joan was very tense and taut.

'Oh, we've got a lot of worry on, Doctor,' she said, 'what with me taking O-levels at night school and things being so hard in the plumbing business.' A large firm of plumbers had recently set up in the town and were in fierce competition with Ray's one-man outfit.

When I passed Ray in the street or he came down to do a job, he looked much more serious, almost as if life was getting too much for him. He had always been versatile and although ostensibly he was our plumber, he would clean gutters for us, put back tiles, put in window cords and even new windows. His bills, which had always been too modest for the amount of work he did, now went the other way and were much more than anyone else's. Instead of his increased prices helping settle his financial condition, they aggravated it because people turned to the less expensive, though not as conscientious, larger firms.

Things got worse and worse until the cold winter of 1963, which was every plumber's dream. I think that every pipe in the town that could burst, did. The plumbers were working round the clock, and Ray was able to stabilise his economic situation.

The lines began to disappear from his face, and Joan looked happier. But still she got progressively fatter. The next time she came in with one of the children — apart from pregnancies she never came about her own health — I felt I had to intercede. She really was getting extremely gross now and as her clothes did not keep up with her weight she was beginning to bulge out of everything.

'Joan,' I said, 'we must do something about your weight.'

She replied, as most over-weight people do, 'Oh, I hardly ever eat anything, Doctor. It must be my glands.'

The next time Ray came round, I mentioned it to him.

'She eats very little, Doctor,' said the defensive Ray. 'I know she does.'

Joan, like Topsy, whatever she said about her diet, growed and growed and growed. Her blood pressure began to go up and she was a good eighteen and a half stone. I remembered that after her first baby she was only six and a half stone.

I screened her with various blood tests but apart from a fairly high blood sugar level, everything seemed normal. I sent her off to Winchcombe to John Bowler who investigated her thoroughly and could find no organic cause for her steadily increasing weight.

I took Ray to task again about how much she ate. He swore that she ate very little. 'Honest, Doctor, there's never very much food in the house. Joan doesn't believe in stocking up.'

I gave her diet sheets and slimming pills but, in spite of all my efforts, she continued to grow.

I discussed it with my partners, but none of them could give me any ideas. I suggested that we admit Joan to Tadchester Hospital to keep an eye on her diet but she refused because of the children.

She really was a sight now, fat and bloated. Her weight, apart from making her uncomfortable, was causing her a great deal of distress.

'Oh, Doctor, I do wish I could lose weight,' she said. 'Isn't there something I could take?'

She made a sorry picture, sobbing, her great big fat arms shaking and tears running down her cheeks.

'I just don't know what to do, Joan,' I said, 'unless we wire your jaw, which I don't think is practical. Let's have a look at your eating list.'

What I found helpful for people trying to lose weight was to make them write down a list of everything that went into their mouth during the day. The fact that they had to write everything down was often good enough to knock off as much as a couple of stone. They had to think before they ate.

As Joan opened her handbag the contents tipped out.

Amongst the lipsticks, powder compact and bus tickets was an envelope of white powder that spilled all over the floor.

'What's this?' I said to Joan.

She had been crying before. She now became completely hysterical. She sat rocking on the chair, arms over her face, crying 'Oh, you've found me out! You've found me out! Doctor, I'm an addict.'

There was very little addiction of any sort in Tadchester and the only people I could think of were the cider addicts who used to congregate near the river bank. I had read in the papers of packets of heroin and cocaine and stuff, but surely Joan would be the last person to be associated with anything like that?

'Addicted to what?' I asked.

Joan through her muffled sobs, said, 'Icing sugar.'

'What do you mean, icing sugar?' I said.

'I eat a pound of icing sugar each day,' she sobbed, 'and I can't stop.'

'I don't believe you.'

'Yes, I do, Doctor. Please believe me. When we had all the worries about money and my exams, I got into the habit of taking a pinch of icing sugar. It wasn't very expensive and I took more and more and now I can't do without it. I keep on having a dab or a spoonful and I'm getting fatter and fatter and there's nothing I can do about it. Please don't stop me.'

'Joan,' I said, 'I'm writing straight to the *Guinness Book of Records*. You must be the first person in history ever to be addicted to icing sugar. You silly girl, why didn't you come and talk to me before? We could have helped you. There's not going to be any trouble getting you off.'

'I felt so ashamed, Doctor,' she said, 'and I always thought that next week I would be able to give it up, but then next week would come and there'd be some child's birthday and I'd be asked to bake a cake and there'd be some reason for buying icing sugar and now I order eight pounds a week — one pound for cooking and seven pounds for myself.'

'Your troubles are now over, Joan,' I said. 'Now you've told me, we can do something about it. In a few weeks this will all be

51

a thing of the past. We'll soon have you back to eight stone.'

But I was wrong. When Joan said that she was addicted, she meant it. She had all the problems of withdrawal that people have from the serious addictive drugs. We were at least six months with some psychiatric help getting her off the sugar and it was a year and a half before she got under ten stone. None of Joan's children ever had cakes iced. She just couldn't risk having any in the house.

A few days after Joan's confession I went into Ron Dickinson's surgery. He was holding up an X-ray, looking at it pensively with a fountain pen stuck in his mouth.

'What's the matter, Ron?' I said. 'Have you taken to smoking fountain pens now?'

'Oh, no,' said Ron, 'I'm addicted to them. I eat them all the time.'

'A fortnight ago, Ron,' I said, 'I wouldn't have listened to you, but I completely believe you now. I think I'll have to start flicking pencils in your ears as an antidote.'

* * *

Mr and Mrs Rollinson were well into their seventies when I first started to look after them. They had been publicans in London most of their lives and had moved down to Tadchester to run a little mixed groceries shop near the bridge. This they did until their retirement when they moved into a semi-detached house off Park Lane. Long marriages are often endured through love or necessity, or through people enjoying arguing and finding that their partner was the most able arguer they had ever met. But the Rollinsons didn't seem to have anything to keep the marriage going, other than the habit that they had always been together and had always worked together.

They lived their lives in mutual hostility. I, as a common factor, was constantly wooed to take one side or the other and had to keep as neutral as possible. They had a couple of children who lived in London, but they never came to see them.

Mr Rollinson spent his time pottering round his greenhouse and would produce tomatoes for me as a bribe, whereas Mrs Rollinson would never let me go without producing a white and sickly toffee from a huge seven-pound jar.

'Can't go without your sweet, Doctor,' she used to say.

I used to hate it. I would pop it in my mouth and start chewing before I left the house. They were so sticky that you couldn't spit them out afterwards and I had to accept that I was going to have a rotten sticky mouth for the rest of the afternoon.

Both the Rollinsons were seriously convinced that Mr Rollinson was suffering from a brain condition. He was always asking for something for his arthritis. I examined all his joints which, for his age, were very mobile and it was some months before I began to realise that what he was really bothered about was that he thought he had arthritis of the brain.

I fobbed him off with some liquid paraffin. 'It oils all the sticky parts,' I said. He seemed content with this and appeared to improve. I thought arthritis of the brain was quite a good condition to have and added it to my armoury of questions for awkward customers.

If somebody sat down and gave me forty symptoms I would look him straight in the eye and ask 'Do you think you've got arthritis of the brain?' If he said yes I would assume that most of his troubles were psychosomatic.

When I first came into general practice my punch-line when people were going on with innumerable symptoms was to ask 'Do you get pain in the back of the neck when you pass water?'

Having done this for some years and been rather pleased with myself about this clever phrase, I went to a post-graduate course where they described a syndrome called the sub-clavian steal syndrome which meant that if you whirled your arm round it resulted in losing your sight in one eye. So perhaps people did get pain in the back of the neck when they passed water.

Mrs Rollinson had all sorts of bladder troubles, and eventually lost her bladder tone which meant she couldn't pass water.

There was no obstruction but her stomach swelled and she could only pass water in dribbles.

I sent her to hospital for investigations. Calling round to see her soon after she had been discharged, I found her sitting grumpily in a chair, a rug over her knees.

'Fine mess you've got me into, Doctor,' she said, 'sending me to the hospital.'

'Well, Mrs Rollinson,' I said, 'you're looking much better and we had to do something, You couldn't pass your water.'

'Guess what they did to me.'

'I've no idea,' I said.

She said, 'They stuck a cafeteria into me and I've got to keep it stuck in me for the rest of my life.' I nearly exploded with

54

laughing. Lifting the blanket I could see an in-dwelling catheter attached to a collecting bag on her knees.

I thought it was probably some sort of neutral justice that if a man was stuck with arthritis of the brain, he should be married to a woman who sported an in-dwelling cafeteria.

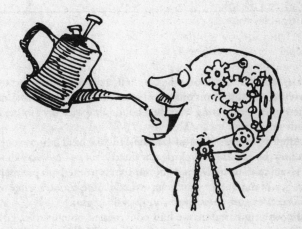

CHAPTER 5

Holidays with the Family

I had been a bachelor when I first arrived in Tadchester, survived the ambitions of several local ladies, and married my wife Pam after meeting her when holidaying with my mother in Bournemouth.

After nine years in a flat Up-the-Hill, we built a house overlooking the estuary. Thinking our family of two boys was all we were going to have, we had got our rooms worked out precisely. Jane, our daughter, was born exactly nine months after we moved. I'm sure there was a very good reason.

In our original plans we had not counted on nurseries, girls' bedrooms, etc. and the tiny study and TV room had to be knocked together to remedy this deficit. The builder said we were the only people he had ever known who started knocking walls down as soon as the house had been put up.

The birth of Jane coincided with the death of Pam's mother, 'Bill'. Pam and her mother had been extremely close but Pam was so occupied with the new baby that frankly she just had not the time to grieve. It was one of those strange balances of nature which can do so much to heal the wounds of tragedy.

But one of the disadvantages of general practice is that the sheer physical demand of the working hours means that the

amount of time you spend with your family, particularly your children, is limited. As I begin to tot up the years, looking back on the things that have given me the greatest pleasure, I think probably the happiest moments of my life have occurred on travels with the family.

It was impossible to have holidays at home, even though we

lived in a delightful rural area near the sea. If I was at home gardening, the fact that my car was outside the house would encourage people to knock at the door with, 'I know you are off duty, Doctor, but...'; even a trip to the beach usually resulted in a queue of people waiting to see me for unofficial and alfresco consultations. So when holidays came round we had to get up and travel somewhere.

All five of us reacted differently to the rigours of travelling. The drug companies which sell travel-sickness preparations have always done well out of us. Pam and Jane take one tablet; Paul, my younger son, has at least two, and Trevor none at all. I need a measure of brandy or whisky to wash down a tablet, providing that I have remembered to take it before I've swallowed the supporting fluid.

Pam is patient, long-suffering and non-complaining. A polite request for the car window to be opened slightly means that the combination of my clouds of tobacco smoke, dust and undulations of the road are too much for her, that she is feeling sick, that she wishes she were dead and would rather have stayed at home anyway.

Trevor is unperturbed by travel; in fact, he is unperturbed by anything. He uses bread as a tranquilliser, following each meal with a few thick slices, and at home slips off to the bread bin every fifteen minutes in between meals. I did, on one journey, find him chewing a tyre-pressure gauge, but put it down to withdrawal symptoms as he had been without bread for two hours.

If Trevor is mentioned in the *Guinness Book of Records* for his bread consumption, Paul must rank as the worst traveller of all time. Once, in a rowing boat on Lake Geneva, on a calm, sunny day, he felt sea-sick before we had left the shore. He distinguished himself on that particular holiday by vomiting all the way from Calais to the Italian Riviera and back.

Although we remembered the magnificent scenery, the Alps and the Dura Mountains, he claimed to be more familiar with the bottom of Continental lavatory basins than anyone else of the same age and weight.

On one occasion, crossing on a new and short-lived route to the Continent — Torquay to Cherbourg — on a boat without stabilisers, I thought we were going to lose him.

Everyone on the boat was sick, standing three-deep at the rail, including two hundred Swedish students, all dressed in their Sunday best on a day trip. It was easy to see what you had had for breakfast because the next person was wearing it.

Pam and I were so ill that we could give Paul only the minimum attention. He lay curled up, semi-conscious, under some seats on a pile of newspapers. On disembarking we carried him to the car and — although this was officially a camping holiday — rushed to book in at the nearest (very expensive) hotel to get him safely into bed.

As a small boy Paul always looked desperately ill even when he was well. He was so thin that we considered he might have a career modelling for famine relief posters. This time he looked worse than usual. It was a tremendous relief to get him into bed and see his small pale face lying peacefully on a huge pillow. I popped back half an hour later to see him stirring. 'Paul,' I said, 'is there anything I can get you: Vichy water, lemon squash?'

To my utter amazement for one so young, his feeble voice answered, 'Yes. I would like a sirloin steak, rare, with chips and a tossed salad.'

This was our Paul all over. Although he goes down quicker than anyone I know, there's no doubt that he gets up even faster. He has sometimes been so dehydrated by travel sickness that if he had been a patient I would have sent him to hospital. But put Paul to bed, give him twenty minutes after he has stopped being sick and he is up, downing a plate of egg and chips before shooting off to play football.

His ability to eat in unusual circumstances could be due to pre-natal influences by his brother. At three o'clock one April morning I was rushing Pam by car, in early labour with Paul, to the maternity hospital. Trevor, aged three, and lying supposedly asleep on the back seat, suddenly piped up, 'We haven't had swede for lunch lately, have we?'

Jane, much like her mother, is the gentlest of the three children: a sweet, tender little soul. She is highly intelligent as well as being painstaking and methodical. She is a fair traveller and takes her medication reluctantly.

I, as the last-mentioned traveller of the family, am the leader, the organiser, and the only smoking member. As I get older I get fatter and balder and more addicted to my pipe. I am one of the few people who smoke a pipe in bed before breakfast and have been known to nip down in the night for a puff. I have an excellent reason for smoking a pipe: I can't afford cigars.

My life has been so permeated with smoke that my partners reckoned they could smell me coming even if I weren't smoking.

A long train journey with Ron Dickinson after a hospital reunion in London, resulted in his wife forbidding him ever to travel with me again. She said not only did his clothes smell of pipe smoke for weeks, but the whole of the wardrobe had become contaminated.

The family has always travelled in rather old and suspect cars. I begrudge spending money on cars and can never understand why they fall to pieces. We take enough food and clothes for a month, irrespective of the fact that our holiday may only be for a week. There are polythene bags hanging out of windows, chairs and tables strapped untidily to the roof rack; every available inch around the car passengers is crammed with shoes, packets of cornflakes, tennis rackets etc.

We would make ideal smugglers. No customs official would ever dream of interfering with the turmoil of our car luggage. From our outward appearance, even if we were illegally trafficking, we were obviously not making a profit out of it.

* * *

River holidays had been a success in the past, so one year we booked a barge holiday on the River Severn and the adjoining canal system.

We travelled by car to the Severn, to a beautiful marina filled with gleaming, modern boats. In previous years we always

60

seemed to have a dirty old boat: perhaps our luck was in this time. There were some 150 boats in the marina. They really were superb, being beautifully equipped and more like floating bungalows than boats.

Our boat turned out to be one of a group of grimy barges moored some 100 yards away from the main huddle. (Perhaps if they were closer they would have contaminated the others.) Our luck hadn't changed. And, as it turned out, we were paying more for ours than for one of the brand new models.

The boat was a 50 foot long, six-berth steel barge. It was the best equipped boat we had ever had, with electric light, hot water, flush toilet, shower, gas stove, fridge and convector heater.

It was also the dirtiest boat we had ever had. No attempt had been made to clear accumulated mud and debris either inside or outside.

We tested the various equipment and found that the water heater didn't work, the fridge didn't work, and we didn't know how to light the convector heater. From time to time we engaged the attention of men in smart nylon overalls. Whoever we contacted seemed to be involved in something else and promised to get his mate who specialised in our particular problem, in five minutes.

Nobody took our inventory, and anyway we couldn't find one. We did note that we had no mop, deck scrubbers, mooring stakes, windlasses for opening locks, mallet, or engine oil. Each time we asked one of our marina staff for some particular missing item, he would soon manage to produce it. It was only later I noticed they were pinching them from other boats.

We had ordered a television set and eventually a battered one materialised. The man who brought it cheerfully said, 'If you can't get it to work, we will give you your money back.'

Having stowed our luggage we sat waiting for someone to come and authorise the hire. In the meantime, relays of men, each saying it wasn't really his job, managed to get our water heater going, our fridge in working order, and instruct us how to use the convector heater.

We were due to take over the boat at 4 p.m. It was 6.45 p.m. before the boat proprietor arrived to conduct the business side. There were one or two surprises, including an extortionate charge for parking our car for the week.

One of the engineers showed us the various working parts of the boat, turned the engine on and we cast off. He opened the throttle handle and it came away in his hand.

'That's definitely not good,' he said.

The boat could do eight or nine knots, it was steel-hulled and weighed a few tons and if not under reasonable control could do a great deal of damage. The engineer screwed the throttle handle back on, leapt off the boat, and we were away.

We had planned to cruise from the Severn to the Avon, go up to Stratford and, hopefully, go to the theatre. We discovered that the lock gates into the Avon were under repair and closed to traffic. So we headed upstream to the canals that would lead us into the Midlands.

We cruised for about an hour then moored out in the country by a field. Although it was a six-berth boat, there was only seating for three round the table, so I stood up having my dinner at the sink and Paul sat on the steps leading up to the front of the boat, with his dinner on his knees. The disadvantage of sitting on the steps was that they were next to the convector heater — which really was hot. Although Paul thoroughly enjoyed his meal he found that he had burnt a hole in his jeans.

Going up the Severn I appreciated for the first time some of the things that Captain Scott put up with. In my exposed position as helmsman I bore the full brunt of the wind, rain, hail and icy cold. It was no comfort to know that I was paying through the nose for the experience.

On the second day, in the teeth of a driving gale, we reached our first lock, on the Severn just south of Worcester. Manoeuvring the boat in the lock I put it astern with full throttle to bring it to a halt.

The throttle handle came off in my hand and several tons of steel barge were bearing down on the lock gates with nothing to stop them. As calmly as I could, I knelt down by the instrument

post and tried to fit the throttle handle into its socket to reduce
the revolutions. Thankfully, with one son holding it in place, I
was able to bring the boat to a stop.

The lockkeeper had various screwdrivers but none of them
fitted the handle. Eventually I managed to effect some sort of
repair by using an assortment of medical instruments. (I had
thrown my medical instrument case in, as I usually run into

surgical difficulties on holiday.) These instruments took a greater beating on the barge than they had during my previous ten years in medicine. My midwifery scissors were used (to their detriment) when we found that the only tin opener provided on board didn't work.

Next day, we reached Stourport for lunch and thought we had come to Blackpool by mistake. It seemed a mass of crowds, fairgrounds, and fish-and-chip shops. We had been told to keep our water tank topped up, with the attendant vaguely pointing to the white caps on the top of the cabin which, as old boat hands, we knew were the covers to the water tank. We successfully started a stream of water going through the hole on the top of the boat. Fortunately Jane was reading below and, hearing a splashing noise, informed us that we were putting water through the bathroom ventilator.

Eventually we were away and up the Worcester and Stafford Canal.

We crept through the dismal industrial area of Kidderminster, past derelict factories, sewage works, and one lock right in the middle of the town with traffic pouring over our heads. Then we were in the country again and found a delightful mooring spot close to a lock pub at Wolverley.

One day the family got back to the boat to find Trevor holding it to the bank by the two ropes. He had got so caught up in a book he was reading in the cabin that he had not heard a party of youths come along, pinch the aluminium mooring pegs, coil the ropes on the barge and push it into mid stream.

Almost as if from a storybook we found a real live blacksmith with a forge by the towpath. He fashioned us some iron mooring pegs, one of which seemed to weigh about three quarters of a ton.

After a few more adventures, we found ourselves back at the mooring on the Severn.

We'd enjoyed the holiday. It had been nice to be cruising along knowing there was a joint roasting in the oven and that the cabin would be warm and there would be a bottle of wine waiting. You have got to get wet and cold to really appreciate warmth and dryness. To manage the boat we all had to leap about and in spite of ourselves we had become quite fit.

We needed the fitness when we got to the marina car park — ours was the only car which wouldn't start.

CHAPTER 6

Rewarding Years

I was called urgently one day to help Jack Hart with a male patient who had collapsed just outside the surgery. In spite of all our resuscitation attempts, he died.

'He was sitting in my surgery half an hour ago, talking to me,' said Jack, 'I'll have to inform the coroner.' (All deaths have to be reported to a coroner if the deceased has not seen a doctor in the previous two weeks.)

'Why, Jack?' I asked. 'You've only just seen him.'

Jack looked a bit sheepish. 'He's not a patient of ours,' he said. 'I've just done a life insurance examination on him.'

'And how did you grade him?'

'An A1 first-class risk.'

I always avoided being pinned down to a forecast on how long people are likely to survive in any particular circumstances. Too often I have been proved wrong. I've comforted families whose elderly relatives I thought would pass away during the night, to be confounded by them being hale and hearty five years later.

New cures arrive almost every day which can completely change the outlook on certain diseases. When penicillin was discovered, five diseases which were considered incurable, straightaway became curable and manageable. This was apart from all the lesser benefits that penicillin and similar drugs brought to the treatment of other diseases.

I also believe that if you tell a man that he only has a certain time to live then, whatever else you do, you reduce the time he has to spend with us.

Two couples defied all the odds.

Commander Hugh Dunlop and his wife Erica were both ex-navy people. Commander Dunlop was 6 foot 4 inches, seventeen stone and practically housebound by a painful arthritic hip. Erica, a pert, very upper crust ex-Wren, was charming, smiling, very attractive and in her early sixties.

The Dunlops lived in a little cottage at the end of a small mews just off the front at Sanford-on-Sea, or rather this was where Hugh held court.

The cottage was extremely tiny and its living room crammed with antiques. It had a kitchen and bathroom at the back and a winding staircase leading to bedrooms upstairs.

The small front garden was packed with flowers and there were roses over the door: the archetypal dream cottage. It was the focal point of local activity, with a constant stream of visitors coming and going.

The Dunlops were the perfect hosts, always charming, although Hugh was physically very limited. Erica looked well but was, in fact, far from it.

I had been visiting them for some years, treating Hugh's arthritis, when Erica asked if I would mind having a look at her. She had, to my knowledge, never had any medical attention before.

We climbed the tiny spiral staircase to the bedroom. On examining Erica I found that she had a widespread cancer. My heart sank.

'How long have you had these lumps, Erica?' I asked.

'Oh, about two years,' she replied. 'I didn't like to bother anybody.'

Erica had to have a mutilating and debilitating operation, and then fight a constant battle against the invading disease.

I would have said that she had about six months to live.

However, she went on leading a normal life to the extent that she ran her household, did her own shopping, did not reduce the amount she entertained and was able to attend local dinners and cocktail parties.

She had to have repeated courses of radiotherapy and various courses of drugs. Although at times she must have felt absolutely awful, particularly when she was on some of the more toxic drug treatments, she never complained. She never ever asked what was wrong with her, she appeared to accept that she had some sort of inflammatory condition — so there was no need to dwell on the reality of her condition. I think she knew the truth but had managed to shut it out.

Erica's disease, though not cured, was contained. She lived a normal life to its full span — and none of us can hope for much more than that.

Hugh knew absolutely everything and everybody. Whatever subject you brought up, he was better informed than you. He made it his business to keep in touch with all the important people he knew and he knew so many: lords, ladies, politicians, generals, admirals. Hardly a day went by without someone calling at the cottage. There were army staff cars, Rolls-Royces, battered sports cars, even bicycles, parked outside. There was always something going on.

Hugh had been injured in the Norwegian expedition during the war, and had been decorated by both British and Norwegian Governments. Manning a Bofors gun on the quay as they left Norway chased by the Germans, with too long an exposure to the flashes, had left him with some weakening of his sight. Although he could hear quite well, his eyes were such that he couldn't read. He was unable to watch television, but he wouldn't have had time anyway. Once when he was admitted to hospital he had twice as many visitors as the person next to him in popularity. He also had the largest fund of dirty stories I have ever known.

For all his cheerfulness and bluff naval manner, Hugh was in considerable pain. I never knew how he got up and down the stairs from his bedroom to the living room: it must have been on his hands and knees.

His hip got progressively worse and it was obvious that he should have something surgical done. I impressed on him that he must see an orthopaedic surgeon.

'Thank you, old boy,' said Hugh. 'We'll think it over and let you know.'

By my next visit — and the visits were usually more social than medical (I could hardly ever get away without a glass of whisky from a cut glass decanter) — Hugh and Erica had thought it over. Said Hugh, 'We have decided to have Chaplin operate on my hips, old boy. All my friends say he is the best.'

'That will cost you the earth,' I said. 'Chaplin is the most famous hip surgeon in England.'

'Oh, I know,' said Hugh. 'We obviously can't afford his fees so I will go and see him privately at first — when he visits the south of England — and then I'll go up and have it done in one of his National Health beds at Wrightington, near Wigan.'

'Hugh,' I said, 'everybody wants him. It's like saying I would like to have the Queen's physician for my bronchitis.'

'Look here, old boy,' said Hugh, 'this is what we want. Please organise it.'

This was how Hugh always operated. I sat down and wrote a long letter to Chaplin who I knew had a waiting list of private patients for two years and National Health for three years. I wrote explaining how ill both Hugh and Erica were, and put forward — tentatively and apologetically — Hugh's proposition.

To my surprise, an appointment came in two weeks for Hugh to be seen at Midhurst in Sussex. Six weeks later he was in Wrightington having his operation under the National Health Service. The logistics of getting him up to Wrightington and back were incredible, but friends stood the costs of all train journeys and went to great lengths to organise cars in between. Hugh was back in two months, having done what he set out to do. He'd had his hip operation by the best man in the land and there was one more story for his repertoire. Of course, by then he was an authority on Chaplin and had another celebrated name to add to his list.

A couple of years went by and Hugh's other hip started to give trouble.

'I'm thinking of getting in touch with Chaplin again,' he said. (I'm sure he was calling Chaplin by his christian name by then.)

'You're damn well not,' I said. 'You'll go across to Winchcombe and take your turn like the rest.'

So Hugh went across to Winchcombe and had his other hip done. Two months later, and for the first time in six years, he was walking down the road. It made a tremendous difference to him. He could walk down to the nearest pub, not that he was a great drinker but he did love the company.

He was able to walk far enough with Erica for them to go out to lunch. They could go and sit on the small promenade at Sanford and soak up the sun. They weren't shackled by the house any more. This incredibly courageous couple were able to go on enjoying many happy years together — two living tributes to the miracles of modern medicine.

* * *

Mrs Diana Thompson was a smart, Eton-cropped, efficient

career woman, the second senior partner in the largest firm of accountants in Tadchester. She had a Cambridge degree, had come from a wealthy background and was a lady (whatever that means). She certainly had poise and style.

She was severe, unapproachable, abrupt in manner and minded her own business, which was about the biggest sin you could commit in Tadchester. Nobody quite knew what she was up to in her spare time, though a lot made educated guesses. She used to spend her weekends and holidays away from Tadchester. It was rumoured that she had been seen going into a night club in London, but nobody ever really knew.

She had extremely good holidays in expensive places like the West Indies, the Bahamas, Bermuda and the South of France. I knew this, as from time to time I was called on to give her injections and immunisations.

She was certainly not short of money, one of the things she couldn't hide. When her father died, his will was published and he left all his money — a six-figure sum — to her. She must also have had a reasonable salary from her accountancy. She was the first occupier of one of a block of luxury flats built at the western end of Tadchester Quay near the park and art gallery. They were extremely up-market for Tadchester, being walled-off for privacy, and with their own swimming pool. As far as anybody knew she had no male friends.

I was surprised one day to get a call from Mrs Thompson. Would I come and see a guest?

I went at the end of the morning surgery and was shown into the large, double bedroom. As there was a nightdress by the side of the bed and a lady's dressing gown hanging on the back of the door, I assumed she was sharing the bed with the wheezing, overweight male propped up gasping on some lace pillows.

'This is a friend of mine,' she said in her curt tone, giving nothing away and with no feeling of tenderness. 'James Fry. He's come down here so that I can look after him while his chest is bad.'

James Fry turned out to be a fifty-year-old Fleet Street journalist, not a big name but someone who had had to hold his own amongst the big names for a number of years. He had a serious lung complaint which finally reduced him to the extent that he could hardly walk.

There was nobody who looked less like a nurse than Diana Thompson, I doubted if she could be very helpful if he really got ill.

On examining Fry I found that he had a chronic, irreversible lung disease with secondary heart failure. He was on a mass of drugs and had obviously been treated by the best physicians in London. Also, obviously, none of them had been able to do a great deal for him. He had been a heavy smoker as well as having a bad chest, and the combination of the two had almost brought him to a halt.

After examining him I suggested various changes in medication, arranged for him to have some domiciliary oxygen then took Diana into the next room.

'Mr Fry is extremely ill,' I said. 'I think it would be as well to get him under one of the physicians here and see what help we can give you.

'Would you like the District Nurse to call or shall we get in a private nurse?'

'I don't need any help at all,' she said, 'I can manage completely.'

'But you are holding down a job,' I said. 'Can you do both?'

'I can manage that as well,' she said abruptly. She wasn't a person to argue with.

I arranged for my friend John Bowler, a physician at Winchcombe, to come over and see him. His findings were much the same as mine: very little we could do, and no benefit in going to hospital. He thought Fry's outlook was very poor and, when pressed, said he thought he wouldn't last more than about six months.

When Fry had been in Tadchester a few months Diana came to my surgery to say she would like to take him to her cottage in the Dordogne for a month.

'I'm afraid I can't recommend it,' I said. 'He's far too ill to travel. A journey to France could well be too much.'

'He might as well die there as anywhere else,' snapped Diana. 'There's no point in his just stopping at home.'

That was that.

James — as I now knew him — was terribly excited about going. Just the fact that somebody considered that he might make it was a tremendous boost to his morale, and he improved visibly. I kitted them out with enough stuff to see them through any crisis, gave them a letter to give to any doctor if they needed help, and even managed to fix them up with some oxygen cylinders.

They had a month in the sun and he came back better than I could have expected. This only meant that he could walk two or three hundred yards but it was enough to get him to the quay, where he could sit and watch the boats.

They told me there was no need for me to call at the flat any more: if they could get to France they could certainly visit my surgery. So once a month Diana used to drive James over for a check-up.

Over the next six years she called me out only twice to see him. Both occasions were during the winter when he had a chest infection superimposed on his already chronic lung disease.

As James got slowly weaker, Diana organised her office routine so that she was in for only three hours in the morning and two hours in the afternoon.

James's health slowly and steadily got worse. It took only a slight chill or a little over-exertion to make him dangerously short of breath. He was unable to leave the flat at all under his own steam.

He was in a pretty desperate state when they came for medication for their annual holiday to the Dordogne, in his seventh year in Tadchester, but I knew better than to try to persuade them not to go. He came back a little improved, still not well enough to go out and walk on his own, but much better in spirit and with a good tan.

During their next trip to the Dordogne, I wasn't surprised to receive a card from Diana saying that James had died peacefully in the sunshine and was to be buried out there.

73

She came back completely broken. The normally tight-lipped and composed woman wept on my shoulder.

'Oh, Doctor,' she sobbed. 'Why did he have to go? Why did he have to go?'

'My dear Mrs Thompson,' I said (I had never even reached the stage of calling her Diana), 'by some miracle you were able to give James seven more years of happy life of good quality, more than anybody expected. No nurse, no doctor, no hospital could have given him what you gave.'

'Whatever I gave him,' said Diana, 'is nothing to what he gave me. He was my life, my mainstay. Now there's no point in going on.'

Diana was extremely ill for about four months, acutely depressed and withdrawn. She didn't even go to work; she grieved desperately, was careless over her grooming and she looked lined and older.

I offered to send her to a nerve specialist, but she refused.

She came to see me once every week for some sleeping tablets. I refused to give her the facility of re-ordering herself: I didn't want to tempt her to take too many.

After six months she slowly began to pick herself up again, looking smarter, going back to the office, but she never went out in the evenings or at weekends.

Gradually she inched out of her shell and occasionally she would go up to London. Then one day she called to announce she was finishing with the Tadchester firm of accountants and taking up a post in the metropolis.

'Dr Clifford,' she said, 'I never thanked you for all you did for James and myself. We would never have managed without you.'

I was again able to tell her what a marvellous person I thought she was, that by transfusing someone with her own energy she had given James at least seven extra years of life at no small sacrifice to herself.

'Whatever I gave him,' said Diana, dropping back into her curt manner, 'was nothing to what he gave me. He was my whole life.'

74

How this breathless invalid gave her so much I shall never know. I do know that I saw the near-miracle of a dying man being sustained for seven rewarding years.

CHAPTER 7

Pearls Before Swine

My senior partner Steve Maxwell had instilled in me the importance of routine visits, particularly to the elderly.

'Sometimes the only medicine needed,' he said, 'is for you to sit and listen. You will find in time that it is rewarding to both you and the patient.'

Over the years in Tadchester I built up a number of regular calls, ostensibly to see people who were ill and enquire about their progress. But just as much, it was somewhere I could catch my breath, have a chat, a glass of home-made wine, a cup of tea, swop a few stories, have a good laugh and generally relax.

One such call was at the Coach and Horses, an old thatched coaching inn halfway between Tadchester and Hovery, to see the venerable Mrs Partridge.

In a small fenced garden opposite the inn stood a genuine coach which, some 150 years earlier, used to ply the muddy track which is now tarmacadam road between Tadchester, Winchcombe and Hovery. With its immaculate thatch, black timbers, white walls, polished high-backed wooden seats and solid wood trestle tables, the inn was a favourite holiday spot for the better-breeched holidaymaker. It had a sort of public school

76

air about it, with the chat in the bar more about Fiona and
Hugo and Clarence than Elsie, Gladys and Albert.

I had been in Tadchester for two years when I was summoned
to see Mrs Partridge, the lady of the inn. She had got fed up with
her elderly doctor, who had a one-man practice out in the
country, and wanted somebody younger to look after her.

I had already met her son-in-law, Group Captain Charles Hunter and his vivacious wife Felicity. Charles and Felicity ran the hotel although Mrs Partridge was still a major shareholder. She was an imperious old lady who very much resented the fact that her son-in-law was now running things.

Most of the time, when she was well enough to be up and about, she sat in the corner of the pub slandering her son-in-law, saying that he had stolen all the family money, was running the pub down and she would advise people to go and stay back in Tadchester. The Coach and Horses certainly wasn't what it was in her husband's day.

The truth of the matter was that Charles had not only put his boundless enthusiasm and energy into the hotel and worked it up to its present high standards, but had also invested a great deal of his own money.

The fact that the atmosphere of the pub was public school, and that by some natural selection the guests were usually gin and tonic, hunting, shooting and fishing people, was because the inn really had a public school foundation. The late Mr Partridge had been a housemaster at Repton and when retirement came he fancied running a country hotel.

He brought certain standards to the running of the inn. Guests had to toe the line, much as any boy in his house at school had had to do. You had to dress for dinner and conduct yourself in a gentlemanly manner whatever you were doing, be it drinking, playing darts, or even bowling in the skittle alley.

One day a leather-clad motorcyclist found that you couldn't break the rules. He came into the public bar and asked Mr Partridge, one of the few men who served drinks in the public bar in a morning coat, for a Harvey's Bristol Cream Sherry. Having downed it like an American film star throwing back a snort of whisky, he asked for a second glass. Gulping that down, he asked for a third. He was refused point-blank by the indignant Mr Partridge, who sent him packing — nobody was going to drink sherry like that in his hotel, and to a man who drank liquors before dinner, he muttered audibly 'Pearls before swine.'

Mrs Partridge had a multitude of small things wrong with her, and one or two large things. I developed the habit of going there every Wednesday evening to have a cup of tea — which was served in her bedroom — and a chat. She would be sitting up in her bed waiting for me in a clean white nightgown. I can't ever remember having to examine her other than superficially, and she was perfectly fit enough to be up and about. But when a doctor called you always greeted him in bed ready for an examination, even if you weren't prepared to let him examine you.

We would discuss Mrs Partridge's medical problems, make a few remarks about things like opening bowels and passing water, and then one of the maids would bring in a tray. I would have a cup of tea from a silver teapot, and eat sugar-coated, wafer-thin biscuits. Then she would regale me with tales of the past. Weekend house parties, hunt balls, titled acquaintances, when ladies and gentlemen were ladies and gentlemen.

The second half of my visit would be spent downstairs with Charles and Felicity. In the summer the place was packed with visitors, and there was not time for more than to say hello and have a quick glass of sherry. But in the winter, most often there were just the three of us, and we would sit round a great log fire in the bar and sort out the world's problems.

Under the incongruities of British law, the hotel had to be open the whole year round. Though it was packed in summer, on three nights a week in the winter, the only customer was a patient who was allowed to come out of the local mental hospital on his own, have a pint and then go back again.

Charles had been captain of football and cross-country at Repton. He was a fine figure of a man: 6 foot 2 inches, proportionally well built, jet black hair, and an infectious, raucous laugh. He had been in the RAF during the war, before which he'd spent most of his years in India working for an oil company. He had a great love of flying and his claim to fame was that he was the first man to introduce gliding into India. He paid to have a glider boxed and shipped over, and opened the first Indian gliding club.

His years in the air force had made him unsettled, and after the war he did not want to go back to India. Wandering around England he happened to book in at the Coach and Horses for the night. There he found his old housemaster working behind the bar and the housemaster's daughter, whom he remembered as a gap-toothed little girl, had now blossomed into the beautiful Felicity.

Charles's one-night stay was extended to three weeks. He and Felicity were engaged after a month and married after six.

Pam, myself and the children were among the privileged few who were asked to dine on Boxing Day lunchtime when Felicity would produce such exotic dishes as frogs' legs, snails and caviare.

Charles and Felicity were made joint presidents of the Gaderene Society. This was a society for those of us who were stupid enough to crawl through the surf at night, dragging seine nets, trying to catch fish off the beaches. All members were treated to an annual dinner one night in the winter, when Felicity would produce clams, oysters, exotic fish dishes — everything a self-respecting fisherman would expect to eat — and we would dance, sing and generally let our hair down.

They were kindness itself. One December they asked my help in selecting half a dozen people who would otherwise have had a bad Christmas or no Christmas, to come and spend Christmas Day with them. Not only did they offer to feed these people, but they would also go and pick them up and run them home.

After much searching I could find only four. These included a widowed father and his spastic son; a retired butler, a tall fastidious man who lived in a tiny bedsit; and a decrepit old lady, Mrs Tuckett, who lived in an equally decrepit old cottage just off the Winchcombe road.

The cottage was filthy, and I doubted if she fed herself properly. She would take anything from anybody, and certainly wasn't proud. She was a cheery old soul, though, and made light of the circumstances she was in.

Her nextdoor neighbours did their best for her. They were old themselves, but produced a meal most days. A

Christmas free of the old lady was a blessing on its own.

Mrs Tuckett loved Christmas Day at the Coach and Horses, and went home showered with presents and tins of food. She touched Charles's and Felicity's consciences and they made a habit of popping in with a gift of groceries, usually once a week when they went into Tadchester shopping.

Old Mrs Tuckett was found dead in her cottage one morning, from either a coronary or cerebral thrombosis. I broke the news to Charles and Felicity on my next visit.

They were both very upset. 'Poor old thing,' said Felicity. 'She had so little. There was so much more we could have done for her.'

I smiled. I'd been there when ambulancemen started to look around for blankets and things to lay Mrs Tuckett out. In every conceivable nook and cranny they found pound notes, saving certificates, share certificates and cash bonds. They totalled £37,173.

'Good God!' said Charles, throwing his head back with a great roar. 'She could have bought the hotel.'

One spring, after nine years of my weekly visits, Mrs Partridge died within forty-eight hours of contracting an acute chest infection. She had been a great old character but the way she belittled the efforts of her son-in-law and daughter was very naughty, and I think she knew it. However, I felt a sense of loss. My Wednesday evening call *was* a medical visit. If I wasn't going to see her I was selfishly going out into the country just for a drink. It didn't feel right.

'I do hope you will still come on Wednesdays,' said Felicity.

'I hope so too,' I said. 'But with your mother's going I have no medical excuse.'

'Well come up next week,' said Felicity. 'Don't stop suddenly — you're part of the scenery.'

I called the next Wednesday. And on the wooden seat by the log fire was a most beautiful leather medical case with the initials R.C. It really was elegant: a case I could never have afforded.

'Just a little memento of mother,' said Felicity. 'Your visits

81

were so important to her. She used to say that it was the high-light of her week.'

I stuttered some modest protest.

'Rubbish,' said Felicity. 'It was so important to her that she started to change her nightdress on a Wednesday after having had Monday as a changing day for eight years. She couldn't pay you a bigger compliment than that.'

I picked up my new case. Would I, I wondered, be changing my pyjamas specially for someone when I was ninety-seven?

*　　*　　*

John Denton solved my problems of conscience regarding visits to the Coach and Horses. He suggested that we formed a two-man fishing club, with John as president and me as secretary, and that we should meet fortnightly at the Coach and Horses and apply ourselves to discuss the different aspects of fishing over a drink.

When I first met John Denton he'd given me lessons on coarse fishing, and since then we'd had one or two very enjoyable days on the river. Now I fancied fly fishing for trout.

'But I never seem to find the time, John.'

'Make the time,' he said. 'It's the only way. Otherwise you'll never get round to it. Tell you what, it won't be long before the mayfly hatch.' (It was getting towards the middle of May.) 'I'll give you a couple of lessons and we'll be ready for the river as soon as the hatch starts.'

He gave me a couple of dry-land lessons on a fly rod, using a scrap of cloth on the line instead of a hook. ('I've only got two ears,' he said, 'and I'm rather attached to them. You can have a hook when you've learned to cast without being a danger to the public at large.')

The thickness of the fly line came as a surprise. The nylon monofilament I'd used for tench when John gave me my first fishing lessons, had been almost invisible.

Casting was tricky to start with. There is no weight to rely on as there is in other forms of fishing. The only weight is that of the line itself. To the end of the line John tied a short length of finer line — the *point*, which takes care of any wear and tear — and to this point he tied the cloth.

The rod had a beautiful action, springy right down to the butt without being floppy. And all the work was done from the wrist.

'Take some line off the reel in your left hand,' said John. 'Then take the rod back with your right, over your shoulder to one o'clock. When the line is fully extended behind you, bring the rod smartly forward. Keep doing that, and release a bit more line with every forward cast.'

I felt like a circus ringmaster, waving the rod from the wrist as if I were flicking at a team of performing horses. Indeed, after a few motions there was a crack just like a whip.

'How about that, John?' I asked. 'Hear that crack?'

'I did,' said John. 'Bottom of the class for that. It's what happens if you bring the line forward before it's streamed out fully at the back. Do it too often and you'll finish up without a hook. And though I've not mentioned this before, a hook is by way of being a necessity for catching trout.'

After a while I'd got the hang of it enough to try some target practice, dropping the rod tip when the cloth was about three feet above the desired spot.

One afternoon a couple of days later, John rang me at home.

'I hear you've got the day off, Bob,' he said. 'The mayfly hatch has started. Fancy trying for a couple of trout?'

'Love to. But I'm painting the shed.'

'The shed can wait. The mayfly won't. Make time. Remember? I'll expect you in half an hour.'

I cleaned up quickly, leaving the shed half-painted, and drove over to John's cottage. He was waiting, with rods, landing nets and creels already packed in his Land-Rover.

In a slow eddy of the Tad, the mayfly were hatching. It wasn't so much of a hatch as a transformation.

The mayfly larvae, known to the angler as 'nymphs', rise to the surface after two or three years of living underwater. On the surface their skins split and the adult flies — the 'duns' — emerge. The duns then fly off to bushes on the bank where one more sloughing of the skin leaves them ready to take part in their brief mating dance; after which they return to the water, near to death, as spent flies or 'spinners'.

On the bank, however, there was not much time to worry about the love life of the mayfly. The water was dimpled by ring after ring as trout rose to suck down the emerging flies.

'There y'are, Bob. Not a moment too soon,' said John. 'Dry fly for these. A dry fly floats, just like the hatching mayfly. Drop it upstream and let it float down. When a trout takes, just the merest lift of the wrist will hook it. Don't make a meal out of playing the things; just get 'em back to the bank and have another go.'

He tied a fine point to the end of the line, and to that an artificial fly — red and green, I think it was — made from gamecock hackles. He pressed the fly in a piece of chamois leather which had been lightly soaked in liquid paraffin. ('That's to make sure it floats.') and handed over the rod.

I looked at the fly.

'Doesn't look much like a mayfly to me, John.'

'Doesn't look like one to another mayfly, either. But it does to the trout.'

I made one or two casts, letting the fly float downstream to the end of the swim, without result.

'Don't worry, Bob. Just keep casting,' said John. 'I'm getting out of your way to try my luck further down. Oh, when you catch one, use this.'

He handed me a short, heavy, lead-weighted cosh — a 'priest' — with which to kill the fish painlessly. One swift clout on the back of the head was much more humane than letting them gasp out their lives in the basket.

'Why is it called a priest, John? I keep meaning to ask.'

'It administers the last rites, doesn't it? Joke. Ha, ha. Not one of mine, so don't blame me.'

Several casts later, the water dimpled under the fly and it disappeared. The point of the line disappeared also, knifing swiftly under the surface. I lifted the rod with a quick flex of the wrist — and a trout was on.

There can never be another trout quite like the first one. I

could imagine its muscular body shaking this way and that as it bore back and forth in its efforts to throw the hook.

Before long I had it close enough to the bank to slip the landing net under it, and out it came. It turned out later to weigh about 1¼lb, but to me it was Moby Dick himself.

One clunk of the priest and it was dead, quivering the whole length of its body. It seemed that almost at once its beautiful speckled sheen started to fade. I admired it for about half a minute then put it in the creel.

I dried the fly on a piece of amadou (a sort of spongy fungus) which John had left with me and squeezed it between a scrap of oiled chamois.

Ten minutes later, another trout. Fifteen more minutes, a third was bucking and boring on the end of the line. Within an hour and a half I had seven beautiful fish. Then suddenly the rise stopped. That was it for the time being.

'You've done well, young Bob,' said John who returned with five fish. 'This calls for a pint.'

We called at John's local riverside pub, where I immediately began to boast. I spread a piece of cloth on the bar and displayed my seven beauties to the landlord. As he was nodding approvingly, I noticed that two anglers at a corner table were also taking out several trout apiece from their baskets.

'Looks as if someone else has had a good day,' I said.

'Yes,' said the landlord. 'Not a bad start at all to Duffers' Fortnight.'

Duffers' Fortnight? I looked at John, who gulped in his beer.

'Ah, well . . . Yes, Bob lad. It's a name given to the first mayfly rises. Sometimes the trout do get a bit suicidal — er, start rising well. But don't worry, there are Duffers' Fortnights when the fish will look at anything but a mayfly. It's no guarantee. You've done well there, lad. You caught those fish fair and square. If it had been that easy, I'd have come back with more than five now, wouldn't I?'

I felt better for that. I didn't find out until later that he'd spent some of his time checking tickets and chatting to other anglers.

Back home that evening I was greeted like a hero. And I must admit I played up to it, thrilling the family — and finally boring them — with a detailed account of how each fish fought like a fiend until it was finally defeated and brought to the net.

Next day there were trout for tea.

'Congratulations, darling,' said Pam.

'Clever old dad,' said Trevor.

86

'Cleverest daddy in the whole world,' said Jane.

'Yummm...,' said Paul.

I blushed and ate on. Feeling, for all my undisputed prowess with the rod, a bit of a fraud. Not to say a bit of a duffer...

CHAPTER 8

Ways of Dying

Charlie Sloper, the local poacher, idler and ne'er-do-well, declined quickly after the death of his old friend and adversary Major Hawkins.

For the last few months of the Major's life, Charlie and he were not speaking — the Major had stormed out of the Tadchester Arms after an almighty row — but for Charlie there was always the hope that the Major would return to the pub and that they could resume the trading of insults.

Perhaps the Major had missed Charlie, too. An almost daily argument with the man who had saved his life under shellfire in World War One was not an event to be passed up lightly. But in their last argument Charlie and the Major had mortally insulted each other. And it seemd that 'mortally' was no exaggeration.

Charlie appeared at the Major's funeral, unrecognisable as a spruce, clean, silver-bearded little man in a neatly pressed suit. But within a couple of weeks he was back to his usual garb of tatters and grime.

His behaviour, never the most conformist in the world, grew more and more eccentric. He wandered about Tadchester's new supermarket, openly picking up odds and ends, putting

them in his greasy haversack, and wandering out without attempting to pay. He was never spotted by the manager, who would certainly have had him prosecuted. The check-outs were operated by local girls who knew Charlie, and who let him get away with it either out of compassion or fear. Charlie had taken to sudden rages and, small though he was, made a fearsome spectacle when he erupted.

I had first-hand experience of this when I greeted him one morning in the market square. He was standing by a vegetable stall, possibly waiting for the moment when he could safely purloin a potato or two.

'Good morning, Charlie,' I said.

He turned and glared, crouching like a wrestler with a tightening grip on his knobbly walking stick.

'And 'oo are you?' he hissed.

'Dr Clifford, Charlie. Surely you remember me?'

'Never seen you before in my life!' he yelled, raising the stick. 'Now git orf out of it! Go on. Piss orf!'

I pissed orf.

Charlie's behaviour in the Tadchester Arms worsened as much as it had outside. He would insult everyone who gave him a cheery greeting or a kind word. Often, if a sympathetic regular handed him a bottle of brown ale, his favourite tipple, he would return it to the bar, tell the barman to put the cap back on, and demand to be given the money instead.

He had always been dirty and smelly, qualities which became more evident at close quarters, especially when the pub had warmed up a bit. Now he was getting really beyond endurance. He would sit at a table designed for six people, and all evening there would be five empty seats.

All that was overlooked by the landlord, Geoff Emsworth, whose genial exterior hid a nature as hard as putty. But things came to a head when the public bar was renovated by the brewery. The first stage was the toilets. They were closed down and the public bar customers had to use those in the saloon.

The saloon bar was frequented by some very up-market types indeed, and they did not take at all kindly to having the peasantry stamp through. Least of all did they take kindly to the smelly little apparition wearing one stout brogue and one frayed plimsoll and carrying an old army haversack. But none of them dared say anything to Charlie. From a face as black as a miner's after a hard shift flashed fierce, ice-blue and quite mad eyes. Charlie had become a dangerous man to cross.

In the end, however, Geoff had to call him to order.

'It's bad enough your stinking the place out,' said Geoff, 'and putting paying customers off their ale. I don't even mind you upsetting some of the pucka sahibs in the saloon. Do some of them good to see how the other half lives, if you can call it that. But keep your grubby little mitts off the freebies. Right?'

Geoff's freebies were luxuries not available in the public bar: bowls of peanuts, cheese nibbles and crisps put out on the saloon bar counter to heighten the thirsts of the gentry; and two ornamental bricks, the frogs of which were full of free matches.

Gcoff had been unable to understand, especially when the saloon was quiet, how all the bowls and the bricks would suddenly become empty. Then one night he happened to see Charlie returning from the gents.

With a furtive glance to ensure that what few customers there were had their backs to him, Charlie emptied peanuts, cheese nibbles, crisps, matches and all, into his haversack. Then he picked up a half-pint glass from the bar, filled it from the soda syphon, and marched back to his lonely table in the public.

'Just a minute...' said Geoff.

'You go makin' accusations like that,' said Charlie, 'and I'll 'ave the Lor on yer. Takin' away my good name.'

'All right, then,' said Geoff. 'Empty your haversack.'

'Piss orf,' said Charlie.

Even that didn't get him banned. Geoff was a patient man. But finally it had to be done, if only for a little while.

The public bar was to be closed for several weeks to allow the renovations to be completed. The regulars then had the choice of drinking in the saloon — a happening much resented by the resident county types — or of finding another pub for the time being.

'Nothing personal, Charlie,' said Geoff. 'But you are definitely not a saloon bar type. I'll have to ask you to stay away, or at least stay in the garden, until the public's done out.'

'That's nice after all the years I've been comin' here,' said Charlie. 'You can stuff your bloody pub. I'll take my custom elsewhere.'

But no other pub would have Charlie's custom. After being thrown out of every one within walking distance — and Charlie was capable of walking quite a way when he put his mind to it — he was back in the garden of the Tadchester Arms. Geoff would serve him through the hatchway, but steadfastly refused to allow him across the threshold.

After a couple of months the public bar was opened again, and Charlie was allowed back in. But it was nothing like the scruffy, cosy, spit-and-sawdust bar he had known. There was a carpet on the floor, soft upholstery on the benches and chairs, a juke box going full blast and a couple of one-armed bandits in constant use.

Worse, the clientele changed. Before long the old regulars deserted the bar and their places were taken by a much younger crowd.

Charlie had nothing in common at all with the youngsters in jeans and mini-skirts, and he winced every time the juke box blared out with another rock 'n' roll record. The youngsters were not nearly so tolerant as the old regulars, and made loud comments about the dirty old geezer in the corner. Visibly Charlie began to age, even to shrink — and he was small enough to begin with.

One night, after closing time, as Geoff went round clearing the tables, he noticed Charlie's haversack slung over the back of a chair.

'Silly old duffer's forgotten it,' Geoff muttered to himself. 'Shall I keep it for him or pretend the bloody thing's been nicked?'

As he reached across to pick it up, he noticed a tattered heap under the table. Charlie.

Though I hate being called out at night for trivial reasons, I am only too glad to turn out for serious cases, and Charlie was serious.

By the time I reached the pub, Geoff had laid him on a bench and loosened his filthy clothes. Charlie's breathing was chillingly shallow and his pulse only a flicker.

'May I use your phone, please, Geoff?' I said. 'We've got to get him to hospital quickly.'

Charlie lived for another month in the hospital. He turned out to be suffering from severe malnutrition and, of all things, dehydration.

Geoff, busy man though he was, visited him every other day with presents of fruit and good wishes from old acquaintances —

though most of the good wishes Geoff used to make up on the spot.

Charlie never thanked him. He recovered enough after ten days to get his old cussedness back and made the lives of the ward staff a misery. He made such a fuss about 'wimmin' gazing upon his scrawny little body that he was bathed only by male nurses.

One night, after a marathon rave at everybody in sight, he simply closed his eyes and died.

The funeral was simple, with only three wreaths. They were inscribed: 'To Charlie, from your friends in the public'; 'From the regulars in the saloon'; and 'From Geoff and Ruby, Tadchester Arms'.

And there was only one mourner: Geoff Emsworth, who had ordered and paid for the three wreaths himself.

'Couldn't have the old lad going as lonely as he'd lived these past few months,' said Geoff. 'Anyway, he should be all right now. He'll have met up with Major Hawkins — if they allow

visitors where Charlie is, and don't mind the stoking being interrupted. Wherever it is, there'll be some right bloody ructions tonight...'

* * * *

Nellie Walters, a small but sturdy matron of seventy-eight, came in to see me again about her knee. She suffered from a form of dry eczema, possibly a legacy from her days in service when she spent endless hours on her knees, scrubbing the stone floors of a large house up the hill. The eczema was always there, but now and again would spread in a flaming red and painful patch.

I prescribed the usual cream and then asked, 'And how is your husband?'

'He's going,' said Nellie.

'Going? Going where?'

'Passing away.'

'Oh, dear! I'd better call in and see him this afternoon. But what makes you think he's going?'

'He's had twelve bottles of light ale in the sideboard for three weeks now, and he's not touched a drop.'

This *was* serious. William Walters, pushing eighty-five, had always been fond of his ale. Now and again the walk to the pub became a bit too much for him, so he stocked the sideboard with bottles of light. Never to my knowledge had the bottles survived more than a few days.

Big and portly, but with the ramrod bearing and waxed moustache of one of Kitchener's men, William had seemed indestructible. His clothes, serviced by Nellie, were always clean and brushed. His trouser seams looked as if you could sharpen a pencil on them. And there was always a flower in his buttonhole, backed by a piece of fern with the stem wrapped in damp moss and clipped in a silver holder.

He had run his household like a barrack room. Meals had to be there on time. Not a second early or a second late. None of his five children had ever dared sit down at the table before he did, nor did any of his nine grandchildren when they came to visit. Both children and grandchildren had to stand behind their chairs until William entered the room — scrubbed shiny, moustache waxed and with a fresh flower in the buttonhole — and sat down. Only then were they allowed to sit and bow their heads for grace.

William's indestructibility had defied all the odds. At seventeen he had volunteered for the Boer War, and been turned down for what was described as 'smoker's heart'. Even at that age he smoked full-strength cigarettes, potent enough to make a blast-furnaceman cough. At eighty-four he still smoked them.

In World War One the medical boards were not so fussy, and William was accepted for army service. Because of his age and his five children, he was not among the unfortunate 'volunteers' marched away by the local squire. But in 1916, at the age of thirty-four, he turned up at the Tadchester recruiting office.

'I was no chicken,' he used to tell his drinking pals, 'but they were glad enough to have me.'

From all accounts, William was glad enough to go. It was possibly not so much patriotism as the strain of living in a small house with Nellie and five lively children. Even William's repressive domestic regime couldn't keep the noise down all the time.

Whenever Nellie had presented him with another child, William had gone off to 'wet the baby's head'. The wetting usually took two or three days and he didn't come home until the money ran out, leaving poor Nellie to be looked after by kindly neighbours.

The first child was a boy, and then came three girls. 'This one had better be a boy,' ordered Nellie as she went into labour with the fifth.

Nellie was so scared of his reaction that, when the girl was born, she pleaded with the midwife to tell William it was a boy. The midwife, equally frightened of William, acquiesced. While William was roistering on a head-wetting to end all head-wettings, the poor child was even registered as a boy.

The sobering discovery that it was a girl, the ensuing almighty row, and the trouble involved in getting the child re-registered, may have been what finally sent William off to fight for King and Country.

He joined the Royal Artillery. Such was the need for men on the Western Front that he arrived in France trained in the rudiments of signalling, map reading and gun laying, but not having the first idea of how to use a rifle.

No time was a good time to be in the trenches, but 1916 was a worse year than most. Soon, Gunner Walters was being carried to a field hospital. Even in the filth of the trenches — and even without Nellie in attendance — William was still a dandy. The medical orderlies were amazed at the cleanliness of his body and underclothes. The body, though clean and free from lice, had

96

been bashed about enough to qualify for a Blighty One. And William was shipped across to a military hospital near Dover.

Back in France a few months later, he was blown up again. This time he was carried into the field hospital wearing the remains of a monk's robe over his khaki.

'I'd got tired of being shot at,' he told me. 'And I came across this dead monk. What he was doing there I'll never know, but he certainly didn't need his robe any more. So I borrowed it. It was lovely and warm, but I was really hoping that the Germans would have some respect for the cloth.'

William had taken the additional precaution of sleeping in an old water tower, the only structure left standing for miles, on the premise that if the Boche hadn't hit it so far, they weren't likely to now.

He was wrong. A shell landed in the tower and blew him right out of it. Neither he nor anybody else knew how he survived the blast and the 30-foot parabola to the ground. His injuries even after that weren't too serious, but again enough to qualify for a Blighty One.

William had never been much of a hand at writing and Nellie hadn't heard from him for weeks. Then one day she met one of his pals, also in the Artillery, home on leave.

'Have you seen anything of my William?' she asked. (Nobody ever called him Bill, incidentally. Nobody who valued his front teeth, that is.) 'I'm worried sick about him.'

'He's all right, Nellie,' said the gunner. 'You should know anyway — you've had him home twice on sick leave.'

'The swine,' said Nellie through clenched teeth. 'If he's been home, he's never got as far as here.'

Nor had he. William's amazing powers of recovery, reinforced by the sight of the lovely young nurses, soon had him out of bed. He was back in bed as soon as he found a nurse compliant enough to join him, and he spent the rest of both leaves wenching and drinking.

His third wound was a terrible one. But again, comparatively speaking, he was lucky.

Sitting in a trench with six of his mates, he bent down to open a tin of beans. As he did so, a shell or mortar bomb landed. The fragments went across his back like a monstrous cheese grater, taking off most of the skin and some of the flesh.

A stretcher party found him bent double, unconscious, bleeding horribly and with a tin of beans and a tin opener still clutched in his hands. All that was left of his six mates were the legs and lower trunks, still sitting on empty ammunition boxes.

I don't know in detail what techniques of patching up or plastic surgery were used in the First World War. Certainly they worked on William, but the results were not very pretty. Fifty years on, his back was sound enough, but it looked like a badly made patchwork quilt, with strips of brown, yellow and dead-white skin jumbled together in a haphazard and rough-ploughed pattern.

It was the end of the war for William and this time he did

come home, to be tended with unstinting devotion by Nellie until he was well enough to get up to his old tricks again.

(It says a lot for heredity that Harry Walters, William's grandson, had the same penchant for wenching and boozing, and finished up in my hands several times needing treatment for the result of his escapades.)

When I called on the afternoon of Nellie's visit to the surgery, William was past any form of roistering. I was shocked by the change as I examined him. He was pale, crumpled and shrunken. Even his moustache, left unwaxed for the first time in fifty years, drooped forlornly.

'Help yourself to a drink, Doctor,' he said, gesturing feebly towards the sideboard. 'Plenty there. I've lost the taste for it.'

I knew what Nellie meant. William would not be with us long.

Nor was he. A fortnight later, after a massive but mercifully brief heart attack, he was gone.

A couple of days after the funeral, Nellie got around to sorting out their affairs. Her middle-aged son, a stable and prosperous Tadchester greengrocer, came over to help. And it was as well that he did.

In William's trunk of souvenirs, Nellie came across faded sepia photographs of several ladies she did not recognise, each photograph inscribed with sentiments far from platonic.

'Look at these!' she exploded, waving the photographs in a trembling fist. 'What *did* that man get up to?'

'Give them to me, mother,' said her son, thinking quickly. 'They're nothing at all. All the troops used to be given photographs of girls who came over on concert parties. The frontline troops never even met the girls; the photos used to come up with the rations. Now go and make yourself a cup of tea and I'll see to the rest.'

In the trunk were bundles of letters, more photographs and a couple of inscribed cigarette cases which indicated that William's war service had not been all mud, blood and bullets. Nor had his ravaged back been any obstacle in time of peace.

There was enough evidence to have had him divorced a dozen times over, were he still around.

The son heavily censored the trunk's contents and took the offending items home for burning.

He told me later that as he threw the letters one by one on the garden incinerator, he had been filled with a grudging admiration for his father's exploits.

'The old bugger,' he said. 'All those years he'd been drilling into us kids the virtues of discipline, fidelity and moderation in all things. And look what he'd been up to...'

There was another shock for Nellie when she went to the bank to check on the joint account she kept with her husband. Every week for years she had saved from their pensions and put the money in the bank. She never saw the statements.

'Leave them to me,' William had said. 'Women don't understand things like that.'

At the bank, the clerk pored over the ledger sheets.

'Your account, Mrs Walters? Let's see now ... ah, yes: a balance of seventeen pounds, three shillings and sixpence.'

'Seventeen pounds, three shillings and sixpence!' Nellie exploded. 'But I've been putting money in every week for years, every pension day!'

'Ah, yes, Mrs Walters. But remember that your husband used to come in every week and draw money out. It did seem a strange arrangement, but apparently you were happy to have it that way.'

Nellie stood there rigid, quivering and speechless. William had done it again.

'We haven't seen your husband for two or three months,' said the clerk. 'Is he all right?'

'All right?' repeated Nellie, dazedly.

'Yes ... er ... I mean, where is he now?'

'Where is he now?' said Nellie, lapsing for a moment from her normal temperate language. 'The swine is where I can't bloody get at him!'

Several years later I was chatting to Nellie, herself then towards the end of her life, about William.

'He gave me some problems, that one,' she said. 'But I knew I had married a man, not an angel with a carnation in his button-hole. And at least I have one consolation: in all that time he was never unfaithful to me.'

'Yes,' I said, trying not to look shifty. 'You certainly had that to be thankful for.'

* * * .

Two of my favourite patients were Mick and Alice. They'd been married more than fifty years and put the secret of their success down to 'a bloody good row' at least twice a week.

Twelve months earlier, Alice had almost died from a bad bout of pneumonia. They were an independent old pair, and Alice had always made little of her ailments. What had started as a mild 'flu was left to 'work itself out'. By the time I was called in it had worked itself up into something much worse.

Alice's recovery — and Mick's survival, because he was not the most domesticated of men — was due as much to the care of their married daughter Phil (short for Philomena) as to any of my ministrations. After a couple of tense weeks, with poor old Mick a frightened and bewildered spectator, Alice pulled round.

The event was signalled by a bloody good row one morning when Mick forgot to make Alice's breakfast. After sitting on the edge of the bed in anticipation for forty minutes, Alice went down to see how Mick was faring. He was faring very well, sitting with his nose stuck in the sports section of the morning newspaper, drinking tea from a pint mug, with poor Alice's breakfast completely forgotten.

'Even as our rows go, that was a good 'un, Doctor,' said Mick. 'I knew straightaway she was back on form.'

Now, a year later, it was Mick I was worried about. Phil was visiting them one day when she heard strange noises coming from the upstairs toilet.

'What's the matter with dad?' she asked Alice.

'He's been having a lot of trouble on the toilet lately,' said Alice, 'Reckons it's piles. I don't know, though...'

101

Phil listened from the bottom of the stairs to stifled cries of real pain and muttered gasps of, 'Oh, no...! Jesus, Mary and Joseph...!'

'That's not piles,' she said. 'Have him ready in the morning. I'm taking him to the doctor's.'

Protesting his fitness, Mick was ushered into the surgery by Phil.

'You're poorly, dad,' said Phil. 'Now be told. I've not brought you all this way for nothing. Tell the doctor about your pains.'

'I don't like to,' said Mick. 'Not in front of you. It's private.'

'That's all right, Phil,' I said. 'Just leave us two chaps alone and we'll soon get to the bottom of it.'

Ten minutes later I wished I'd chosen a more fortunate phrase. Even as a sick joke, that was not funny.

Mick had been having pain and increasing difficulties going to the toilet. I followed my brief internal examination by making an urgent appointment for Mick to see Henry, my surgical partner.

Henry confirmed my fears, Mick had a growth of the lower bowel, a condition which, if caught reasonably early, has a good outlook, and the meticulous Henry would have almost guaranteed a cure. We would now have to wait until the operation to assess Mick's chances.

Major operations at Tadchester Hospital were a team effort. Henry operated assisted by Ron Dickinson, with me helping Jack Hart with the anaesthetic and being responsible for saline and blood transfusions that were part of many major operations, as well as making myself generally useful.

Mick's operation lasted five hours; he had come too late, the growth had spread and all Henry could do was to lessen any chance of obstruction, and remove as much of the growth as possible.

'I'm afraid Mick's time is running out,' said Henry, as he wearily put in the final closing stitches.

'How long do you give him?' I asked.

'He will do well if he lasts twelve months,' said Henry.

Mick survived the operation but was left extremely weak and debilitated.

I had to break the news to Phil and left it to her own good sense whether or not to tell her mother.

Rightly so, she did; the family had been through some hard times together in earlier years and was well used to accepting harsh facts and coping with them.

A bed was made for Mick in the living room and a cheery fire was kept burning. He was kept well supplied with his favourite reading — pulp Westerns — and in the evenings he would sit in his own armchair and watch television.

He and Alice were both staunch Roman Catholics, well-loved members of St Malachy's Church, and their religion was a great comfort. Father Daly, the parish priest, would call round to discuss with Mick the latest football results and the prospects of horses in the forthcoming races. He would call again once a week to give Mick Communion and hear his confession, not that the poor old lad had much to confess.

I am by no means a religious man, let alone a Catholic, but perhaps faith like Mick's is contagious. During his agonies, I found myself in Liverpool at a conference, and visited the Roman Catholic cathedral. Inside, bathed in a cool, dim, almost underwater light which came in through the windows, it had a peace and calm authority I have seldom come across anywhere else. Sceptic that I am, I found myself kneeling in a pew and saying a short prayer for Mick: 'Please, God, if at all possible, a miracle. If not, no pain.'

As an added bonus to Mick's home comforts he had his 'girlfriends': three local nuns who used to turn up with fruit, cowboy books, and often a bottle or two of Guinness. Such was the eagerness with which Mick looked forward to his girlfriends' visits, and such was the laughter coming from the living room at times, that Alice, bless her, actually got jealous.

'Well,' she said, 'he wasn't always old and poorly, you know. He was a bit of a devil as a lad, that one.'

The bloody good rows went on. I called round one evening to find the living-room window panes vibrating with the ding-

103

dong going on inside. Mick had wanted to catch the sports results on the television and Alice was insisting on watching a soap opera. That was all, but it sounded like a full-scale riot.

'Don't you worry, Doctor,' said Phil, who was making a cup of tea in the kitchen, not bothered in the least. 'My mother knows what she's doing. A row bucks my dad up no end. He's not a little invalid any more, lying there feeling sorry for himself. He's master in his own house, laying down the law.'

Full marks to Alice for applied psychology. And it certainly worked. Six months passed, twelve months. Mick was still with us, enjoying visits from Phil, her husband Jim and their two young children; Father Daly; the nuns; friends, neighbours and relatives — and having a row with Alice whenever things got too quiet.

Mick had no illusions. Early on in the illness, after a sudden twinge of pain, he said to Alice, 'I'm dying, love, aren't I?'

'Don't be so daft,' said Alice brusquely, turning her face away. 'I've got a nice bit of mince for your tea, and you're not missing that.'

'It's all right, love,' he said. 'You don't have to kid me. I'm on the transfer list all right. But I'm not complaining; I've had a good run.'

After about fifteen months came the inevitable decline. Even with pain relievers and heavy sedation Mick was in great discomfort and would have restless nights which he sweated through determined not to wake Alice upstairs. Alice herself was not too well. Her devotion to Mick was unstinting and she was becoming worn out.

'It might be best,' I said to Phil, 'if we thought about moving your father to hospital now. He'll get every attention there, and it will take this enormous strain off your mother.'

'He wouldn't take too kindly to that,' said Phil. 'He hates hospitals. But I tell you what he might accept — a bed at St Bernadette's Hospice.'

In Tadchester was a Roman Catholic Hospice for the terminally ill. It was run entirely on money accrued from massive fund-raising activities and publicity stunts which didn't even stop short at nuns entering sponsored roller skating marathons. Though equipped with hospital facilities, it was not a hospital. Its function was to care for people who were past hope of recovery — not only Catholics, either — and to make their last days tranquil, even happy.

There was no strict routine. Mobile patients could come and go as they pleased during the day, and guests — which is how the patients were regarded and treated — were free to wander from room to room on social visits.

There was an atmosphere of calm and serenity about the place and oddly (or perhaps not oddly at all) a cheerfulness as well; an atmosphere personified by the smiling nuns who moved quietly about their business of tending the terminally ill.

Mick needed a couple of days to think about the Hospice. Though he knew he could not live long, he still had to make a big mental adjustment to move into a place specifically devoted to the actual act of dying.

Finally he agreed. 'With all those nuns I'll be better off for girlfriends than ever,' he said.

'I'm keeping my eye on you, lad,' said Alice.

Phil and Alice went to see him every day at the Hospice, and he still had all his other regular visitors. The nuns really were saintly characters and did a great deal to help Mick prepare himself for the inevitable.

For a couple of weeks the bloody good rows went on, causing the nuns to glide silently away whenever they heard the first warning shots. This was effective family therapy, and they recognised it as such. But as Mick's pain increased, so did the doses of morphine, and he would sit up in bed perfectly relaxed and happy, smiling so contentedly that Alice knew he didn't need the rows any more.

One evening he died. Quietly, and smiling. The morphine had taken care of his pain. Father Daly and the nuns had taken care of his fears. Jesus, Mary and Joseph had given him comfort and strength all his life, and now in death he had gone serenely to meet them.

*   *   *

Alice, though heartbroken by Mick's departure, took comfort from his way of going, and held up well for the funeral. Even then, her old sense of humour did not desert her.

She was helped into the church by the undertaker, a family friend for whom Mick had once worked. She was weak and frail, and her steps were faltering, but the undertaker held her firmly so that she would come to no harm.

'Don't go spreading rumours about us two,' she said in an aside to Phil. 'He only wants me for my body.'

CHAPTER 9

A Fate Worse than Death

As Medical Officer to Drake's College in Tadchester, a boys' boarding school that had been built up from fifteen to three hundred boys in eleven years by my friend George Tonbridge, I had a range of problems that I didn't meet generally in the rest of the practice. Many of the boys came from abroad and, particularly at the beginning of each year, there was that complicated and heart-rending condition to deal with: homesickness.

Every October term I had to wade through seventy or eighty routine medical examinations on the new boys. Though most tedious, it was worthwhile. There were always half a dozen boys with either one or no testicles, hernias, perhaps a blind eye that had been missed in the past, and the occasional one with some heart condition. Nearly all those with something wrong turned out to be sons of doctors. As with my own children, being the child of a doctor can have many disadvantages: you either overwhelm them with treatment or miss them out altogether.

Drake's College, for all its newness, with an enthusiastic staff and high *esprit de corps*, was soon competing at all levels with much bigger schools at rugby, cricket, swimming and athletics. For one period the First XV went for seventeen matches

without defeat. Good schoolboy rugby is probably the best of all to watch and I used to go and cheer them from the touchline whenever my duties as President of the Tadchester Rugby Club permitted me to.

The First XV had become a tough, sophisticated, organised unit and their seventeenth victory was over a very vigorous Old Boys XV. The Old Boys had a ground in London and the Drake's team were allowed to play them as the last fixture on a short tour of London-based schools. They were entertained after the match and the enlightened headmaster, George, had allowed them to spend a night on the town with the Old Boys — to acquire, he said, a bit of worldly knowledge.

After that night, their rugby skills went to pot. From being a brilliant, well-oiled machine, they had become tired and dispirited. They lost three games in a row, two of them to sides that the Second XV would normally have beaten. Haggard and jaded they had lost spirit not only in their rugby but also in their schoolwork and general life as well. They were fifteen very worried boys.

After a chat with the distraught games master, I asked the team captain to come and see me. He was so adamant that there was nothing wrong that I knew there must be, but there was little I could do except watch and wait.

The following week I got my answer. The scrum-half, a short, ginger-haired boy from Wales, asked Matron if he could see me, privately and confidentially, after the next surgery.

He was reluctant to talk when he first came in, hanging his head. I made some preliminary small talk about the fortunes of the First XV and then asked how could I help him.

He stood there looking tense and desperate, and then burst into tears. Something was very seriously wrong.

'Come on, lad,' I said. 'What is it?'

'I'm giving all the others away, Doctor, but I must tell you. I'm afraid we've all got venereal disease.'

Although this was not impossible, it was very unlikely.

'And where do you think you got it from?' I said.

'We got it in London . . . from prostitutes,' he said.

Oh dear. Perhaps he was right after all.

'And how does it affect you? Does it hurt when you pass water?'

'Nothing like that,' he said, 'but it's awful — I'm almost too ashamed to show you.'

'Come on,' I said, 'down with your pants. Let's see what the trouble is.'

Shamefully, half-covering his most private parts with his

hand, he lowered his pants. There, in each groin, spreading down into the thigh and on the inner half of his scrotum were large areas of red, sticky skin.

'It's terrible. Will I go blind, Doctor? What shall I tell my parents?' he stuttered between strangled sobs.

'Put your trousers back on,' I said, 'and tell me how you contracted this.'

'Well,' he said, 'the Old Boys took us to a night club . . . and then there was a stripper . . . and then . . . [amongst more sobs] she came and sat on three or four of us — on our knees. A few days later nearly all the team came out in this — we must be giving it to one another.'

'You bunch of lunatics!' I said, struggling not to laugh. 'What you've got is a very common condition called Dhobi's Itch. It's nothing to do with venereal disease. It's a fungal infection in the groin that athletes get through sweating and showering. I've seen fifty boys with it already this term — and none of them had been near a stripper. You've all worried for nothing. For God's sake, why didn't you see me earlier? Some powder and ointment will clear that up and you'll be as good as new.'

He looked at me as if he'd won the football pools.

Word spread like fire. As I was just about to go, the other fourteen players arrived at the surgery.

'Sorry we're late, Doctor. Could we just see you for a minute?'

Each produced identical red areas in the groin. Their relief that they'd only got a small fungal condition in their groins was indescribable, after spending sleepless nights worrying about VD. They were back on form the following Saturday and thrashed their local rivals 37-3.

* * *

Not sleeping, or sleeping too much were among the commonest conditions I met in general practice. A great number of people came for various forms of sleeping tablets. The commonest cause of not sleeping was having formed a habit of waking up too early and I was a believer in giving short, sharp courses of tablets to ensure a full night's slumber.

I probably had no more than my fair share of insomniacs, but I seemed to have more than my share of people who couldn't stay awake. Nearly every day somebody would come in convinced that there was something medically wrong with them because they felt so sleepy and tired all the time. Many of them claimed to have sleeping sickness. I had to explain that you had to be bitten by a tse-tse fly before you could acquire this condition and, as far as it was known, there weren't too many tse-tse flies in Somerset. The likely commonest cause was boredom or anxiety. In the whole of my medical life I've only met one man where sleepiness or too much sleeping was the actual condition. The disturbances in the sleep pattern were usually not an illness in themselves, but were symptoms of some other thing that was going wrong: very often financial trouble, trouble at work or at home.

The heaviest sleeper of them all was Frank Preston, a charge-hand at the electronics factory. He prided himself that he'd been never late for work since the factory opened, there every day at 7.15 sharp. But he did complain that he seemed to fall asleep at every opportunity and that once he was asleep it was very difficult to rouse him.

I did what I could for Frank, but I was much more concerned for his wife, Jenny, who insisted that she was going to have her second baby at home in spite of the fact that she had had a difficult forceps delivery with her first baby in hospital. I tried to persuade her to go to Winchcombe to have the baby but she insisted that she was going to have it at home.

'If you don't want to come, don't, Doctor,' she said. 'I'll manage on my own.'

Even the indomitable Nurse Plank, a stalwart support at home confinements, was worried about it.

However, the ante-natal time went perfectly well, with no complications. The baby was in a good position, and on time Jenny went into labour.

I was called at about 11 o'clock at night to say she was getting on well, but that I had better come along in case a hand was needed. She wasn't quite fully dilated and ready to push when I got there. Jenny was in a large high-ceilinged room with two single beds in it. Her bed was in the middle of the room, its head against one wall, and the other bed with a heap of bedclothes on it stood against one of the side walls.

Jenny did extremely well until the last stage and then she shouted the rooftops off.

The baby wouldn't come the last inch or so and I had to call in Jack Hart to give Jenny a whiff of chloroform while I put some low forceps on and lifted the baby's head out.

Jenny had a fine baby girl. After a couple of stitches, she was as fit as a flea, sitting up in bed and cuddling her newborn. Her mother-in-law came up from downstairs with a cup of tea, and Mrs Preston, Nurse Plank, myself and Jenny sat round chatting. We'd worked hard. We'd been there nearly all night and it was just approaching 6.30 in the morning. Suddenly an alarm clock went off with a shrill clatter next to the bed covered with a heap of bedding. A hand snaked out of the bedding and turned the alarm off.

'Good God!' I said, startled out of my wits. 'What's that?'

'Don't worry,' said Jenny. 'It's only Frank.'

A tousled head appeared above a mound of bedclothes, looking in complete disbelief at the group of people thronging his bedroom. 'Frank,' said Jenny, 'you've got a lovely little girl.'

'Thank God for that,' said Frank. 'When I first saw all these people I thought I had woken up on Tadchester Station.'

*　　*　　*

It was too late to go to bed when I got home so I took Pam up a cup of tea, got myself a bacon sandwich and arrived at the surgery a bit early.

'Oh, I'm glad you're early, Doctor Bob,' said Gladys, 'We've got a man who hasn't an appointment but insists on being seen. Would you mind fitting him in before the surgery?' 'Fine,' I said. 'Give me five minutes then send him in.'

My first patient was a cocky, independent little man who did

the garden at the local convent. 'Won't keep you a minute, Doc,' he said. 'I'd just like something for my knee.'

'What's the matter with your knee?' I asked. 'I don't think I've seen it.'

'No, no, you haven't,' he said. 'But I've got a touch of anthracite.'

This I had to see.

'Hop on the couch,' I said, 'and let's have a look.'

He had a large swollen knee.

'How long,' I asked, 'do you think you've had anthracite of the knee?'

'Oh, about two or three weeks,' he said. 'My mother's got it — or my mother used to have it.'

'Well,' I said, 'I hate to disappoint you, but what you've got is a bit of *arthritis* of the knee. The only time you can get anthracite of the knee is if you sit too close to the back-boiler in your kitchen.'

The sarcasm was lost on him. He accepted my tablets with some disdain and went off happy, convinced that he was being treated for that very common condition — anthracite of the knee.

*   *   *

Aubrey Cattermole looked normal enough when he came into the surgery. Smartly dressed, he carried a trendy executive briefcase in his left hand and had a well-cut trench coat over his arm. His right hand was bandaged.

'Take a seat, won't you?' I said.

'Thank you, Doctor,' he said, glancing vaguely this way and that, although the chair was directly in front of him.

'Ah,' he said, finally locating it. He stepped towards it, caught his coat on the back and knocked it over.

'Oh dear. Silly me,' he said. He then attempted to pick up the chair with his bandaged hand, winced, and tried with the other hand which was still holding the briefcase. Briefcase, coat and chair got into a terrible tangle, resulting in the kind of panto-mime act which usually involves a drunk and a deckchair.

'Allow me,' I said, walking round the desk, separating him and his encumbrances from the chair, and setting it back on its feet.

'Most kind,' said Aubrey, sitting in the chair, placing his briefcase on the floor and draping his coat over the top of it. The briefcase toppled over and there was another pantomime ses-sion as he tried to right it and replace the coat one-handedly.

'What seems to be the trouble? The hand, I take it?'

'Yes, Doctor. I lit a cigarette at work this afternoon and stupidly flicked the match into the wastepaper basket. I hadn't noticed it was still alight. The basket went up in flames and I tried to beat them out with my hand. Burned it rather badly. It was treated in the first-aid room, but I think it might need looking at properly.'

The hand was blistered pretty badly. I cleaned it, covered it with burn gell and re-dressed it.

'Quite a bruise on your temple there, too,' I said. 'Did you do that trying to put the flames out?'

'Er . . . no, Doctor. I bumped into a door jamb at home this morning. Nothing serious.'

'Here, I'll prescribe some cream for that to get the swelling down. Anything else?'

'No. My big toe was painful for a while, but it seems to have settled down now.'

'Toe?'

'Yes. I stubbed it on the bed leg a few days ago.'

'I'd better have a look while you're here.'

The toe was badly discoloured, but there was no swelling, and a little manipulation established that nothing was broken or dislocated.

'You seem to have been in the wars lately,' I said.

'Yes . . . the landlord in my local was saying that only the other night after the pile of pennies on the bar fell on me. Pure accident, of course. I must have caught them with my elbow as I turned round.'

'You'd had a few, had you?'

'No. I'd only just gone in. The wife had sent me to the pub to get me out of the house. She was a bit peeved because I'd broken her favourite vase.'

I was looking at a walking, talking natural disaster area.

'I'd take it steady from now on,' I said. 'And be careful crossing the road.'

'I certainly will, Doctor. I always look both ways. Ha, ha. Well, thanks a lot.'

He stood up, knocking the chair over backwards as he did so, and then repeated the earlier performance as he rescued coat and briefcase.

'Thanks again, Doctor. Bye...'

He tucked the briefcase under his right arm, grasped the door handle with his left, and jerked the door open. Straight back into his face.

That abnormal was normal I'd accepted. But Aubrey was more normally abnormal than anyone I'd seen that day.

'Just a minute, Mr Cattermole,' I said. 'Could you spare me another five minutes?'

I asked a few questions about his seeming accident proneness. Casting his mind back, he reeled off incident after incident in which he'd knocked things over, tripped over things, set fire to things, cut himself, bruised himself, winded himself and almost killed himself. It was a habit of his wife to send him out to the pub just to get him out of the house and prevent his doing any more harm to the furniture, fixtures and fittings.

It sounded very much like a particular disease of the nervous system, a condition which manifests itself by lack of co-ordination, clumsiness and a general pre-disposition to accidents.

I booked him in at the hospital for some aptitude and co-ordination tests which later confirmed my diagnosis. He was treated with a drug which corrected his nervous circuitry, and he recovered from his tendency to go bumping around.

But at the moment I was faced with this apparently upright and responsible citizen who couldn't even get out of a room without doing himself some damage.

'When these tests are done,' I said, 'I'm sure we'll be able to give you something to cut down the number of accidents. I hope they don't affect you too much at work.'

'As a matter of fact, they do,' he said. 'I get a bit tired sometimes of people laughing behind my back. And often in front of my face. A bit embarrassing in my position.'

'What position's that, then?'

'I work in the public relations department at Tadchester Electronics,' he said. 'But I'm also unpaid Safety Officer...'

CHAPTER 10

Trouble at Mill

There were problems in Tadchester.

After the coal mine had shut, a government inducement had attracted an electronics firm to work there. This had absorbed some of the redundant work force and had offered many new jobs for women. Then, just as the ex-miners started to drift away, one of the big international chemical companies decided that there was still some life in the slagheaps that surrounded the village of Thudrock, and Thudrock colliery, and a huge works was built to convert the slagheaps into plastic.

Over a period of two or three years after the mine closed down, the two new places of employment actually brought labour into the area. The town boomed and the population slightly increased. As the electronics company was part of a larger corporation it brought in a proportion of skilled men and middle management people to run it.

But then there was unrest over pay at the plastic works and, owing to some worldwide recession, there was a reduction in demand for electronic components. This resulted in a reduction in staff and some redundancies at the electronics works.

Both these two aspects of industrial unrest brought new medical problems.

The trouble at the plastics factory was over pay. I never knew the details. Both the employers and the work force claimed to have right on their side. There were go-slows and processions in the town, and the pubs were full of excited men intent on showing their virility and industrial muscle. If their demands were not met on the following Monday, they said, they would be out on strike. They would show the bosses. Somehow it seemed to give a new awareness to the town. The atmosphere was buoyant.

The demands weren't met and the strike began, with picketing and a general air of euphoria.

Only one or two older people remembered earlier strikes, particularly the miners' strike of 1926.

One old collier told me in the surgery, 'Nobody wins in a strike, Doctor, whether it's right or wrong. You lose money while you are out, the wife and the kids suffer, and when you get back you very rarely make it up.'

Perhaps somebody, someday, will devise some other means of settling industrial disputes which will do less damage to both sides.

The strike had full union backing and at first everybody was full of beans. The strikers' cause and enthusiasm seemed unbeatable.

But this enthusiasm lasted barely two weeks. If you asked any of the strikers how things were going, they seemed as determined as ever. But they weren't as cheery; the excitement had gone. The first week there had been income tax repayments but these were smaller the second week, and with so many commitments

119

like hire purchase on televisions, washing machines and cars people began to wonder how long they could go on. The cheerful, virile strikers now were subdued; the pubs had started to empty. I had more and more worrying mums coming into the surgery about one thing or another, but their basic reason was the lack of security and increasing shortage of money.

After the strike had been on for four weeks there was almost complete demoralisation. Although the strikers were still vehement about their cause and the pickets were still at the factory gate, it was as if the work force had been humiliated. Moneywise, many were in dire straits, and it would be a very, very long time before they recovered from the financial setback, whatever the pay rises.

The strike was finally settled after six weeks. The workers gained practically all they had taken action for and it was almost certainly justified.

What effect it had on the company I have no idea. They were part of a huge international concern, but it certainly cannot have helped them.

The strike left its aftermath. This was the first really serious industrial upset in Tadchester for many a year. Apart from the economic problems it gave people, it left a wake of uncertainty that took a couple of years to finally subside.

People were depressed. Their basic security had been challenged and it showed in many different forms. And the pattern of life had been disturbed.

Men being at home for six weeks with nothing to do, proved to be a strain in some households. A number of marriages broke up, not because of the financial difficulties, or because the partners agreed or disagreed about the strike, but because there was a new aspect to their married life: the husband, the breadwinner, was humiliated by being at home. He had been under his wife's feet for six weeks and their relationship had changed.

I hadn't realised that one little strike in such a small place could have such deep and long-lasting effects. And I remembered the words of my old collier: 'Nobody wins'.

*　　*　　*

120

The redundancies at the electronics plant were mainly among the unskilled labourers. To some it was a bonus. They were given redundancy pay and there were plenty of seasonal and other jobs to be found.

The nature of their work, whoever they worked for, hardly changed, so working in one place differed little from many others and a change of scene suited many of them very well.

The worst casualties were among the middle management, the men aged between forty-five and fifty-five; those who had travelled down from large cities, perhaps from London, when the electronics works was first opened.

They had uprooted themselves and come to work in Tadchester. It meant new homes, and new schools for their children. They had settled themselves into the community, perhaps joined the golf club. They became accustomed to eating out, company cars, and a good standard of living. There were perhaps not more than a dozen involved, but at least six of them ended up at my surgery. Here again I had new medical conditions to deal with.

As with the strikers, these men were humiliated — not only because they were no longer wanted in their jobs, but also because they didn't know what to do with their lives from then on. These men of substance and standing were suddenly taken out of the day-to-day battle of earning a living. They retired on reasonable pensions, but there were no more perks and they had nothing to do.

They were also virtually unemployable. Their special skills lay in one particular type of electronics, and I had men in their prime condemned to a life of golf, gardening, and pottering about their homes. A move away would be difficult. The house prices in Tadchester were less than they were elsewhere, and to venture forth into a new area was therefore virtually impossible.

Two of my six managed fairly well. They had an interest in music which they were able to expand. There were several light orchestras in the area which played at local operettas and various concerts, some of which brought in a modest financial return.

I did my best for the other four men, all leading figures who had cut a dash in the community but who were now humbled and had nothing to look forward to. There was little that I could offer, other than tranquillisers, night sedation, and suggestions of pursuing hobbies and taking up other interests.

They were crippled as surely as a man who has had both legs amputated.

I discovered that industrial unrest presented medical problems of its own, and I found I was almost groping in the dark trying to find solutions.

I depended heavily on my senior partner, Steve Maxwell, for advice and guidance. He was probably the wisest, kindest man I have ever known and rather than just catch him for a few minutes at coffee, I asked him if he could come and dine one evening and spare an hour or two in unravelling problems.

Having Steve to dinner was always a great pleasure. He was good company, laughed uproariously at my jokes, was appreciative of Pam's cooking and very good with the children.

Pam left us with our coffee after dinner and got on with the washing up.

'Well, Bob,' said Steve. 'What are these great problems you have? How can we put the world to rights for you?'

'It's mainly things I don't understand,' I said. 'I don't understand why with a fixed population that we see more and more patients.

'With the strikes and redundancies we seem to be having new diseases which I feel at a loss to cope with. I remember some years ago you telling me the answer to society's problems was better individuals but we don't seem to have made much progress.'

'I think there are two major factors,' said Steve. 'First, over the past four or five decades society has changed more than it did over the previous five or six hundred years. Up to and after the First World War the vast majority of people worked for somebody. We were all sheltered, or most of us, by umbrellas. For generation after generation families would work in the same

122

environment. Society was very much in groups and there was somebody at the head of each group or community who would take the responsibility for us.

'Now there is just about only the doctor and the Citizens' Advice Bureaux who are directly available for advice and counselling.

'Although we have a comprehensive social service system with psychologists, social workers and psychiatric workers, experience can't be learned from books. A young man in his twenties with a degree in psychology or sociology, however intelligent he might be and however able, can only have had a certain amount of experience of life and life situations.

'We're at a time of evolution where individuals are becoming freer to express their own ideas. They're not quite sure yet how to do it or whether or not they should do it or even if they want to do it — at least a good number of them.

'The other point is that we are going through a new industrial revolution. Technology is changing and it looks as if, progressively, in the future, machines will do the work and men will be less necessary. We are already at a stage where machines make machines. We have yet to accept that there is a new industrial revolution and tackle the problem in a new way. I don't think anyone's going to go around breaking up looms this time.

'We can't necessarily call it progress: man will always keep moving on to new projects and new ideas. What we have to decide is how to utilise this time we have. To be unemployed demeans a man, takes away his dignity. We have, and that includes you and me, to work on some way of re-organising society.

'It's fine being armchair politicians and deciding how the country should be run. What we have to do is to recognise the real problem, because it is not going to go away, and as a community, a county, a nation we have to tackle this problem, each of us trying to contribute. Perhaps we can look forward to the day when we only do two or three days work a week and the rest of our time is spent in leisure, whatever that means.'

I knew Steve spent every minute of his spare time digging

away at his garden. He once said, 'My salary's now big enough for me to be able to afford to be a farm labourer.'

'Steve,' I said, 'thanks for your advice. I shall vote for you as a future Prime Minister.'

Steve smiled.

'But me,' I said, 'how do I cope with all these people who come into the surgery: the depressed, redundant executive; the disturbed striker?'

'One of the most important things,' said Steve, 'and one of the most effective treatments is sitting patiently listening to people, whatever their troubles.'

'You mean a bit like the way you sit and listen to me?'

Steve smiled again.

'Yes,' he said. 'Something like that.'

CHAPTER 11

Changing Times

I was growing older. When I first came to Tadchester I had been completely involved in local affairs, playing for the rugby club until Steve Maxwell suggested that a two-legged partner might be more use than a one-legged one. I played cricket in the summer, went seine fishing off the beaches, and was part of the Round Table tableau in carnival processions.

I now had to leave the Round Table and move up into the 41 Club.

I became president of the rugby club instead of one of its players. I was on the carnival committee, vice-chairman of two cricket clubs and both the rowing clubs — offices which really meant that they came to me for subscriptions — medical officer for two or three horse shows a year, and deeply involved in Red Cross work.

As if life wasn't busy enough, I was asked a couple of times to stand for the council. I talked to old Billy Beer about it. He was a builder Up-the-Hill, with a family business that went back several generations.

'They asked me to stand several times,' said Billy. 'But I refused. Two or three of my builder friends were elected and the difference between them and me is that they went bankrupt and

I am still going. You've got to have plenty of spare time if you want to do council work properly.'

Tadchester had a tremendous depth of history. At one time it had been a major centre for the importation of tea into this country, and the old historic buildings in the town were jealously preserved and guarded. It was a town to be proud of.

The biggest danger to its identity came with the increasing numbers of holidaymakers who came pouring down every year. Holiday camps and caravan sites at Sanford-on-Sea grew and grew.

Broken-down cottages all over the countryside and in the small creeks and bays were steadily being bought up by people from the cities. A couple of new hotels were built, with sophisticated bars and dining rooms and large swimming pools. It was like a leap into the space age for Tadchester.

But in spite of these fairly obvious changes, the heart and strength of the town was little changed.

Many an entrepreneur came down to settle and thought he'd take over the town, get on the council, be mayor, but he would always come across the same rigid defences. There was only one certain way of getting elected to anything in Tadchester and that was to be a Methodist.

During the General Election at the end of the Second World War I was in South Yorkshire, working as a Bevin Boy down the coal mines. The locals said they would vote for a pig if it was Labour.

Here in Tadchester if you weren't a member of the Methodist Church, then it was pretty hard going. The only man ever to beat the Methodist stranglehold was an itinerant builder from Up-the-Hill who could neither read nor write, but he did have 630 relatives who all put their crosses on his ballot papers. It was typical of Tadchester that once elected, the illiterate councillor should be put in charge of choosing books for the library.

Tadchester Hospital had been built by the local community, taken over by the National Health, and was now being run down from an active hospital to a geriatric unit. All major cases were being referred to Winchcombe Hospital ten miles away.

When Henry retired, it was likely there would be no more surgery at Tadchester. It was rumoured that the Government were going to build a health centre in the grounds of the hospital and that we should vacate our surgery premises.

This was all in the name of progress but there was only one way out of Tadchester, across Tadchester Bridge on the Winchcombe Road, and in the summer this was a terrible bottle-neck. In June, July and August, if a woman was on her way to Winchcombe in labour, she had about a fifty-fifty chance of having her baby in the ambulance.

What midwifery facilities we had had in Tadchester had been withdrawn. The old St Mary's Maternity Home had been closed down. We missed it terribly. Home confinements got fewer and fewer and we had to accept the fact that we were losing our skills as obstetricians.

Strangely, the old St Mary's Maternity Home with its lack of hygiene — in fact a dog came and lifted its leg in the delivery unit when I was making my first delivery — never had any troubles with infection.

This small unit was probably overrun with the local germs of the local people. Now our young mothers had to go over to a big sterile unit in Winchcombe. Immediately there was an increase in various infections picked up by both mothers and babies.

My old friend, Bob Barker, at the bookshop, smiled when I complained about all these changes.

'It's part of an unending pattern, Bob,' he said. 'These are fashions. Big is beautiful and then small is beautiful, we can only really find out by trying. If we could learn by our mistakes each time we got some new project, then we might advance.

'The trouble is that when you have new brooms, changes are made for changes' sake. It's not always wise.

'By and large there are probably better medical services down here than when you first came. This has been at the expense of the personal, caring sort of medicine that was practised before.

'The next move will be for somebody to discover all sorts of disadvantages in medicine being de-personalised. There'll be

127

the great move back again to small units, until somebody decides that it is time that we had bigger units again. I've seen it all happen in every sphere of life.

'Everything goes round in circles. All the time we do edge forward, but not nearly as much as we think.'

He reached behind him for an old book which catalogued prices of goods on sale at an apothecary's in the seventeenth century.

I looked down through the lists. About half the things I recognised as still being in use today — senna, rhubarb, opium, isinglass — a few we didn't use — sea horse pizzle, crabs' eyes and a lovely sounding medicine called skink.

'What is skink?' said Bob Barker.

'I've no idea,' I said, 'but if it was available I'd certainly use it.'

'Now,' said Bob, 'you say about half the things on this list are still being used today. I wonder how many times they have been discovered and abandoned and re-discovered over the last three hundred years?'

I looked at them closely. I could think of a couple of items that had been picked up and discarded at least three times in my time in medicine.

'What you should do,' said Bob, 'in addition to having a go at writing, is to interest yourself in music and painting or even writing poetry. It's only in the arts that we can make any real advances, break new barriers, find new methods of communication.

'I don't mean to be disrespectful to the medical profession,' he said, 'but all you can do is get better at keeping people alive. I wonder if that on its own is enough.

'I remember the Roald Dahl story of the obstetrician who used all his skill to procure at last a live birth for a woman:

'"What are you going to call the baby, Mrs Hitler," he asked her.

'"Adolf," she replied.

'Perhaps,' he said, 'as we have more and more leisure time there will be more time to cross new barriers in the artistic world.

'We might even reach a stage where you would have to justify having some medical treatment,' he said with a grin. 'You are keeping us all alive so long nowadays we might reach a stage where to have your appendix out you might have to produce a certificate to say you are a worthwhile case.

'Thank goodness,' he said, 'I'll have gone before all these things happen.'

Steve Maxwell and Bob Barker have been a great influence on my life. Wise, kindly men, unselfish and almost without prejudice.

*   *   *

129

Pam and I were sitting on the balcony one day looking out over the estuary.

'What will happen,' I said, 'when Steve Maxwell and Bob Barker have gone? Nobody lasts for ever. Whom will I chat to then about the world and how to put it right?'

Pam said, 'Well, you'll be a bit older then. And the likelihood is that the ageing Dr Clifford will be one of the wise old men of the town, and it will be you who'll be offering tea and sympathy.'

'I can't ever see that happening,' I said.

'Oh come on, Peter Pan,' said Pam. 'Let's go off and have a swim.'

* * *

For some years it had been my ambition to write. I was encouraged to try by Bob Barker and by Joan Courage, a local author who took me to the Writers' Summer School in Derbyshire.

The writers at the school liked to have a doctor around. I was useful because I could clarify medical situations and plots, give details on how to poison somebody or how to perform an operation. There were questions such as when did anaesthetics first start to be used? Could I suggest how somebody could be killed in hospital by a visitor apart from being bored to death?

The first two scripts I wrote — both short stories based on courageous patients of mine — were accepted by the BBC. I broadcast both of them and was beginning to regard myself as an author and broadcaster of great talent. The BBC must have thought differently because they rejected the next twenty-seven scripts.

Pam had a friend who was about to do her first BBC recording of a script she had written. Was there any advice I could give her? With the experience of a full eight minutes on the air behind me, I was prepared to advise anybody. I gave the friend the benefit of my vast knowledge and asked if she would put her script on tape for me. This she did. The lady had the broadest Devon accent and all she did was talk about the pigs on her farm and the paying guests in the summer. It really was appalling — so I thought — but I kept my counsel.

While I was getting my twenty-seven rejections Pam's friend, Nancy Horner, was asked back again and again to do more and more recordings, and soon became an established radio personality. Though over the years I was to do many broadcasts for the BBC, I was never anywhere near as accomplished or successful as the fascinating lady I had first thought so appalling.

Tadchester rugby team asked me to write some first-aid instructions for them. I knew that these big, hairy rugby players would never look at normal first-aid instructions, so I decided to funny them up, to use the laughs to get the message across.

I finished up with enough for a small book, so I sent it off to a publisher. Like my first broadcast, it was accepted straightaway and I went up to London to meet the publisher.

I was ushered into a huge room. Sitting behind a vast mahogany desk was a man of about my own age, smart-suited, wearing executive glasses and smoking a huge cigar.

'Pleased to meet you, Dr Clifford,' he said. 'Congratulations on your book. I think it will do well.'

'Thank you,' I said. 'When is it likely to be published?'

'Monday, 17th September,' he said. 'We've chosen a Monday because on that day there is more space given to book reviews in the Press. After the weekend people read their papers more intently than any other day of the week. And we have found that books published on a Monday do better, by and large, than books published on any other day of the week.'

'Sounds great,' I said. 'But the 17th of September is a Thursday.'

The publisher did not bat an eyelid.

'Thursday,' he said, 'is a good day as well.'

He sounded exactly like a consultant physician.

I enjoyed my writing and broadcasting, attaining small successes but never achieving any great heights. It was a tremendous help to my medicine to have an outside interest and to meet such different groups of people.

Although I was never going to win the Pulitzer Prize, I had found something that I enjoyed doing, and which in some strange way held me steady for my main work of being a family doctor.

CHAPTER 12

Letter from America

An unexpected letter from America brought memories of student days flooding back. It was from Paul Young who had been one of my firm friends during that time.

Pre-clinical years, three in number if you get your exams at the right time, are some of the most frustrating years of medical training. Although nominally a medical student, you know nothing about medicine and any self-respecting ambulanceman or first aider could leave you way behind in the management of even minor accidents.

This did not deter a couple of fellow students in their first year (when their nearest approach to medicine had been the dissection of a dog fish) from offering their medical services. The inference that they were nearly doctors gave them introductions to all sorts of functions: football matches, boxing matches and even some expeditions. They would tackle everything, nipping back to read a book on the management of casualties between cases. Providing they followed what they read, all was well.

Being a first-year medical student as opposed to a schoolboy you could wander around with the hospital scarf thrown nonchalantly round your neck, drop into pubs at lunchtime and revel in the fact that you were an embryo doctor.

133

Then came the second-year slog. Corpses that had soaked in formalin bore no relation to anybody you knew. Dissection, which implies bold strokes with a knife, was in fact scratching through grubby plasticine-like tissue trying to identify nerves, arteries, muscles and bones which were nothing like the beautiful pictures in text books.

We were taught some medical testing, prefaced by a classic,

lecturer's trick. A jar of urine was placed in front of us. The lecturer announced that a crude test for diabetes was whether or not you could taste the sugar in urine. He then pushed his finger into the urine, put it in his mouth, and said he wasn't sure about this particular sample.

Three or four 'volunteers' were asked to come up and repeat this procedure. They all pulled funny faces, one of them was sick and none of them could decide whether there was any sugar in the urine or not.

'The main thing I am teaching you here is observation — the single most important thing in medicine,' said the lecturer. 'If you had looked closely you would have noticed that it was my index finger that I placed in the jar and it was the third finger that I put into my mouth.'

Paul Young was an American. He was a six-foot, thirteen-stone American football player who had come to England after having taken an organic chemistry degree at an American university. He was on a scholarship and intended to go back to America with an English degree in medicine.

He was also anxious to enjoy every minute of his stay in England and absorb much of its culture. He would have a go at anything; he played rugby enthusiastically and got himself a place in the hospital second team on the wing. His loudly shouted American football terms were a great asset although often confusing, not only for the opponents but also for his own side.

He was a beaver for work and put us all to shame. He wore a large pair of horn-rimmed spectacles and was usually seen carrying great tomes under his arm. He was always eager to get into discussion about the various work projects we were involved on. He asked endless questions in lectures without causing irritation.

Anatomy and physiology are never really a test of one's ability; they are much more a test of application, stamina and determination and one just had to sit down and solidly learn things. There Paul Young had the advantage over us. If given an area of textbook to cover, he could quickly commit it to

135

memory and could recall it almost word for word. In fact, he could sometimes recite two or three whole pages of text.

But for some reason he didn't do terribly well when we had our terminal examinations. He came in the top third in the organic chemistry examination at the end of the first year but didn't do as well as expected of a man with a degree in this subject. He was well liked by all the lecturers and it was quite obvious he knew his stuff. They did their best to explain to him that he was answering questions in the wrong way and it wasn't a lack of ability that was getting him such low marks.

During the last three months before the final pre-clinical examinations you have to memorise so much information. There is very little to be worked out, one simply has to amass the detailed knowledge of the body and its workings which will be the basis on which you build your medical career and which must last you for the rest of your life. We were obviously well taught, for even thirty years after qualifying, odd bits of anatomy that I thought I had forgotten come into mind when required.

We were all nervously entered for our second medical examination; you were nothing until you had passed second M.B. In Oxford and Cambridge you get a degree for second M.B., in London you get nothing. Once you have passed your second M.B. then you are certain to qualify eventually for a degree of some sort or another that will enable you to practise medicine.

Paul had worked at least as hard as any of us and, looking at our group, if anybody had to put a bet on who would pass highest in the rankings, it would be Paul. And yet he got the lowest marks in anatomy ever recorded, which absolutely shattered him.

I hadn't expected to pass. I hadn't worked hard, had played a lot of rugby and was secretary of the rugby fifteen. I hadn't really prepared myself. You have another chance in the summer and I wrote off the summer to swotting hard for the second M.B., which that time I got.

Paul failed again, and I gathered that his second attempt was only slightly better than his first.

It certainly wasn't exam nerves, and it certainly wasn't a lack of ability or application. The main reason must have been some difference in the way we are examined in this country as opposed to the United States. It is not that our system is better or that we have a higher standard: it's just in some way different.

Paul was at least as well informed as any of us, and better than most. He understood what he was doing, had a good grasp of everything, was able and intellectual, but somehow he could not come to terms with the British examinations. He returned to America, settled back into medical school there, passed all his degrees with honours, specialised in paediatrics and became a well-known paediatrician.

Although we didn't see each other after he left for America, we kept in touch and a letter from him saying that he was coming to London on a post-graduate course meant that Pam and I would travel to London to stay with my mother and have a few days with him.

Paul was in a party of six, his wife and two other Americans and their wives, all delightful charming people. They were mixing their morning lectures with various London entertainments. They were determined to absorb as much of London culture as they could, and were going to a matinee every afternoon, the theatre in the evening and sometimes a late-night film as well. What suckers they were for punishment.

Paul had changed very little: he was slightly stouter, still wore thick horn-rimmed glasses, was as friendly as ever, and more British than the British. His wife was a very striking dark-haired woman called Peggy. She was extremely smartly dressed and came from one of the great Californian wine families. Like myself, she had an interest in writing.

We took them as our guests to see our friend Joan Miller in the 'Three Ladies' starring Dame Flora Robson, and Peter Cotes, Joan's husband, entertained them all after the show. They were delighted to be in the presence of such famous English stage people.

Their stay went all too quickly and almost before we had realised it, it was their last night here.

They wanted to take us out somewhere, and after careful

planning they decided to treat us to a meal in a hotel which specialised in the re-creation of the Elizabethan scene. As they didn't know where the hotel was, I, as the only Englishman and part-time Londoner, was elected to select our mode of transport to the site of this repast.

After careful enquiries I managed to find a bus which unfortunately dropped us off over a mile from the hotel, leaving us to complete the journey on foot. I explained that, medically, exercise was the best thing for us, especially in view of the volume of food we were about to consume, but there was little enthusiasm from the rest of the party.

We arrived at our destination late, to be ushered into a candlelit room by a number of wenches who characterised the age by having the top half of their bosoms exposed. If you are interested in bosoms, as I am, it is worth going for that alone.

Being the last in we had to sit at the top table (the only one vacant) and our host, Paul, had to sit in the grand armchair as lord and master, whilst Pam, who sat on his right, was informed that she was his mistress for the night. On enquiring tenatively about her duties, to her relief she found that she was required only to put food on his plate.

We were above the salt, i.e. the landlords, which meant that we had the right to collect taxes from the people who were seated below the salt, and didn't have to pay taxes ourselves. I immediately determined to visit my local income tax office the next day and explain my change of status. The demarcation line was a large box of salt at the end of our table, forming a barrier to the next one.

We started with a mead aperitif, followed by a mulled wine which (to my distrusting palate) had some Spanish ancestry. We had instructions to greet each other by shouting something like 'Hail, Wassail!', which is apparently Elizabethan for 'Bottoms up'. I shouted 'Seig heil!' all the time and nobody appeared to notice. (It was so much easier to say.)

The tables in front of us were filled with lively Americans from a special 'Three-Week Five-Country Tour'. Owing to my travel arrangements, they had a head start on us and were already busy drinking and wassailing when we arrived. This was their second meal in three nights at this establishment, and being the last night of their tour, they were determined to go back to their mother country having experienced a bit of Old England or bust in the effort. (Nothing to do with the wenches.)

The chief wench, who also happened to have the largest bust (probably this is an example of natural selection), was trying to describe medieval customs but had to shout above the surrounding din. We discovered that 'If you didn't leave some of your hog's head salad for your beef, you were fined,' and 'If you were on a lower table and wanted salt, you were dependent on the whim of the lord and master.' Meanwhile an attractive green-clad singer was plucking her guitar (or Elizabethan equivalent) and singing Elizabethan ballads. As the Three-Week Five-Country Tour rapidly lost their inhibitions, her music disappeared amongst cries of 'A drink for Milwaukee . . . now one for Kansas City!'

Meanwhile we were served with our first course: soup; and in true Elizabethan style had to drink it straight from the bowl. We had a quick international discussion and found that all children of our party, both British and American, drank their soup in this way, and we decided that this must be some sort of infantile subconscious recognition that Elizabeth II was on the throne.

Next hog's head and salad.

The food was good and the wine, if I questioned its origin, was available in abundant quantities.

It was leading to the complete disintegration of the Three-Week Five-Country Tour in front of us. Everybody in this party was embracing everybody else, and one group of women with the experience of five countries behind them, had started to tackle a group of British businessmen who had unwisely entered this un-native scene. Soon the wine began to act on them too, and they proceeded to match the embraces of the American Amazons, one for one.

One girl in a bright-red frock stuck loyally to her own party and began to 'eat' in the most vigorous manner a thick-set man with a hairline moustache, sitting next to her. One older lady of

the party, with a high nasal whine, turned and said, 'That girl had the worse luck of the trip. She lost her bags [presumably cases] in Amsterdam and her passport in Paris.' I hated to think what she was likely to lose tonight, but suggested she would be able to put in her diary, 'The night my luck changed.'

Paul managed to rescue the minstrel and we grouped to form a protective ring about her while she sang us some delightful Elizabethan ditties. Some had exactly the same music as well-known rugby songs, thus dispelling the legend that this game started when Tom Brown, at Rugby School, picked up the ball and ran. I'd always thought, when I saw pictures of Sir Walter Raleigh, that he looked rather like a scrum-half.

The Three-Week Five-Country Tour were getting quite

worked up now and a few of the wenches who moved in to keep the party clean probably gave the impression to later diners that bruised bosoms were the fashion round about the time of the Armada.

Then suddenly 'Auld Lang Syne', and the party was over, and everybody went quietly home (though I did see one man and a wench slipping upstairs and wondered if she was going to show him an old Elizabethan bed).

It had been a great evening. I told Paul I was grateful to him, for at last I had found out about my own heritage.

We promised to go and see Paul and his wife in the States, and it was pleasant to know that this delightful man, who somehow did not fit into the British examination system, had prospered in the different academic climate of America.

CHAPTER 13

Diets and Boat Trips

We very much enjoyed our house, which was sited on three-quarters of an acre of wooded garden overlooking the estuary.

I could watch salmon boats rowing up the river and herons fishing from its banks, and could see Tadchester's two fishing trawlers coming home on the incoming tide with their following flocks of gulls.

Far away, across the other side of the river, was the main road to Winchcombe. The seasons could be noted by the volume of traffic on this road, a much better guide than the unstable British weather.

Since Pam lost her mother, her father Gerry had become

142

increasingly despondent. He had had an unsuccessful attempt to set up house with a musical housekeeper — part of her job was to play piano accompaniment to his violin — and they talked of buying a property near us. Finally he built a bungalow extension to our house, and it gave him an even better view of the estuary and river than we had.

Food was a very important part of Gerry's life. He could smell a mile off if we had anything special cooking and was very hurt if he wasn't asked to any dinner party that was going. At Christmas he hovered round to see that his trifle with hazelnuts on it was prepared in the way that he liked it (he didn't like Christmas pudding). When, on a visit, my mother offered him some bacon and egg pie, he was quite affronted: he considered that food for peasants. Only the very best for Gerry.

'To keep fit,' he said, 'you've got to have a well-balanced diet. You ought to know that, Bob m'lad.'

I was never quite sure what a well-balanced diet was and always failed to persuade Pam that there was probably as much nourishment in a glass of milk and a ham salad sandwich as there was in roast beef and Yorkshire pudding.

One of the fittest men locally was Trevor Robinson, a confirmed bachelor — not that he did not like women, he liked them so much he could never settle on any particular one.

A great keep-fit enthusiast, he rowed and played squash, badminton and cricket. Although forty-seven, in temperament and outlook he was really only in his middle-twenties. He drank like a fish, often stayed up all night drinking and playing cards, but never seemed to be tired. He was always in demand for local hospital functions. Having an eligible bachelor like Trevor as make-weight for the many nurses who were without partners was invaluable and every new woman who met him felt that she might be the one to break down his barriers.

Pam and I had been to one particularly late-night dance and staggered home about two o'clock in the morning. We were aroused about ten o'clock by the noise of motorboats racing up and down the river. I peered through the window to see Trevor Robinson water-skiing.

143

We had left him at two o'clock with the party in full swing. I doubt if he had been in bed before five and, knowing Trevor, probably not alone. I waved to him from our balcony as he came back up the river and he slipped his rope, glided to the bank, pulled off his water-skis and walked up to our house for coffee. 'Good God, Trevor,' I said. 'How on earth do you manage it?'

'Diet,' he said. 'Purely diet. Apart from the odd time I dine out or am invited for a meal, I only eat two things — tinned· salmon and pineapple chunks.'

'Isn't that expensive?' I said, only half believing him.

'No,' he said. 'I get them all free.'

Trevor was the senior sales rep for a canned foods firm and it was a perk of the job that salesmen were able to keep goods damaged in transit. I gathered that most of the salesmen in his firm fed themselves for nothing. When their supplies were dwindling, a packer could very easily be persuaded to drop a case accidentally.

Trevor one day showed me his larder — and he hadn't been joking. The whole of the left side of the pantry was stacked with tinned salmon and the other side with pineapple chunks. All, of course, with dents in them.

'Don't you ever get bored?'

'No,' said the ebullient Trevor, 'I love them both.'

I have no idea what magic ingredients tinned salmon and pineapple chunks possess to ensure a well-balanced diet. I know Trevor reinforced this basic minimum with plenty of beer.

When he was away from home, he must have eaten normally. He specialised in holidays abroad and would bring back colourful slides from far-off places such as Thailand, Morocco and South America. He used to give talks about his travels to all the various bodies in the town — Rotarians, Round Table, Women's Institutes — and then after drinks in the Tadchester Arms, you would hear the unabridged version of his exploits in Thailand massage parlours and South American brothels. He was a great laugh, was Trevor. I never knew if the stories he told us were true but they were very entertaining. Perhaps his brief

144

intakes of foreign food balanced his tinned diet, anyway it worked.

* * *

Gerry tried to get involved in as many local sporting activities as he could. He was a good shot, he fished a bit and played very mediocre golf. Music was his real love. He had been a very good violinist and now played in orchestras for the local operatic societies and was a member of various trios and quartets whose playing sounded absolutely ghastly to me, but it obviously gave all the participants great pleasure.

We had a small dinghy with an outboard motor. A nice boat, but it had its limitations. It wasn't really big enough to go out to sea for a start. When we took it out on the river the tide had to be right, otherwise several hundred yards of sticky mud had to be traversed; also the weather had to be right; and I had to be off duty to supervise the children.

Gerry came into our house for coffee one Saturday morning and we looked out over the estuary together. He pointed to our small boat, rocking gently at its mooring.

'You could do with a bigger boat,' he said. 'With a 25-foot clinker-built job and an inboard motor we could do a bit of deep-sea fishing. I fancy my hand at that.'

Gerry was now seventy-six and I thought this was a bit old for taking up deep-sea fishing. But he had successfully taken up camping at the age of seventy-five so nothing was impossible.

'Chap's written to me,' said Gerry, 'saying he's got a 25-foot clinker-built boat with an inboard, lying at Abersoch in North Wales.' (What a coincidence.) 'If we'd like to have it brought down we can have it for nothing.'

'You're not going to sail it down?' I said.

'Good God, no,' said Gerry. 'We'll have it brought down by trailer.'

'That's fine,' I said. 'Shall we fix it up?'

'Better have a look at it,' said Gerry. 'What about going up on your next weekend off?'

It was February now. We were down on the Somerset coast. I didn't fancy driving up to Wales overnight. In the end, Gerry persuaded me and one Friday night we set off.

It was bitterly cold. The car didn't have a heater and the windscreen wipers weren't working quite as they should. The further north we went, the colder it got. I was driving Gerry's car, a Morris Minor Traveller, which was slightly better than mine.

Dawn was breaking about fifty miles north of Bristol when we came across an accident. A little A30 bubble car had driven into the rear of a lorry, and the scene was quite appalling. The lorry driver and his mate had pulled out the driver of the A30, who was sitting at the side of the road with blood streaming down his face. The lorry driver and his chum were standing near the cab talking away as if nothing was amiss.

I pulled up and asked, 'What happened?'

'He's crashed into the back of our lorry, mate,' said the driver.

'Have you sent for an ambulance?' I asked.

146

'No,' he said, 'there's nowhere to phone from.'

We were way out in the country.

'What are you doing?'

'Waiting for a passing car.'

'Well, has anything passed?'

He said, 'You have. Do you know any first aid?'

'I'm a doctor.'

'Good, I'll leave it to you, mate,' he said.

The injured man was sitting holding his head in his hands, blood running through his fingers. He was an awful sight.

His car had run under the extended tailboard of the lorry, smashing his spectacles and putting glass into both eyes.

'I think I'm blind,' he said.

'We'd better take him to the nearest town,' I said. I knew that Netherton was only ten miles off and should have some sort of hospital.

We managed to get him into the back of our Traveller, wrapped him up in a blanket and drove off towards Netherton.

We found a cottage hospital with a rather diffident sister on duty.

'What can we do for you at this hour?' she said.

'There's been a road accident,' I replied. 'This man's eyes are badly damaged.'

'I don't know if we can get a doctor at this time of day,' she said, 'but you'd better bring him in.'

We brought him in and sat him down. His face was still bloody and he was in obvious pain.

'Hm,' said the sister, 'I expect I'd better ring the doctor. He won't like to be disturbed at a time like this.'

She went off to the phone. 'He's in his bath,' she said. 'He'll come when he's finished.'

Gerry had noticed as we drove into the hospital that the police station was only just up the road.

'I'll walk up,' he said, 'and report the accident.'

He came back ten minutes later looking exasperated.

'How did you get on, Gerry?' I asked.

'Well,' he said, 'I went up there and there was a chap digging in the garden of the police station. I went up to the police station and knocked on the door. There was no reply. I knocked again. There was no reply so I said to the chap in the garden, who'd been watching me all this time, "Do you know where the policeman is?"

'"Yes," he said, "I'm him — but it's no good talking to me: I'm off duty. You'll have to go and ring up the station in the next town."'

Gerry was fuming.

'May I use your phone?' he asked the sister.

'Why?' she said, looking suspicious.

'I must phone and report this accident,' said Gerry as patiently as he could.

'Oh, all right,' said the sister.

Gerry rang the police sation in the next town. 'I want to report an accident,' he said.

'What's your name?' said the voice at the other end.

'Never mind my name,' said Gerry, 'I want to report an accident.'

'What's your name?' said the voice at the other end.

'I'm not involved in the accident,' said Gerry. 'We just happened to have helped somebody involved in it.'

'What's your name?' said the man at the other end.

Gerry gave a description of the accident and slammed the phone down.

The casualty sister came up to him.

'That's sixpence for your phone call,' she said.

Gerry was getting redder and redder in the face.

'Where's the bloody doctor?' he said.

'We won't have that language in here,' said the sister. 'This is only a cottage hospital and he's on call. It is very good of him to come at all.'

I was getting a bit impatient too by now.

'Look,' I said, 'this man's got glass in his eyes. Can I be doing something?'

'Hm,' said the sister. Realising the man was in a bad way, she volunteered to give the doctor another ring.

148

We'd been at the hospital an hour by then. The sister came back. 'The doctor will be here in half an hour,' she said, 'he's just having his breakfast. He says if you do feel you can do something, he would be very grateful.'

I cleaned up the chap's eyes as best I could, bandaged them to protect them from the light, gave him something to ease his pain and saw him settled down in the ward.

'Come on, Gerry,' I said, 'we're off. There's nothing more we can do here.'

We set off in the car. It had now begun to snow. We had to call in on Gerry's friend who was donating the boat and it meant a diversion through the Llangollen Pass.

In the Pass it had obviously been snowing for a long time. We crept along in blinding snow over treacherous roads and eventually reached his friend's house.

'They'll give us a bloody good breakfast here,' said Gerry, smacking his hands together.

We arrived at nine o'clock and were obviously very unpopular. The man hadn't told his wife we were coming for breakfast. We were shown into a cold dining room, where we sat shivering until eventually we were reluctantly brought some tea and toast and given directions how to get to the boat at Abersoch. We set off on our way again.

The car was bitterly cold, the road was very difficult to drive, Gerry hadn't had the breakfast he had expected, the windscreen wipers had frozen almost to a stop — and then suddenly the car slid gently into a ditch.

It wouldn't budge. The wheels just spun and it was too heavy to push.

'Christ,' said Gerry, who had been getting steadily more irritable. 'What else can happen today?'

After about half an hour a tractor came along the road. It stopped near us and a bewhiskered farmer got off.

'You're in trouble,' he said, perceptively.

'Can you help us?' I asked.

'I don't know,' he said. 'I'm not really licensed to do this sort of thing. Don't think I can, really.'

I put my hand into my trouser pocket and saw his face brighten. I extracted two pounds from my wallet.

'Will this help?'

'Have you out in a jiffy, sir,' he said. A rope from the back of the tractor tugged us out of the ditch and we were on our creepy crawl again.

As we got nearer to Abersoch the weather and the road got better. The sun gave a sort of wintry smile and after numerous enquiries, we found a little cove. There, covered by a tarpaulin, was the boat we'd come to look at.

'It's been worth it,' said Gerry. 'Look at it.'

She certainly was a beauty, with sturdy but graceful lines. I could already imagine us riding the waves as we went out to Tadchester bay. This was just the boat for a fisherman like me.

Gerry reached into his pocket for a penknife and stuck it into the nearest planking.

'Bloody rotten,' he said. 'It's no good. It's a wasted journey.'

Both sides of the boat had areas of rotting timbers. Though it looked good from a distance, the craft was complete rubbish. We would have been doing Gerry's friend a favour by taking it away.

'Come on,' I said. 'Home we go.'

It was late afternoon and we had had just about enough. We decided to stay for the night in Criccieth.

Gerry was very disgruntled by now. 'Bet the food'll be bloody awful,' he said.

The hotel was quite comfortable. There was a big log fire and Gerry improved as he sat with a glass of whisky, toasting his feet in front of the roaring logs.

'By God,' he said, 'I could eat a horse.'

The food was simple fare but not at all bad: a great big bowl of oxtail soup, roast beef, Yorkshire pudding and roast potatoes with great mounds of soggy cabbage.

Gerry packed food in like a man stoking a raging furnace. He smacked his lips as he pushed away his empty plate.

'Now for something tasty,' he said, 'just to finish it off. What have you got, Miss?' he asked the fat, pimply waitress in the grubby white pinafore.

'Well,' she said, 'there's some prunes and custard, semolina pudding or you could have a bit of Stilton.'

'God,' said Gerry, 'I don't want semolina or prunes. I'll have to settle for the Stilton.

'I expect it'll be a little bit of dried-up stuff,' he moaned. 'What a bloody waste of a journey. All these miles...the windscreen wipers don't work... I'll have to have the car serviced...blood all over the back of the car...frozen...' but then his face suddenly lit up. Across the dining room came our dumpy waitress almost staggering under the weight of a huge half Stilton.

'My God,' said Gerry. 'This is perfect.'

A large glass of port, a great wooden spoon, a pile of biscuits, and butter — Gerry was in business.

'Not such a bad trip after all,' he said, munching away. 'I feel like a man restored. The best bit of cheese I've had for years. Now then, what are we going to order for breakfast?'

Gerry's port and Stilton had certainly revived him. I was still exhausted. We'd missed a night's sleep, been cold and wet, I had been driving a strange car, we had come all this way for nothing and I felt low and exhausted.

'Come on, Bob,' said Gerry, 'I see they've got kidneys. Not often you get kidneys offered for breakfast.'

'Well, if you insist,' I said, 'but I'd rather have some tinned salmon and pineapple chunks.'

They were the only things I could think of that might give me sufficient energy to make the journey home.

CHAPTER 14

First Pike

I had fixed up to have a day off on October 1st to go fishing for pike with John Denton.

'Why wait till then?' I asked, having seen several pike brought into the Tadchester Arms during the summer.

'Tradition,' said John. 'On some waters you're not allowed to fish for pike at all until October 1st. This river authority doesn't like pike, so people are allowed to catch them all through the coarse season. But October 1st is the accepted date. Worth waiting for: gives you more a sense of occasion.'

Although the Tad was a mixed fishery, it held a good head of trout, topped up by John's re-stocking every year. The trout fishermen certainly hated pike. They claimed that they played havoc with the stocks, and they kept up a strong lobby with the river authority to have the numbers kept down.

'Pike do knock off a number of trout,' said John. 'But in the main, trout can look after themselves better than most. And if I know a particular pike's doing a lot of damage, I'll soon have him out.

'But what the pike do is to keep the river healthy, keep the head of fish in balance with the food supply. Take all the pike out and you'd end up with a water full of stunted, sickly fish.

'That's one thing pike do: see off the sick fish. They're bone idle by nature and only hunt in short sprints. So any fish which is off-colour and slowing down a bit makes an ideal target.'

'Vicious-looking things, aren't they?' I said, remembering the monster in the glass case above the bar at the Tadchester Arms.

'They are,' said John. 'Freshwater shark, they're often called. And that's another reason they're treated so badly — they frighten people.'

I found out how much they frightened people on the morning of October 1st. John and I were walking along the bank towards the chosen swim, when we saw a man booting something through the grass. He kicked it some distance away from the water, then stamped on it hard three or four times.

'Hey up,' said John. 'If this is what I think it is...'

The man was short, bespectacled, balding, middle-aged, with a round face which, as we discovered later, was normally quite pleasant. A typical family man out for a day by the river. He was filling his pipe as we reached him, and looking at the thing in the grass. He was trembling quite noticeably.

'By the...' he panted, his eyes wide and triumphant. 'Took some putting down, that one. Thought it was going to have my hand off.'

'That one' was a pike. Badly mangled from the kicking and stamping, still quivering but very dead.

John took a tape measure from his pocket and ran it down the length of the fish.

'Know what length this is?' he asked coldly.

'Ooh... Three feet if it's an inch,' said the little man, his trembling subsiding as he drew on his pipe.

'It's 23 inches long,' said John. 'Which gives it a weight of $3\frac{1}{2}$ lb. And 23 inches is an inch under the minimum length. That fish should have been returned to the water straightaway. Unharmed.'

'Get away,' said the man. 'I nearly lost my fingers with that thing. Who the hell are you, anyway?'

'That's me,' said John, producing his bailiff's identification card. 'Now then, I could have you banned for a season for what you've just done. Taking an undersized fish for a start. And kicking the bloody thing to death for a second.'

'I'm sorry,' the little man stuttered. 'I didn't know...'

'Well you know now,' said John. 'If I ever catch you doing it again, that's your fishing up the spout for a while. Now get back

155

to that water and try for another. When you've got one on, give me a shout — I'll only be round that bend — and I'll show you how a pike should be treated. Right?'

'Right,' said the man, flushing with relief. 'Thank you.... Thanks very much.... Most grateful.... Thanks...'

'Thank me by behaving yourself in future. Now off you go...'

John and I went round the bend in the river to a spot facing a small spring which trickled into the river down the opposite bank.

He kitted me out with a 10-foot, hollow fibreglass rod — which I found out later was really designed for carp fishing — and baited up with a dead and very smelly fish. The fish, a sprat heavily soaked in pilchard oil, was attached to the line with a single and a treble hook on a wire trace under a long, thick float.

'Get it over there, Bob,' he said. 'Just where that water's trickling in, downstream of that fallen log. There's a slow eddy there: just what the old pike likes.'

I cast in, the bait sank, the float righted itself, and I reeled in the slack line.

'Right,' said John. 'Keep your eyes on the float. You'll soon know when a pike takes the bait.

'For a start, let it run. It won't go far. The pike will stop to turn the bait in its mouth — it takes it sideways and swallows it head first — and then it will run again. On that second run, give it the hammer. Tighten up your line, stand up and strike firmly and smoothly. Nothing to it.'

We sat there for an hour, talking about this and that, but mainly pike.

'What was wrong with that man?' I asked. 'He seemed to be in a state of shock.'

'He was,' said John. 'Pike bring out the worst in people. All the buried frustrations, fears, aggressions, you name it. When a man catches a pike, all those complexes can explode.'

'But it's only a fish.'

'True. But weight-for-length it's a big one, and the most evil-looking we've got in this country. Mouth like a bear trap, lined with hundreds of needle-sharp teeth. All pointing backwards.

What goes in never comes out. But the biggest fright comes from the eyes.'

'Really evil, are they?'

'Not so much that as the fact they look straight at you. A pike needs binocular vision for hunting. so the eyes point straight ahead, not sideways as in other fish. The eyes, actually, are quite beautiful. T. H. White once said . . .'

Just then there was a loud yell from round the bend.

'T. H. White will have to wait,' said John. 'Me laddo's got himself a fish by the sound of it.'

He got up and moved off with long strides, keeping low so as not to disturb the fish in our stretch, putting his big feet down quietly. Leaving me staring at my float.

I am particularly prone to Sod's Law, and this time was no exception. Hardly had John disappeared than my float did the same. It shot underwater as if it had been snatched and moved swiftly upstream. Then it stopped and bobbed to the surface again.

Frantically willing myself not to panic, I waited for what seemed an age. The float waggled and bobbed and jiggled, and then slid firmly under, curving back downstream. I reeled in the slack line, stood up and struck with a long, firm, copybook strike over the right shoulder.

Thank God for the carp rod. Its flexible action absorbed the shock of the hooks going into what appeared to be a rock. Damn. It was snagged. I held tight to the rod for a second to work out how best to free the hook, then — *bang*!

There was a fierce tug on the line and the rod started to buck like a wild thing. The line thrummed with a jagging, side-to-side movement that pulled the rod tip almost down to the water. Remembering John's previous fishing lessons, I let out a little line, then turned the rod sideways to put sidestrain on whatever was threatening to drag me into the water.

The line went slack as the thing turned back upstream and I reeled frantically to make contact again. As soon as it tightened . . . *whoosh*! An enormous shape, like a blunt-headed torpedo, leapt clean out of the water, the tail thrashing the surface and the great head shaking from side to side in an attempt to throw the hooks.

With a great splash the fish belly-flopped onto the water and set off for another run, whipping the rod violently through the whole of its length. Some more line out, some more sidestrain and ... *whoosh*! Out came the thing again, skittering upright on its tail across the surface, with the great mouth agape and the head shaking like a terrier with a rat.

'John!' I shouted, or tried to. What came out was a high-pitched squeak.

'What are you, Clifford? A man or a mouse?' I thought. Ignoring the answer of 'Pass the cheese', I followed the thing through as it crashed once more into the water, and this time dealt with the run a bit more calmly.

The fight seemed to go on for hours. Run after run and leap after leap, always with the same spectacular thrashing and head-shaking.

Another run. Here we go ag ... But this time there was no leap. The pike ran frantically back and forth across the eddy, jagging all the time but now perceptibly weaker.

This was it. The Moment of Truth. John had taught me never to fight a fish to the point of complete exhaustion just for the fun of it. It was time to bring this thing across the river and net it. Thank God, too, for another of John's basic angling-for-idiots instructions: always make up the landing net before you start to fish. With this thing on the line, I could never have coped with screwing the net into the handle.

I started to pump the fish across, lifting the rod tip and then dropping it, reeling in the slack line every time. Got you now, me proud beauty. Another couple of ... *whoosh*! A monstrous shape rocketed out of the water near the bank in a last desperate skittering bid for freedom, and so close now that I was splashed by its re-entry.

Right. Contact made again. One more pump. Net in water. Rod up slowly. Firmly draw the fish. *Eek!*

What faced me was a primaeval nightmare. A huge, scoop-shaped head. A mouth glittering silver with hundreds of tiny,

158

vicious teeth. And a pair of immense eyes which accused me of every sin committed since the beginning of time.

My knees turned rubbery and my stomach cold and knotted. What the hell was I to *do* with this thing?'

'Hang on, Bob! I'm coming!' John's voice from a distant planet.

I couldn't lose it now. Not in front of witnesses. With a silent prayer and a firm grip, I drew the apparition over the submerged net. Such was its length that its snout was over the nearside rim of the net before its tail had touched the far one. Now or never — *hup*!

The fish thrashed, doubled up like a U-bend into the capacious mesh. I ran crabwise up the bank and at a safe distance from the water swung the net onto the grass with a scything movement which made sure the fish was covered by the mesh. I leaned hard on the net's rim. What on earth do I do now?

'Good lad, our Bob,' said John, kneeling beside me and pulling on a pair of thick leather gloves. 'I'll see to this — unless you fancy a go yourself.'

'No thanks, John,' I panted. 'He's all yours.'

John gingerly parted the mesh until the fish's great head was free. With his left hand John gripped the fish by the bony sockets behind the eyes. His right hand held a pair of long surgical forceps. Forcing the pike's mouth open with his knuckles, he probed into the great cavern and, with a couple of expert twists, freed the hooks.

(I discovered later that it was not uncommon for unenlightened anglers actually to stick finger and thumb into the eyes, blinding the pike while they forced in a cruel gag to hold the mouth open.)

'Nice one,' breathed John, taking the pike from the net and holding it down firmly on the grass. 'Tape measure in my right-hand pocket, Bob. Run it from the nose to the fork in the tail.'

This I did, warily. 'My God! Three foot one. Must weigh a ton.'

'Fifteen and a half pounds,' said John. 'Bloody good going by any standards.'

159

'What size do these things run to?'

'English record, about 37½ lb.' (That year it was to become 40 lb and is even more now). 'Scotland, nearly 48 lb; Ireland, 53 lb.'

'Sheesh! Makes mine look a bit sick.'

'Nay,' said John. 'That's a good 'un. You did well to hold him.'

'My, my,' said a voice behind me, almost repeating my words. 'That makes my little ones look a bit sick.'

It was the pike basher from round the bend. Now, seemingly, a reformed character.

After letting me admire the pike for a bit, John picked it up and laid it gently back in the water, head facing upstream. He held it for a minute or two, 'walking' it against the current to get the oxygenated water flowing over its gills, and with a final shove gave it its freedom. After a couple of confused shakes, it found its bearings and dived deep out of sight.

'I'm grateful to John here,' said the pleasant-faced little man. ('John' already. They must have got on well.) 'He took all the fright out of that second pike of mine. A five-pounder it was, too. What was that bit from T. H. White, John? You'd just started to tell me when your friend here screamed.'

Screamed?

'Ah, yes,' said John. 'My favourite quote about the pike. From *The Once and Future King* by T. H. White. You probably know it, Bob; where the future King Arthur, swimming in the moat after he'd been changed by Merlin into a fish, came across the old, giant pike.'

'Er, no. I can't say I do...'

'Sadness,' said John. 'That's what the pike's eyes hold if you look closely enough. And once you've recognised it, you'll never bash a pike again as long as you live. This is it...'

John intoned slowly and carefully, as if he were in a pulpit:

'"He was remorseless, disillusioned, predatory, fierce, pitiless — but his great jewel of an eye was that of a stricken deer, large, fearful, sensitive and full of griefs. He made no movement but looked upon them with his bitter eye."'

For a few seconds I was unable to speak. Those beautiful words, coming from this big, bluff man who would normally deny any pretensions to culture, spoken in a magical riverside setting with the murmur of the water as a background, were almost too much.

'Ahem,' I coughed, finally. 'That says it all, John. But I didn't know you were a literary man.'

'Nor I am,' said John. 'But T. H. White is special. Tells a good tale, that lad . . .'

CHAPTER 15

Leaving the Nest

My schooldays weren't the happiest days of my life, in fact some of them were very unhappy. I didn't do well in my early years at school neither distinguishing myself at work nor at games. It was only in my final years, when I started to apply myself, that I got any real sort of satisfaction and had any fun. As a result, I was determined that my children should enjoy their schooldays.

Pam and I had to decide whether or not to send the boys away to boarding school. Practically all my colleagues nearly ruined themselves sending their children to public school, really so that their children in turn would be in a position to nearly ruin themselves sending their own children to public school.

We decided that if there was adequate education locally, we would keep ours at home, perhaps selfishly, because we wanted to enjoy them and be involved in their growing up. We did have the advantage of living in a lovely area as part of a community

162

with plenty of local amenities and satisfactory local schools.

Having the children at home meant that we could support them in all the various functions they took part in. We became (I reluctantly) members of the Parents' and Teachers' Association and other such organisations.

If we supported one child in a particular activity we really had to support the others. We saw Jane at the age of four and a half tottering onto the stage with acute tonsilitis to say her bit as Noddy in a school play. We saw the disgruntled Paul in the school pantomime. Trevor and all Paul's friends were soldiers. Paul, to his disgust, was a dicky-bird. Zara made him the most superb bird costume, all fluffy blue feathers and a big yellow beak. Paul was outstanding in that; out of twenty birds, he was the only one with his beak pulled down over his left eye.

We sat right through one tedious play at the grammar school in which Trevor was to blow his trumpet. Having watched this badly acted, badly produced and badly directed play for three hours we were rewarded with our son's prowess — he came on at the last minute to blow a single note.

I have an open mind about religion and feel it's best for each to find his own way. Both Paul and Trevor became choirboys which meant that they attended church not for the religious service, but to perform as singers. They were thus exposed to religion but could make up their own minds whether they wanted to accept it or not.

School sports days could not be missed: Jane, grim and determined, always came in the first few; Trevor, good natured and determined, always came last but never minded; Paul, nervous and agitated, was never satisfied with less than first.

There were school concerts, picnic bathing parties, barbecues, birthday parties and our share of mumps, measles, chicken pox, scarlet fever and german measles.

There were cubs and scouts, junior bands, and judo and dancing classes. Trips to grandma in London and pantomimes, circuses and tournaments. There was always a mass of children in the house, plus friends and friends of friends. We were very lucky.

163

All three children first went to a local convent, up to the 11-plus examination. Trevor managed to pass this without too much trouble, Paul scrambled through by a miracle and Jane passed easily. This enabled the boys to go to the local grammar school and Jane to stay on at her convent without having to pay fees.

It meant that we didn't have to scrimp and save quite as much as my colleagues and could spend money on things like good holidays.

Whether we were right or wrong is difficult to say. Whenever we met the children of medical colleagues, not just our Tadchester partners but friends from medical school, Trevor and Paul felt excuded from the public school club. They used to think it all very funny and were great mimics.

Trevor was already established at grammar school when Jane went off for her first day at the convent: proud in her big red blazer and a satchel that almost dwarfed her, excited and serious, and with Pam keeping back the tears.

Ron Dickinson's daughter, Louise, was just a month younger than Jane and these two little tots used to go everywhere together and would be seen coming out from school with their huge satchels and huge blazers, holding hands, blonde pigtails sticking out at the back of their felt hats.

Trevor enjoyed school, pottering along at his own pace, watching it all from the distance. Paul hated it, apart from the sports, where he was always one of the team leaders. He much preferred to be lost in games of imagination, and at home he would race about as a pirate or a soldier, or run a gang from the old caravan we kept in the garden.

Jane loved school wholeheartedly and took part in every single school activity. She was always near the top of the form and seriously involved in whatever she was doing.

Trevor was very much the elder brother, totally dependable and always the first boy at school. He would set off at about 7.15 in the morning, walking three miles. I didn't even know if the school was open when he got there.

The age difference between the children was such that they

were not really in competition with one another. Jane, ten years younger than Trevor and six years younger than Paul, adored her brothers and they in turn thought they had the best little sister in the world and woebetide anybody who upset her.

School life went on serenely, apart from Paul's bad reports, until Trevor came to his first nightmare of O-levels. (I wonder if the examination system puts too much strain on our children and whether there is not some better way.)

Trevor worked solidly and hard, didn't ask for help, did well and got eight good O-levels.

There was a party to celebrate the results. That night we heard Trevor coming in late and crashing about more than usual. He wasn't very well the next day and when he'd gone to school we found a funny stain on the wall and the carpet. He'd been drunk for the first time and had come home, vomited and tried to clear it up. In the evening I asked him how he had got on the night before.

'Sorry, dad,' he said. 'I wasn't very well.'

'What had you been drinking?' I asked.

'Well,' he said, 'I don't like beer very much and I knew that you liked a glass of port. So I stuck to port — but I felt very funny.'

'How many glasses of port did you have?'

'Oh, about thirteen,' said Trevor. 'It does make your head swimmy after a time.'

Paul showed no interest in things academic. It was almost as if he had shut his mind off when any learning was floated in his direction, but he was captain of cricket and football, first the under-12s, then the under-13s, and so on. He was always organising, always busy.

Trevor and his friends could be members of the Sanford-on-Sea Golf Club for ten shillings a year. They made a profit on their subscriptions very quickly by caddying in the bigger matches and tournaments.

The golf course at Sanford-on-Sea was hazardous in that it was shared with people who had grazing rights in the area. You played golf in the company of rather wild horses, sheep, goats and any other thing that could get some nourishment from the sparse grass behind the natural pebble ridge breakwaters. Trevor came home once in tears, a great hole in his new golf bag. He had put it down at the edge of a green and a horse had chewed it.

He was a quiet, self-contained and happy boy. He worked hard towards his A-levels, and decided that he wanted to do law. He had an offer from Birmingham University and his master thought he should manage the grades comfortably. But his A-levels and the run-up to them were absolutely traumatic. He worked day and night and became a total wreck. We hardly dared make a noise in the house for three months.

When the results came he was completely distraught: he'd done much worse than he thought. His grades were one B, one D and an E; Birmingham wanted two Bs and a C so there was no chance of going there.

Dejectedly, Trevor started to ring and write to polytechnics to see if he could find a place at the last minute.

Of the polytechnics that did law Kingston appeared to be the best. They had a special course on criminology which he thought might be interesting. They wrote back to say that all the places were full, but perhaps he would like to try again next year. Trevor was heartbroken. 'I just can't go through A-levels again, dad. Now what shall I do?'

I said nothing would be lost if he wrote to Kingston again saying how much he wanted to go there; there was always a chance that someone would opt out. Trevor despatched his letter with little hope and began to scan the papers for job opportunities.

For his eighteenth birthday we had a little family party. A bottle of red wine and great big steaks, his favourite. As we sat down to eat, the phone rang: a call for Mr Trevor Clifford. It was Kingston Polytechnic, a vacancy had occurred and could he start the following Wednesday?

What a marvellous birthday present. Pam looked a bit downcast: it had just come home to her that the first of her chicks was about to fly the nest.

At last the day came for Trevor to go. We saw him off on the train with the usual last-minute advice about washing and brushing his teeth, and gave him some extra money so that if he really got fed up he could come home for a few days. He leaned out of the carriage window, a grinning face under a mop of fair hair, waving goodbye. Poor Pam had tears running down her cheeks and I felt just as bad.

'Come on, darling,' I said. 'Dry your eyes. He'll soon be home again.'

'I know he will,' said Pam, 'but I'm afraid that life is going to be different from now on.'

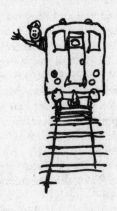

Postscript

There is the fable of the old man sitting outside a town, being approached by a stranger.

'What are they like in this town?' asked the stranger.

'What were they like in your last town?' replied the old man.

'They were delightful people. I was very happy there. They were kind, generous and would always help you in trouble.'

'You will find them very much like that in this town.'

The old man was approached by another stranger.

'What are the people like in this town?' asked the second stranger.

'What were they like in your last town?' replied the old man.

'It was an awful place. They were mean, unkind and nobody would ever help anybody.'

'I am afraid you will find it very much the same here,' said the old man.

If it should be your lot to ever visit Tadchester, this is how you will find us.

Surely Not, Doctor!

For Pam, Trevor, Paul, Gill and Jane

Contents

Prologue

Life is a tragedy, for we are all born eventually to die. We survive our tragedies by laughing at them.

A friend once told me that when he was under the influence of ether he dreamed he was turning over the pages of a great book, in which he knew he would find, on the last page, the meaning of life.

The pages of the book were alternately tragic and comic, and he turned page after page, his excitement growing, not only because he was approaching the answer, but because he couldn't know, until he arrived, on which side of the book the final page would be. At last it came: the universe opened up to him in a hundred words: and they were uproariously funny.

He came back to consciousness crying with laughter, remembering everything. He opened his lips to speak. It was then that the great and comic answer plunged back out of his reach.

Christopher Fry

CHAPTER 1

Toeing the Line

Glancing from the bedroom window of a bronchitic patient whose chest I had just been examining, I noticed, on the lawn of the bungalow next door, a man who seemed to be sitting by some sort of red fountain which was spraying over the grass and his idle lawnmower.

I watched the scene blankly for a moment or two before I realised exactly what was happening. The red fountain was blood . . . and it was coming from the man's foot. For once it looked as though I might be in the right place at the right time.

I shot downstairs and ran into the garden, vaulting the fence into the next-door garden which belonged to the bungalow of Jack Johnson-Peel, a leading London publisher who used the bungalow as a summer residence.

Jack was sitting in the middle of his lawn as if mesmerised, looking at the toe of his left shoe, out of which an intermittent stream of blood was spraying the surrounding turf and lawnmower.

'Good heavens, Jack!' I said, 'what have you done?'

'It's this new rotamower,' said Jack, still watching the fountain and looking rather disappointed as I applied firm

1

pressure with my grubby handkerchief, stopping the brilliant red cascade.

He said, 'I was trying it out for the first time. I've just realised that where it says "place foot here", you should put your foot on top and not underneath.'

Momentarily I lifted my handkerchief off his foot and blood gushed out again. There was just a gap where his big toe should have been; he had taken it clean off at the junction with the foot.

Suddenly there was a shriek from the house and out rushed his wife Penny, who had woken from her afternoon nap to see her husband lying flat on the lawn, blood all over the place and somebody clutching his foot.

'Good God, Jack!' she cried. 'I told you not to fool about with mechanical things! You don't know the first thing about them. What's he done and what have we got to do, Doctor Bob?'

'If you can get me some strapping and some clean linen, we can tidy up his foot,' I said. 'We will have to get him to hospital and I'll get Henry, my partner, to see him. And we must pick up his toe. There's a good chance we'll be able to get it stuck back on – it's a fairly clean cut.'

It took only a few minutes to get things sorted out, the foot dressed, and the bleeding staunched. All we needed now was the toe, which was nowhere in sight.

'Pack him off in the car straight away, Penny,' I said. 'We've got to be quick. I'll bring the toe along as soon as I find it.'

I helped Jack into the car and then made a minute search of the garden; the toe surely couldn't have gone far. It would certainly be covered with blood – there seemed to be pints of it about – but what might have been a toe turned out to be a pebble. I searched and searched but could find nothing. I couldn't believe it: toes don't just vanish.

I was distracted by a movement in the bushes. I went over to find Jack Johnson-Peel's beagle chewing happily at what I could imagine was his first human toe. When I tried to wrest it from him, I was met with a most fearsome growl. A couple of seconds later, the problem was solved: with two quick gulps he had swallowed the lot. Anything they offered the dog for dinner was going to be small beer after this. This was going to be very difficult.

I got in my car and drove to the hospital to find Henry, my surgical partner, all scrubbed up ready to operate.

'Did you find the missing link, Bob my lad?' he said.

'No,' I said. 'Um ... er ... I think it must have been shattered to bits by the mower. Perhaps absolutely disintegrated.' Which, in the true sense of the word, it had.

'Right,' said Henry. 'Then we'll just tidy him up.' And Jack Johnson-Peel was wheeled off to the operating theatre to have the amputation area patched up.

They kept him in hospital for about four days and I came to see him the first day he was home. He was sitting with his foot up in a chair. The chair was almost in the place of his

accident. A rounded semi-circle of luxuriant growth which marked the outlines of the lawnmower and the area that the blood had sprayed on, showed that, whatever else Jack Johnson-Peel was made of, some of him was a very good fertiliser.

I made a point of dressing his foot myself. This would normally be a job for the district nurse but I reasoned that (a) he didn't live too far away from me, (b) I enjoyed his company and he was a most distinguished and well-known publisher and (c) the job wasn't a great deal of trouble.

But subconsciously the real reason was that he was the managing director of a famous publishing house . . . and one day, who knows, he might well consider publishing a book of mine.

I visited him and dressed his foot daily for ten days. Sometimes he was sitting out in the garden and at other times, when the weather wasn't so good, he was inside. But every time I visited him his beagle sat obediently and devotedly by his side. On my tenth visit, as I was finishing the dressing, in came Penny.

'Look at this,' I said. 'The master and his dog. What a picture, almost a Landseer.'

'It's funny you should say that,' said Penny. 'Bozer is really my dog. Jack's never liked him very much and the dog's never had much to do with Jack. But it just shows how intelligent he is. He knows Jack's hurt and can't get about, so he sits by him, guarding him; he must have been very fond of him after all. In fact, he's never left his side since the accident.'

'Yes,' I said. 'There's very little doubt that he has a great liking for him . . .'

4

CHAPTER 2

Water, Water Everywhere

I was the fourth partner in a group of five in a little Somerset town called Tadchester. Tadchester (population 6,500) stands on the estuary of the River Tad, in one of the most beautiful parts of the Somerset coast. It is a market town, with some fishing, some light industry, and a great deal of farming.

The town is split in two by the River Tad, and further split by the large hill which dominates one side of the river. The other side of the river is flat pastureland, stretching off to marshes and the sea coast. You are not just a Tadchester resident – you are strictly Up-the-Hill or Down-the-Hill.

We were the only general practice in the town, and also took care of the local hospital. The five partners each had his own area of responsibility at the hospital: Steve Maxwell, the senior partner, had a special interest in medicine; Henry Johnson, the second senior, was the surgeon; Jack Hart, the third partner, was the anaesthetist; I, as the fourth partner, was reckoned to be the expert on midwifery and was pretty good at piercing ears; and Ron Dickinson, the fifth and junior partner – an accomplished athlete who spent a great deal of his time running, jumping, swimming, sailing and water skiing – was our ENT specialist and removed the local tonsils. We were a happy and well-balanced team.

5

When I first came to Tadchester there were great social divisions between Up-the-Hill and Down-the-Hill. By and large those living Up-the-Hill tended to be the Have-nots and those living Down-the-Hill the Haves. Of course there were exceptions on both sides of the river. After the coal mine had shut, various light industries began to appear in Tadchester: most of these, apart from the plastics factory which was near the coal mine, were built Up-the-Hill and they attacted with them new and more expensive housing and a growing population. This in no way diminished the rivalry between the two halves of the town, in fact, if anything, it increased it. It was almost like two sides having equal weaponry.

A landmark Up-the-Hill was St Peter's church, and the Victorian forefathers of Tadchester must have anticipated that one day there would be a population boom there. In 1870, or more accurately between 1870 and 1875, they built a church only slightly smaller than the Parish Church of St Mary's. Where St Mary's served a large congregation in the town, St Peter's, certainly at the time of its building, covered a very sparsely populated area.

The incumbent at St Peter's church was the Reverend Darch. There were few people who could remember Tadchester without him. He came there as a curate at the age of twenty-three, never marrying but remaining faithfully wedded to St Peter's for a further sixty years.

He was an old and confused man when I first came to Tadchester, and time certainly didn't improve him. He was the only man I've ever known, fishermen included, who continually wore rubber gum boots day in, day out, summer or winter, at church or cocktail party.

As far as I could gather, he had always worn gum boots. They were not related to his present disability, namely that he had very little control over his waterworks. Whenever he saw running water or heard the sound of splashing, he was unable to prevent himself joining in. This was particularly bad at christenings when he had to splash water over infants' heads. He was always completely unaware of his own contribution to

6

the service and the trail of water from the font back to the pulpit was holy water of a unique kind. Whatever he originally wore his gum boots for, they were now an essential part of his equipment.

He drifted around in a private and cosy haze, and was famous for an incident during his eighties when, at one winter's evensong, remembering that he'd left his car outside with its lights on, he asked his congregation to kneel in silent prayer. Then he nipped out of the pulpit, got into his car and drove home.

His sermons were unintelligible and there had been constant pressure from the parishioners for him to be moved. At their bidding, I suggested many a time that perhaps he should take things more easily, but he would hear nothing of it.

'Plenty of work in me yet, Doctor,' he would say in his booming voice. 'Plenty of the Lord's work still to do.'

Without the support of two industrious lay preachers the church would have folded. He always refused to have a curate, claiming that he had managed on his own quite well for sixty years so there was no need to have anybody else. He was quite impervious to hints.

Eventually he became such a passenger, such an embarrassment to his church and the community that the Church Council wrote to the bishop, pleading with him to ask the Reverend Darch to resign, or even to sack him. The bishop, who was always reluctant to take this sort of step, but knowing that church ministers usually take the hint, wrote a firm letter to the Reverend Darch. He thanked him for his services in the past and pointed out that the church, the body of the church, the head of the church and all the church, felt that the time had come for him to retire.

The response was a letter from the Reverend Darch saying: 'Dear Bishop, When your predecessor' – and he named a bishop fifty years back – 'first appointed me, I had no idea that my position here was only a temporary one.'

Things were at an impasse. There seemed no solution until fate took a hand.

Sadly, but mercifully, two months after the bishop's letter, the Reverend Darch absentmindedly stepped out in front of his car. He was knocked down by a lorry and killed instantly.

Ron Dickinson and I arrived at the scene of the accident, both about the same time. There was Reverend Darch lying crumpled at the side of the road, gum boots sticking out at right angles to the gutter, with a puzzled smile on his face as if he was wondering, 'Did I jump or was I pushed?' An enigma to the end.

'The poor old lad's got one consolation,' said Ron Dickinson as we tidied him up while waiting for the ambulance. 'At least he died with his boots on.'

CHAPTER 3

Warm Hearts

Times were changing at the surgery. Although Gladys, our senior receptionist, still reigned supreme she was muttering about retirement. Her sidekick, the ever loquacious Grace, had been saying it was her last year for some years, and, alas, none of us was getting any younger. Ron Dickinson, our junior partner, was the only new medical face in the practice since I had joined. The pattern of medicine was changing; the hospital had almost completely gone. Henry would soon reach the age when he would be retired as a surgeon and there would no longer be a surgeon at all in Tadchester. Already he was reduced to mainly casualty surgery work, many of the hospital beds having been taken over for the care of the elderly. The midwifery unit was now at the nearby town of Winchcombe, apart from the odd case dealt with at home. When I had first come into the practice I could reckon on three home deliveries a fortnight. Now, if I got two or three a year, I was lucky and they were becoming so rare that I had almost forgotten the routine procedure. Fortunately our midwife, the ever-faithful Nurse Plank, was still in practice and she took charge of the whole situation.

We had a variety of staff coming and going at the surgery.

Young girls arriving, marrying, having babies, going, being replaced; an ever-increasing staff as we expanded our facilities with a nurses' treatment room, electrocardiogram unit and so on.

It often took some of our newly trained, highly qualified staff some time to adjust to the idiosyncrasies of our patients. I remember a new dispenser coming to me almost in despair at the end of a heavy day.

'However do I interpret a note like this?' she asked, showing me a crudely written letter that read, 'Grandma says please could she have another bottle of emotion, and not the sort that leaves a lot of sentiment in the bottom of the bottle.'

'That's easy,' I said, recognising the handwriting. 'It means a quart of liquid paraffin for old Mrs Smithson. I'm never sure whether she cooks with it or puts it in her all-night heater. I'm sure she never uses it as a medicine.'

The biggest change had been in the increase in the number of people who had their own transport or who had friends who could transport them. Now we had bigger and more frequent surgeries and did fewer home visits; the home visits being confined to acute medical cases and routine visits to the frail and elderly.

The days when we had twenty-five to thirty visits a day had vanished. If we had a dozen visits a day to do, we thought we were hard pressed. And perhaps we were.

There were many advantages in seeing people in their home environment, but of course there were also many advantages in seeing people in the surgery where you could do so much more for them in the way of investigations and minor nursing and surgical procedures. A few years ago I spent most of my day buzzing around, leaping in and out of my car at a great rate, whereas now I spent most of my time sitting behind my desk.

I don't know if I like this new way of medicine as much.

I still had one clinical attachment at the hospital, where I looked after a medical recovery ward and once a week used to do a round with John Bowler, the physician at Winchcombe, who kept some beds at Tadchester. At the end of his ward round I would sit and glean from him information on all the most recent medical advances, techniques and new drugs.

I kept an appointment free to see one representative from a drug house each week. They would always bring beautifully illustrated magazines, copies of articles, and some gift, like a ballpoint pen or a car windscreen scraper.

Gladys was very much in charge of everything at the practice. Only the outrageous Grace could take liberties with her – even Steve Maxwell was rather frightened – and it was usually Gladys and Grace who decided which patient should see which doctor. We were, of course, not all in surgery at the same time so sometimes we would have directed to us a patient whom we would reckon was not really our 'type'. I always used to say that I was a working-class doctor and to an extent I meant that for, having been a coal miner, I felt I had a better understanding of people who came from industrial or agricultural working backgrounds, than of people who came from the rather more sophisticated ones. But even I, sometimes, had to go out of my class as it were . . .

It is never easy to accept patients who are registered with another doctor. Would-be new patients come in with complaints about their own doctor, but only very occasionally are they justified: there are many more difficult patients, in my experience, than there are bad doctors.

It is important that you are able to communicate with your doctor. If you can't, then you have reasonable grounds for finding somebody else, but it is very difficult, having been registered with one doctor, to get another to accept you: you're under suspicion.

One day I noticed among the pile of cards on my desk, a plain slip saying 'New Private Patient' from Winchcombe. I asked Grace about it when she came in to tidy up the desk before I started my surgery. 'You've got a real toff there, Doctor Bob,' she said, as only Grace can say without causing offence. 'She's a Right Hon. You're moving up in society.'

I couldn't think of any reason why somebody who had lived

11

in Winchcombe, which had excellent doctors and lots and lots of them, should want to travel at least twelve miles to Tadchester to see me. I looked forward to meeting this Right Hon. with interest. She had booked a double appointment, again another ominous sign; it meant she had a lot to talk about.

I visualised a hawk-faced, dominant lady who had worn out every doctor in Winchcombe and now wanted to tell me the story of her life. When the turn of the Right Hon. came, I was pleasantly surprised. She was an extremely smart and very nice lady of about forty-five. Her name had rung a bell somewhere, and as she sat down I remembered that she was a magistrate in Winchcombe.

I'm not always very good at assessing people; I can often make the most terrible mistakes. But this lady did not seem at all like a disgruntled patient. Here she was, however, obviously having explored the medical situation in her own vicinity and travelling twelve miles for another opinion.

'What can we do to help you?' I said, smiling. 'You've come a long way.'

'Yes, thank you, Doctor,' she said, 'there are one or two things I'm worried about. If you could give me a general overhaul, I would be exceedingly grateful.'

My heart sank. Patients who want complete overhauls present problems: it's not just physically possible on the National Health, not without presenting some symptoms. But this lady was private and she'd booked double time.

'I'm afraid I'll have to ask you what brings you over to Tadchester,' I said. 'There are so many good doctors in Winchcombe. Can you tell me what happened?'

'Nothing's happened, Doctor. I have no complaints about them at all. I have heard that you are sympathetic and will listen to people. I don't really want to go into the matter too deeply but I would be most grateful if you could see me today and possibly continue to look after me. I can assure you that I don't ever expect you to come and visit me.'

It was very unusual for a patient who was changing doctors

not to have some criticism. She looked slightly embarrassed about it all and I did wonder – for she was certainly attractive – whether she and her doctor had got too close to each other and felt it better for both if she were medically looked after elsewhere. But the Right Hon. didn't look as if she dillied and dallied and it's difficult to do anything in the Tadchester/Winchcombe area without everybody knowing.

We got down to her medical problems. They seemed minor: she had a slight difficulty in holding her urine – she passed water when she coughed and sneezed; she had a bit of a cold. She said that no doctor had examined her fully (and this was without innuendo) for some time. She was anxious about blood pressure and one thing and another.

I told her to go to the examination room, get undressed, and I would come and see her.

I had a good look at her. Her chest was clear, blood pressure normal, nothing in her abdomen. She did have a degree of prolapse of the muscles that supported her womb. It might be helped by exercises but would probably need a repair operation sometime, although it wasn't essential.

I told her to get dressed and asked if she could manage a specimen of water. With a blood test and chest X-ray arranged she would have had a really good five-thousand-mile service. I saw another patient and then the Right Hon. came in with the urine specimen. Obviously she'd been crying.

'Look', I said, 'I don't want to pry, but clearly something's been upsetting you. What's the matter?'

'I'm crying with relief,' she said. 'It's you. Thank God I've found you.'

'Why?' I said. 'What's so marvellous about me?'

'It sounds so silly,' she said, 'but . . . you have warm hands. I cannot bear anybody touching me with cold hands, particularly in the more intimate places. If anybody puts a cold hand on me I react in the same way most people do if they have their feet tickled. I scream and wriggle like a schoolgirl – I just can't help it. And I've not found a doctor yet with warm hands.

'I've had all sorts of worries about my health – I'm sure they have been groundless – but I literally daren't go to a doctor locally. I know there is this strong medical code of complete confidentiality, but who could resist telling somebody in confidence how I screech and scream as soon as they lay a hand on me?

'I can just imagine sitting on the Bench with everybody sniggering at me. It's like one of the town councillors at Winchcombe said: "It's not we who break the confidences of the Council, it's the people we tell in confidence who let all the secrets out." '

'Well my hands are usually cold,' I confessed. 'You know what they say, "Cold hands, warm heart." I don't know why they're warm this morning – I must have had them in my pockets.'

'Thank God they were,' said the Right Hon. 'I was just about at my wits' end. I was thinking I would have to go to Taunton every time I had a sore throat. What's happened now is that I've broken the ice, literally and metaphorically. I know I can come to you and say, "Now don't forget, I'm the one who can't bear cold hands." Thank you so much for seeing me. I will accept your advice and see a gynaecologist and, if I may, whenever I'm worried, about anything medical, come and see you again.'

'I promise,' I said, 'that I'll keep our secret and I won't tell anybody about it, even in confidence.'

She smiled. She knew and I knew that even the fact that she was travelling from Winchcombe to Tadchester just to see a general practitioner, would have tongues wagging in a country district like ours. It would put my status up but both she and I could bear that. Thus are reputations made.

* * *

In Tadchester reputations could actually be lost in a flash!

The death of the Reverend Darch was not the end of the troubles for St Peter's. A brand new, progressive young vicar was appointed and a grand summer party was held to

introduce him to his flock at the house of the Gentrys – Mr Gentry being the senior sidesman at St Peter's.

There must have been fifty or sixty people in the large room that overlooked the lawn with a view across the estuary. It was a hot summer's day and most of the women were in backless, strapless types of dress, including the big-bosomed Mrs Gentry who, rather overcome by being hostess to such a large gathering, was laughing more loudly than she should at any minor witticism of the new vicar.

During one outburst of laughter, with her head pulled back to give better volume to her appreciation, she failed to notice that the right-hand one of her magnificent two had popped out over her dress. The quick-witted young vicar had the situation in hand in a second.

'Quick everybody,' he said, 'look out of the window!'

Everybody turned at his dramatic appeal. He didn't actually lift up and replace the offending article, but he was able to indicate to Mrs Gentry that some of her laughter was out of place. He then turned to join the rest of his flock, who were gazing out on to the immaculate lawn, in the middle of which were an Alsatian and an Airedale, making love in the only way dogs know how.

CHAPTER 4

Family Affairs

We had waved our eldest son Trevor goodbye to Kingston Polytechnic. He had the usual problems settling in, ringing home most nights to begin with but gradually settling down. Before going to Kingston he had been a shy boy, awkward in manner, who always kept in the background, and I think his first year, although he never said so, was rather difficult. He did have some fun: he played his trumpet in the band at the Christmas pantomime. He also joined one or two clubs, one of which was a completely new activity for him: amateur dramatics. (My first date with Pam, my darling wife, was to see her in the Fetcham Players, so perhaps acting was in the blood.)

After an unsettled period, in the early part of the second year when he wondered whether he wanted to go on with the course, he became very enthusiastic about acting. As proud, and greatly surprised, parents we went up to see him take the lead in *The Threepenny Opera* which, after its run in Kingston, went on to a Student Drama Festival in Paris. Since his choirboy days we had no idea Trevor could sing, and acting – this completely new venture – became his first love. The student company toured Cornwall in the holidays and our retiring son who used to shun the limelight, now became very

17

much more extroverted, full of life and confidence, highly organised with everything: money, clothes and studies, all worked out to a definite plan. I agreed with his view that you couldn't absorb more than two hours' study a night – after that you were just satisfying your own conscience – and that you were much better getting up and going and doing something else. Even so I was a bit worried about his cavalier attitude to his studies, but in the end, in spite of all his acting, in spite of not doing more than two hours' study a night, and in spite of the fact that he took a larger and larger part in the social life, conducting the orchestra for the pantomime and engaging in all major college activities, he finished with a 2.1 honours degree and nobody in his year did any better than that.

He was also awarded the Law Student Prize. This was for the best all-round student, voted for by the staff and the students themselves. He was thrilled.

If Trevor was organised, his brother Paul (four years his junior) was about as disorganised as he could be, unless it was in dressing himself for some activity. Whichever sport he undertook, he was always perfectly turned out in the appropriate gear. He had a great urge to leave the grammar school and go to the local technical college: you are thought much more of as a man of the world at the tech. and it doesn't have school discipline. So having scraped through a few O-levels, Paul went off to the tech, where he had so many free study periods that he could do all his homework before he came home. I didn't know of any other boy who was doing A-levels who had every evening free, but Trevor had managed to do well in his degree with his own regime, so perhaps Paul was the same.

Trevor had fallen in love with acting; Paul's passion was music. The Beatles and Rolling Stones were going to be nothing compared to the group he got together. For sheer application they should have been the best in the world. They worked hard, wrote their own music, and practised in our garage until a round robin from the neighbours suggested that they practised elsewhere as the noise of the amplifiers was having an unsettling effect on the foundations of the houses. One neighbour complained, 'I don't mind the boys playing but when I can't hear my own TV set with all the doors and windows closed, I have a feeling they've got to tone things down a bit.'

The group was made up of Paul, Brian, John and Dick — two guitars, bass and drums. The boys had quite a number of local engagements and gradually they got bookings further and further afield. They even made a journey to London and played in the top of Ronnie Scott's Club.

Jane was beside herself. Ronnie Scott's! Why couldn't she go? There were many reasons why I didn't want our young and impressionable daughter unaccompanied in London at night. The only way was for me to go with her, so I trekked up to London to endure five hours of continuous noise and flashing lights that nearly made me blind and stone deaf as

19

well as being totally confused by the unintelligible words of the songs. I was relieved to catch the three a.m. train with Jane back to quiet Somerset. She loved it. But it was not, as they say, my scene.

What the boys needed was a manager, and they suddenly produced a man who was going to lead them to great things. His first action was to get them involved in the hire purchase of seven thousand pounds' worth of equipment. The HP company arranging the finance said as many people as possible should sign the HP agreement. A friend of the lads, Mick Brown, who was nothing to do with the group and had just popped in for a cup of tea, was inveigled into adding his name to the list of signatures.

'Look, Dad,' said Paul, 'the decision is ours. We're all in this together. We've got to have this good equipment if we're going to get anywhere. The manager's paying his share too. Don't worry – we're going to be famous. We're going to buy houses for all the family eventually.'

The amplifying gear, I think, was really built for the Albert Hall. When the group played for a local concert they could be heard ten miles away.

The manager's reign was short-lived. After three months – and some dispute over whether he'd passed on the boys' instalments to the HP firm – he disappeared. After a further three months, two of the boys dropped out. As I'd feared, in the end Paul and I were left with a bill of about six thousand pounds to pay. Two of the boys chipped in for a time. I took legal advice and the solicitor told me that the best thing was to keep on paying and try to sell the equipment. We had absolutely no success over this – what group of lads could afford six thousand pounds? – and before long the equipment was out of date. For three years I had to pay a hundred pounds a month. Paul, who was working in a garage, still hell-bent on music but just doing something to tide him over until he hit the big time, had to put fifty pounds of his precious wages into paying the thing off. For the last two years of the contract Paul and I were the only ones who made any contribuions at all. When we finished paying the equipment was worth nothing.

At the beginning of his music days Paul had fallen madly in love with Gill, the beautiful blonde-haired daughter of leading jockey Eddie Cracknell, one of whose claims to fame was that he won the first horserace to be shown on BBC TV's 'Grandstand'. Apart from minor attachments, Paul and Gill never had any other boy or girl friends and very soon she became an extra daughter in the family and close friend and confidante of Jane.

Paul's academic record of a few O-levels wasn't anywhere near Trevor's, but he did have one great gift – he was an absolute dab hand at poker. As we forked out the monthly instalments, I couldn't help wishing that the Job Centre would come up with an opening for a riverboat gambler.

'I want to be a musician, Dad, that's all I want,' he said, as members of the group came and went. Paul could write beautiful songs and could sing good ballads but it was the razzamatazz of life in the music business that really interested him. A record company offered to buy his songs but he wouldn't let them go without his group. Gradually, although still a most accomplished musician, he realised that he might have to find other ways to earn his living. He managed to find a job with some prospects with an electronics factory Up-the-Hill, while Gill went on an art and design degree course that took her up to Maidenhead and Southampton. They were now miles apart, but still their friendship flourished.

The children were all growing up far too quickly. What was pleasing was their relationship with each other; they didn't try and rival each other in any way but supported each others' activities. Trevor drove the van when Paul's group went on an unsuccessful tour of the south coast, where he had to be restrained from throttling the manager.

Jane, who had been a model schoolgirl at the local convent, studiously getting all her O-levels, had decided that A-levels must be done somewhere else, and quite emphatically decided

21

that she should go to the comprehensive, formerly the grammar school, for her final two years of schooling.

Jane was young enough to be in a different age group from her brothers. She held them in tremendous awe and was completely spoiled by them. At a party she gave in the church hall, Paul's group provided the music and Paul was general master of ceremonies. Much to Jane's dismay, he shut the party down at ten because some of the boys were getting the worse for drink. As most of the children's parents weren't due to pick them up until eleven, it caused some consternation when they had to stand outside in the cold for an hour. But nobody was going to muck up Paul's younger sister's party, even if he mucked it up himself by shutting it down early.

Although Trevor had left home, we always used to try and manage one week as a family together somewhere: a week in Kent, a week in a farmhouse flat near Evesham, or a week on a boat. Whatever the children's ambitions, and none of them seemed to be quite sure what they wanted, they all knew they would never practise medicine.

'It sounds selfish,' said Trevor, 'but we really don't want to work weekends and nights.'

They were good-humoured, caring children; my wife Pam and I were indeed blessed.

* * *

Pam's father, Gerry, was ailing. He had developed a condition that we knew we could contain for some time but would not be able to stave off forever. Happily his illness did not interfere too much with the last two years of his life but it meant he had to receive blood transfusions from time to time. He had become much more religious in his later years and had a stained-glass window commissioned in memory of Pam's mother in Sticklepath Church in Barnstaple, where they had lived for some years and where Pam's mother, Bill, was much remembered.

Gerry was a great character; a marvellous *bon viveur*. He

22

loved his fishing and enjoyed a bit of shooting. He raced greyhounds in his younger days and was a great follower of the horses. In his middle years he had several friends who were jockeys. He would probably go to three or four race meetings and back only one horse.

'Only back when you know it's trying,' he used to say. 'You've got to be in the know.'

He was always fully engaged with life. He maintained that his racehorse punting saw his family through the leaner years, and in the very early lean years, as well as doing a job during the day, he played his violin in London theatre orchestras in the evening. He had a great passion for golf but, alas, was never a natural.

After he had lost his wife he fitted in well with the family. The extension he had built on to our house meant that he was always with us but never on top of us. When I look back, I realise how self-contained he was and how much he got out of life with his racing, his work as an engineer, his shooting and fishing, and his music. He held up very well until his last few terminal months, but we were able to keep him at home and in comfort and he died peacefully at home with Pam, myself and the children always near.

There was a memorial service in St Mary's church then Pam, Trevor and I and the vicar of St Mary's travelled over to Winchcombe for a cremation service which the vicar conducted. It was all very nicely and tastefully done. On the way back in the hired car, the vicar, who was rather pompous, said to Trevor, 'Do you remember the last thing your grandfather said to you?'

Trevor hestitated for a moment, and said, 'Yes.'

'Always remember those words,' said the vicar. 'Always remember them.'

Trevor was quiet, embarrassed and strangely silent for the rest of the journey.

We got home and over tea he said to Pam, 'Mum, do you know what Gaga's (the children's name for Gerry) last words to me were?'

'You did look a bit confused when the vicar asked you about them,' said Pam, 'What were they?'

'I couldn't really tell the vicar,' said Trevor, 'that his very last words to me were "What won the Grand National?" '

It was a fitting epitaph.

CHAPTER 5

A Collection of Characters

Albert Coaltart was one of the most patient, meticulous men I knew. His hobby was making models and on the top of my sideboard I have the most beautiful model of a French haycart, accurate in every detail. When Albert came to the surgery he would often bring his latest piece of work to show me: perhaps a minute caravan complete with everything from door hinges to cooking instruments, each hand crafted and often improvised from bits of cocoa tins and such like. Not for Albert the ready-made fixture; he made every part of every model himself. He really could have made a good living from his models, but his pleasure was in making them and I never saw him sell one.

Healthwise he had a chequered history. He had worked for the Ministry of Defence at the waterproofing establishment at Stowyn, involved in underwater work the nature of which he would never divulge – it was classified as Top Secret. This injured his health and he was retired early on medical grounds.

Digging one day on his allotment he strained his back and the resulting back pain spoilt everything for him. I tried most of the anti-inflammatory drugs and pain relievers. He had physiotherapy, saw an orthopaedic surgeon, wore a surgical jacket, but we could not get his back right. Although he kept on with his model-making and kept himself busy, he was slowly but steadily getting more and more depressed. Instead of the smiles and the new models that he brought to the surgery, he would come in hobbling and stand rather than sit while we searched for some new preparation that might help his back.

It didn't really register with me when one day he came in, not smiling but not looking unhappy, and sat straight down. I noticed, however, he was limping a bit.

'How are things today, Albert?'

'Something for the book here, Doctor,' he said. 'I was sitting on the toilet, reading, with the door partly open – the rest of the house were out – when the cat jumped through the lavatory window, onto my knee and made for the door. It scared the wits out of me.

'I aimed to kick it as it went and stubbed my toe on the door. It bled, so I wrapped a handkerchief round it. I searched all over the house, but I couldn't find any dressings, so I decided to go across the common to the shop.'

Albert lived in Elfin Cross, the small hamlet to the west of Tadchester, which consisted of a couple of pubs, a garage, about thirty houses, and a shop that sold everything.

'I was half way across the common,' said Albert, 'when I fell smack, straight on my face. Some kids had put a trip wire across the path, the little beggars. I hardly made it to the shop.'

'Well, let's have a look at the toe, Albert,' I said. 'You do seem to go in for misfortunes in a big way.'

I looked at his badly bruised toe, cleaned it up and put a fresh dressing on it. Then I saw that he was grinning.

'Have you noticed anything, Doctor?'

'No, Albert,' I said.

'That fall has cleared my back – I'm better!'

'Ah ha!' I said, 'this is how new cures are discovered. Perhaps you can get that cat for me. I've got several patients whose backs need sorting out.'

'I don't think the cat would be much use to you, Doctor,' said Albert. 'I'll wring its neck if I find it . . .'

* * *

Penelope Smith was a keep-fit fanatic. She ran the flourishing League of Health and Beauty in Tadchester, and her own private gymnasium. Though an attractive and pleasant personality, she was not being pinned down (as it were) by any admirer until she had reached the age of thirty-two. She was an extremely pleasant lady, believed in what she did, thought rightly that keeping fit was the basis of good health, and always had time to listen to people who wanted to get themselves into better condition. She once even dared to suggest that she might have some exercises that would help me lose weight.

I saw very little of her. I was vaguely aware that she was engaged and about to be married and thought no more about it until I was called urgently to her home one Saturday. She had got out of the bath, her back had locked, and she couldn't stand up properly.

'Is it very painful?' I asked her mother over the phone. 'No,' she said, 'but would you come as soon as you can? She's supposed to be getting married at two-thirty today.'

I rushed round to the house to find a small pantomime in progress: Penelope bent double in the bathroom and father and mother wandering around distractedly, muttering 'Tut-tut,' 'Fancy that,' and 'Well, I never . . .'

I do a little bit of manipulating, and so I gave her back a tweak. I offered her some pain relievers and a small dose of tranquilliser. I wondered if part of her problem was anxiety, but whatever it was, my manipulation, the pain relievers and a relaxant would certainly unbend her back. I went away confidently and gave her a ring at about half past twelve to see how things were going.

'She's not much better, Doctor,' said mum.

'Her tablets should be working now,' I said. 'Stand her up and get her moving about slowly.'

27

There was a frantic phone call at about quarter to one.

'We stood her up, Doctor, and she fainted.'

I rushed round again where the rather slapstick atmosphere of a couple of hours before had changed. The mother wasn't dressed; the father wasn't; the bride hadn't washed her hair; things were getting out of hand. I was in a bit of a fix myself.

Penelope really did seem to be in a lot of pain and well and truly locked in her uncomfortable and undignified position.

'Try sitting her up gently in a chair,' I suggested. 'I think I know of somebody nearby with a wheelchair. I'll go and fetch it. We'll certainly be able to get her into that.'

There was an old lady with Parkinson's disease who lived at the opposite end of the village. She had a marvellous husband who had nursed her and taken care of her for years so I went down and explained the situation to him.

'Could I borrow the wheelchair for a wedding?'

'By all means, Doctor,' he said. 'Good luck to the bride.'

I took the wheelchair back but, by the time I got there, it was a quarter to two. The wedding was due to take place at two-thirty in a village about ten miles away and the bride had decided that her hair must be washed before she went. I gave the most strict instructions that she should be sat in the chair and wheeled to the car. When she got out, she must not try to stand. She must be wheeled into the church and stay in the wheelchair throughout the whole of the ceremony. When they got back from the ceremony, they were to let me know and I'd come and see her.

The couple were flying off somewhere for a honeymoon the next day. It was all terribly sad. I heard no more from the family that day and as I didn't know where the reception was being held, I couldn't make my follow-up visit.

The next morning, around came the beaming father and mother of the bride.

'Thank you for all your help yesterday, Doctor. We got Penelope into the car and when she got to the church she managed to get up and actually walk up the aisle, and by the

28

end of the reception she was well enough to go on her honeymoon.' There were great big pieces of wedding cake both for me and for the old couple who had lent the wheelchair.

Penelope shouldn't have walked, but I don't think she would ever have dared to raise her head at her keep-fit studio if it had been known that she had been wheeled up the aisle in a wheelchair for her wedding.

I heard no details of the honeymoon, but from her sprightly walk and beaming face on her return, she'd obviously had plenty of keep-fit exercise.

* * *

Mrs Tomlinson was nearly raped more often than the rest of all the ladies in my practice put together. She and her husband, a retired civil servant, had been careful in the way they lived. They had planned their retirement meticulously, especially with regard to their finances. They had a small house with very little garden, and had budgeted so that they could have four holidays abroad every year. I would receive postcards from all corners of the earth: Antigua, Yugoslavia,

Brazil, Florida – they were completely meticulous in their postcarding, too.

Every time they returned from their holiday Mrs Tomlinson came to see me.

'Terrible men in Ecuador,' she would say. 'There I was, trying to sunbathe in a quiet spot. They just wouldn't leave me alone. Chased me all the way back to the hotel.'

The story was repeated in Fiji, New Zealand, Australia, the Costa Brava, and although I realised that in areas where women were more or less in purdah men were uninhibited in their approach to the opposite sex, especially tourists, Mrs Tomlinson probably wouldn't have been my first choice.

I would sit with her after each trip, congratulating her on yet another narrow escape, trying to find what magic it was that stirred men of all nations to such a high pitch of emotion. It was only on her last holiday, which was a trans-Saharan one, that I got some information that led me towards the diagnosis of this phenomenon.

'How were things, Mrs T?' I asked.

'Oh,' she said, 'the men were terrible. I was very, very nearly raped on a camel trip. Look, I've brought you some photos.'

There was a picture of some grinning Tuaregs getting on their camels and there was the seventy-eight-year-old Mrs T. mounting hers, clad in a pair of shorts and nothing else. When I say nothing else, she did have sandals on, but otherwise nothing – she was completely topless. I was taken aback by the pictures.

I said, 'You're topless, Mrs T.'

'Of course, Doctor,' she said. 'I always go topless whenever there's a bit of sun about. I'm not ashamed of my body.'

'You mean,' I said, 'that in all these places you visit, as soon as the sun comes out, it's jumpers off?'

'Why, yes, Doctor,' she replied. 'They say the sun's very good for the body. Gives you vitamin A or something.'

I had this sudden image of Mrs Tomlinson sunbathing in little coves all over the world, stripped half naked, being spied

30

on by some lusty shepherd or gigolo who would then creep up towards the reclining body. On studying the photos carefully I realised why, though Mrs Tomlinson was so often nearly raped, there was heavy emphasis on the *nearly*.

*   *   *

Two of my favourite patients whom I saw regularly over a number of years were Jackie Dean, who suffered from most named medical conditions and a few un-named ones and who was virtually bedridden, and Reg Dawkins, who had an obscure muscular disease and, although confined to a wheelchair, was able to drive a car.

Jackie Dean was hunting mad. Following the installation of an electric chair-lift, which enabled her to get up and down stairs with the help of her sister Mary, she would chase the cat up and down this route, trying to re-create the hunting scene. When the novelty of this game wore off, never dismayed, she began to wear a riding hat in bed with a whipper's-in whip in her right hand. She would have a go at mosquitoes, moths . . . anything that came in her range. I suggested that she try and get in the *Guinness Book of Records* as the only person who went hunting from a bed. She laughed, shouted 'Tally ho!' and expertly flicked the thermometer out of my breast pocket with her riding whip. I felt sure that one day I would enter her room and find a pack of hounds and a couple of horses in there.

Reg Dawkins, who lived in a cottage down near the river, was always battling with the authorities for better facilities, and the authorities fluctuated between doing nothing at all, or seemingly doing everything at once.

Having put on weight he was waiting ages for a new wheelchair when, suddenly, two chairs arrived, one for indoors and one for outdoors. The outdoor chair, however, was too big to pass through the door.

'No problem,' said the man from the equipment department. 'I'll soon fix that.'

The next day he was round again and almost before you

31

could say 'Jack Robinson', he had knocked a hole in the wall below the window making French windows. So Reg now had two chairs and an extra door; in addition, the man fixed the faulty bar on Reg's bathroom hoist, a useful gadget that enabled him to get in and out of the bath.

I once stayed with Reg and his wife Mary when my family was away – I was on call and needed somebody to man the telephone during the night. It was like staying in a five-star hotel. They completely spoiled me: meals in front of the fire, home-made wine, piles of clean towels, more than I could use in a week. They even offered to bath me by lowering me with the electric hoist; this I politely declined.

Jackie Dean and the Dawkins made great successes of their lives. None of us can do more than fill our days industriously, adventurously and looking out for others. In my early days in practice I had an old lady patient who led a successful life, although she had been bedridden for forty-seven years. Similarly Jackie Dean and the Dawkins lived fully in circumstances that had physical limitations but no limitations on courage, adventure, effort and fulfilment.

CHAPTER 6

Maggots Galore

My advice to patients suffering from stress – to get away for forty-eight hours to a place they'd never been to before – usually worked in helping them to get their problems in perspective. On their return, I sometimes advised the men to take up fishing as part of the longer-term therapy.

It was usually met by the stock objections: 'I'd never have the patience . . .'; 'Don't know the first thing about it . . .'; 'Haven't got any tackle . . .'; 'Can't spare the time . . .'; 'Don't see the sense . . .'

'Just try it,' I'd say. 'And the fewer fish you catch, the better – only don't tell John Denton that: he'd skin me alive.'

John Denton was the water bailiff on the River Tad, a Mancunian who had opted for the country life to pursue his passion for fishing. He was big, bluff and fond of his ale, with a forthright manner and blunt northern speech that didn't endear him to everybody in Tadchester. But underneath it all he was a big softie and always ready with advice and practical help on fishing. With youngsters he was especially good, and he gave free coaching lessons to the junior section of Tadchester's Anglers' Club.

The juniors owed many of their recruits to John's methods

with juvenile poachers. After discovering that some of the kids he nabbed on the river could not afford tickets because their parents were among the growing number of unemployed in the area, he'd send them along for enrolment to the Tadchester Anglers' Club secretary.

'Say bailiff Denton sent you,' he'd tell the youngsters – after first giving them a dressing-down that frightened the life out of them – 'and don't worry about the membership fee for the first year. That'll be taken care of.'

And so it was, out of John's own pocket, though he did not like that to be known. 'People'd think I was goin' soft or summat,' he'd growl into his pint pot at the Tadchester Arms. 'But I've not forgotten what it was like when me dad was out of work before the war. Wasn't funny, that.'

John combed the jumble sales, and had contacts among auction room staff, ever on the lookout for fishing tackle going cheap. He'd repair any broken gear and take it along to the club to loan to youngsters short of the necessary. Special bits of tackle he would donate as prizes in the junior competition, and devised enough awards to make sure that practically everybody won something.

It was to John that I sent my adult patients for their introduction to angling. He'd kit them out and spend a morning with them on the river. The combination of the right tackle, right bait and John's expertise – and the fact that given enough notice, he would pre-bait the swim the night before to attract the fish – meant that almost everyone caught something on their first outing.

At the stroke of twelve on the town hall clock, John would announce: 'That's it, lad. Twelve o'clock and they stop biting. Pack it in now while you're winning and you won't be disappointed.'

The fish often did stop biting around noon, though sometimes they'd carry on feeding quite happily. But one o'clock was time for John's lunchtime ale in the Tadchester Arms. Twelve o'clock gave him plenty of time to pack up and get there, and to allow him to give in gracefully to the pleas of

'Aw . . . just one more?' A few sneaky tricks known to John alone made sure that there would be just one more, but never two.

'Told you,' John would say as 12.25 approached. 'That's yer lot. Never mind – there'll be other times. Er . . . fancy a pint?'

With a rosy glow that didn't owe everything to the morning in the open air, the novice angler would lurch happily from the Tadchester Arms at 2.35, completely hooked on fishing and all that went with it. Another case of stress was on its way to a cure; another potential depression avoided; another small drain on the health service resources removed, and another member enrolled on Tadchester Anglers' books.

*　　*　　*

No matter how many times I went fishing with John, I could never get used to handling maggots, either singly for the hook, or in handfuls as groundbait to attract the fish. It was partly the reaction to the discipline of medical hygiene, but also the fact that a mass of writhing bluebottle maggots looked like an eruption from the primeval slime. Not a pretty sight.

Their size, too, never failed to surprise me. Bait maggots were much bigger than the bluebottle maggots I'd seen on dead creatures in the wild; bigger even than those on corpses I'd had to inspect *in situ* after the discovery of a dead tramp or a suicide in the local woods. I'd never bought maggots at the local tackle shops, either: John always had plenty stacked in an old fridge in his garage and had told me to help myself whenever I was out on the river. Whoppers, they were, every one.

'Wonderful maggots, these, John,' I said one evening at his home, picking out the equivalent of an Olympic weightlifter from his latest batch. 'Do you breed them yourself?'

'No need,' said John. 'I raise my own gozzers on pigeons, and now and again some special butter-fed jobs, but I get most of what I want from Up-the-Hill. Don't even have to collect 'em; there's a few gallons dropped off at my door every Friday.'

'Up-the-Hill? John, you're kidding. I know that times aren't too good up there, but surely they're not breeding maggots to make ends meet?'

'Correction,' said John. '*Over*-the-Hill. T'other side. You've never been to Bleasby's maggot farm? Never heard of "Bleasby's Blockbusters – the Biggest and the Best"? You've led a sheltered life, lad. If you haven't been to Bleasby's, you haven't lived. We'll go there tomorrow.'

'But . . .'

'When's your day off this week?'

'Tomorrow.'

'So no buts. We'll go there tomorrow. Pick you up at nine. Come just as you are.'

John picked me up at nine. Just as I was, which was dressed in my scruffy old fishing clothes after a hasty change and a hastier breakfast. I didn't have the heart to tell John that I'd been out on an emergency call since five that morning.

'Right?' asked John.

'Right,' I yawned.

'Oh, give over,' said John. 'It's not as bad as that. I promise you that you won't be bored. I can tell you've had your breakfast by the marmalade on your top lip, so you've no excuse.'

I followed the intrepid Denton to his Land-Rover, and off we set.

The area over the hill was foreign to me. It was a bleak, windblown stretch of moorland with not a house for miles. Few tourists visited it: it had a desolate *Wuthering Heights* atmosphere about it that was quite depressing. The fact that the few people who did live on the moor were in the catchment area of another practice meant that I did not even know them as patients.

'By heck, John,' I said, as the sturdy Land-Rover was buffeted and rocked by the winds which cut across the moor, 'it's a bit breezy out there.'

'Make the most of it, Bob,' said John. 'There's not much fresh air where we're going . . .'

John drew up outside a solitary bungalow and rang the bell.

He was answered by a pleasant-faced lady in a mob-cap, holding a duster, who turned out to be Mrs Bert Bleasby.

'Morning, John,' I heard her say. 'Bert's over at the farm.'

Declining with thanks the offer of a cup of tea, John strode back to the vehicle. 'Oh, John!' called Mrs Bert after him. 'Just be careful of the dog!'

'So they don't live on the farm, then?' I asked.

'It's not the sort of farm you live on,' chuckled John.

'And what was that about a dog?'

'Dunno,' said John. 'They did have an Alsatian pup a few months back, but she can't mean that. Soft as putty, it was.'

After a five-minute drive, John turned off the road and up a bumpy stone track which led through a screen of stunted trees. Past the trees lay a huddle of low buildings – 'Used to be a pig farm,' explained John – surrounded by a barbed wire fence. There was a sharp whiff in the air, vaguely reminiscent of old stables, which I couldn't quite place.

John opened a gate in the fence and led the way through. Suddenly there was a savage and furious barking and a huge crossbred Alsatian came rushing straight for us. I closed my eyes, covered my vitals, and waited to be dismembered.

'Down, Daffy! DOWN!' roared a voice, and the barking stopped. I opened my eyes to find the dog sitting in front of me, growling menacingly but wagging its tail. A man in a white coat and wellingtons was clumping towards us.

'Oh, it's you, is it?' he greeted John. 'Might have known. How are yer, y'old bugger?'

'All right, till the Hound of the Bleasbyvilles frightened the bloody life out of me,' said John. 'Oh, this is my friend, Dr Clifford. He's fascinated by maggots and I thought you wouldn't mind showing him around.'

'Glad to,' said the man, drawing off a slimy rubber glove, and sticking out his hand. 'Bert Bleasby. Pleased to meet you.'

Bert shook hands with the pair of us and then said, 'Just one thing before we go in. Daffy here had better be introduced. Once he knows you're OK, you've got nothing to worry about. Friends, boy. Friends! Shake a paw.'

The Alsatian, by now thumping its tail frenetically on the ground and slobbering over an enormous tongue, raised its right paw to John and myself in turn. We shook it solemnly. Much better to be a friend of this thing than an enemy. I couldn't work out what its mother had been crossed with – possibly the Creature from the Black Lagoon – but it was certainly bigger than the average Alsatian. There was a hint of soppiness in the eyes, too, which indicated that it was either better-natured than it first appeared or was suffering from repressed schizophrenia.

'Right,' said Bert, leading the way to a little wooden office, 'Let's get you kitted out.'

He gave John and myself a lightweight anorak, a pair of overtrousers and a beekeeper's fine-mesh hood apiece, and picked up a hood for himself.

'What's this for?' I asked, as I put the hood over my head.

'I can tell there are no flies on you, Doctor,' said Bert. 'And I want to keep it that way.'

We went into the nearest building, through a double set of doors.

'Airlocks,' explained Bert as we walked through the first pair. As they closed behind us there was a hissing sound and a fine spray misted the air above us. 'Fly killer,' said Bert. 'Takes care of any bottles who try to run for it.'

Inside the building was a scrubbed concrete area, with several sets of large trays stacked in the corner, and then a door set in a whitewashed breeze-block wall. We walked through this door into another airlock, and again there was the hissing of an automatic fly-killer dispenser.

'This is it, Bob,' said John, as Bert pushed open the second door. 'Be prepared.'

I didn't know what I was supposed to be prepared for, but even if I had, I'd never have believed it. We stepped into a huge room, thirty feet square or more, lit by dazzling neon lights. The air was hot and humid, and buzzing with thousands of black specks. The smell – a weird compound of old dustbins and neglected abattoirs – was revolting. The

38

floor and walls were black ... and, on closer inspection, *moving*. The noise of several million feeding and breeding bluebottles filled the air like a massed choir of buzz-saws and dentists' drills.

'Don't panic, Bob,' said John as he saw me flinch. 'Bert's never lost a visitor yet. Well, not many ...'

'This,' announced Bert proudly, 'is the fly room. Honeymoon Hotel for these little beauties.'

As the 'little beauties' crawled all over me, buzzing loudly in my ears through the gauze of the hood, Bert led the way to a series of racks, stacked one above the other.

'Brown sugar,' he said, batting at the black surface which rose with a protesting cloud to reveal the glistening demerara underneath. 'Their wedding breakfast.'

'How very ...'

'And here,' Bert continued, doing the same to the rack underneath, 'is their nuptial couch.'

I've seen some sights in my time, but at this I nearly threw up. The black cloud rose to reveal chicken heads – hundreds of them – over which the bluebottles were crawling and laying tiny white clusters of eggs.

'Sorry about that,' said Bert, as he noticed me stifle a retch. 'You being a doctor, and that, I thought you'd appreciate these. In the other fly rooms we're starting them off on fish, but that doesn't have the same impact for visitors. Not so spectacular, if you follow my meaning.'

'Please don't apologise,' I muttered, trying not to breathe in. 'This is ... this is ... er ...'

'I agree,' said Bert. 'Fascinating, isn't it?'

As we left the fly room and walked over to another building, Bert explained the system. A constant temperature of 72°F and controlled humidity kept the bluebottles in breeding fettle. When the bluebottles' brief courtship was over, the chicken heads with their clusters of eggs were removed to the hatching bays in the next building; just a few of them being reserved for the next lot of breeding stock.

Then the bluebottles were killed off by spraying with

insecticide – a bit drastic, but no doubt they died happy – and the whole room cleaned down with a high-pressure steam hose. 'When we've finished cleaning, you could eat your breakfast off the floor,' said Bert. I didn't doubt him, but I was glad I'd had breakfast before I came.

'You can take your hoods off now, lads,' said Bert as we walked into the next building. 'You'll find no flies in here.'

Whoof! I now recognised the smell I'd first noticed outside – ammonia. Except that in here it was a thousand times stronger, sending me into a coughing fit and bringing tears streaming down my cheeks.

'Does pong a bit,' said Bert, happily. 'But don't worry, it'll clear your tubes. The county health inspector's over here regularly to check the ammonia levels. And I've got a chemical air-cleaning system that not only changes the air every ten minutes, but neutralises the ammonia before it gets outside. The neighbours would have nothing to complain about, even if we had any.'

The new building we were in was vast, and the floor was divided into dozens of concrete pens, each about eighteen inches deep. Pens at one end had been cleaned out to await the next batch of infant maggots from the hatchery, where heated hatching bays had the maggots wriggling out from the eggs within six hours of laying in the fly room.

But the rest of the pens in here were filled almost to the top with a writhing, wriggling and ammonia-smelling mass of maggots, all feeding heartily on pulverised . . . pulverised *what?*

'You name it,' said Bert. 'Fish, horses, pig, poultry, offal . . . all good stuff. We don't just chuck it in, mind. It takes maggots about six days to reach full size, and during that time they shed their skins about seven times. As soon as they shed, they're ravenous, and that's the time to give 'em the fresh grub. It's like a five-star hotel here: they get a different mix for every feed to build them up quickly. We can't have them just lying around, eating me out of house and home . . .'

I watched the mature maggots being shovelled out of the

end pens and into a huge cleaning machine which riddled them through sawdust to leave them shining bright and free from smell. The cleaned maggots were dumped into a trough about fifteen feet long and easily three feet deep, in which they wriggled and heaved in their millions, waiting to be packed and refrigerated for transport by the lorryload to the big cities and even abroad.

Bert ran his hands through the writhing mass, lifting up a double handful of maggots and trickling them lovingly through his fingers. 'Little beauties,' he breathed. 'Just look at 'em: Bleasby's Blockbusters – the Biggest and the Best!'

Several of the farm's workers hailed Bert as they passed with barrowloads of maggot food, minced and unidentifiable.

'They seem a cheery lot,' I remarked.

'They love it,' said Bert. 'Gets in your blood, maggot-breeding.'

'Where do they get all that stuff from?'

'The cold room,' said Bert. 'Next stop . . .'

As Bert led us into the cold room, I made a mental note to stop asking questions. Around the walls of the room stood thirty or so bins, full of offal. The rest of the place was stacked with frozen corpses: horses, ponies, pigs, poultry, fish, a couple of old milch-cows and – most gruesome of all – crates

containing stiff and cold dogs and cats, strayed or old, and put down at local animal homes.

Next to the cold room was the defrosting room, again littered with corpses. These were being dismembered with a chainsaw by a cheerful lad of about seventeen, and fed into a gigantic crushing and mincing machine.

'Look at that,' said Bert proudly, as a former horse poured out of the machine, transformed into a glittering torrent of mince. 'Prime stuff, that. I could eat it myself.'

It was now time to go. I couldn't say that I was sorry, but it was pure squeamishness on my part. Bert was running an efficient, clean and profitable farm, the produce of which gave pleasure to thousands of anglers and employment to locals who were obviously happy in their work, and there was certainly no distress evident among the millions of wriggling maggots, battery-farmed though they were.

'Thanks very much indeed,' I said to Bert as we left. 'It's certainly been an unforgettable experience. But one thing still puzzles me – why have you got barbed wire all around the place? Surely you're not expecting burglars?'

'Expecting 'em?' said Bert. 'We've *had* 'em! With a place as remote as this it's easy for a bunch of cowboys to drive up with a truckful of bins, shovel the maggies in and drive off. There's money in maggots. The blokes who broke in here must have made a tidy sum. That's the reason for the barbed wire – and for Daffy.'

'I knew there must have been a reason for Daffy.'

'Yes. Guard dog, he is. I don't envy the bloke who runs into him on a dark night. Trained him myself. Watch.'

He called Daffy, who'd been wandering around us, slobbering happily. 'Heel, boy!' he commanded. Daffy carried on wandering.

John started to smirk, but soon stopped when Bert handed him a sack. 'Wrap this sack around your arm, John,' said Bert. 'I'll show you.' A bit apprehensively, John wrapped the sack around his right arm.

'Daffy!' commanded Bert. 'Get 'im!'

With a short run and a ferocious burst of barking, Daffy leapt. Teeth closed sickeningly over forearm – and poor old Bert was pulled to the ground and dragged along by the growling dog.

'Geroff, yer daft bugger!' he shouted, cuffing with his free hand. 'Not *me*, you fool!'

John grabbed the dog's collar with his left arm and bashed its nose with his sack-covered right. Eventually the thing cottoned on, let go of Bert and sank its teeth into the sack.

'By 'eck, Bert!' exclaimed John, clouting the dog around the ears until it let go of the sacking and ran off whimpering. 'He's a devil when he's roused.'

'He'll be fine,' panted Bert, 'once he's tasted blood.'

'You're dead right,' said John. 'Just make sure it's not yours.'

We made our farewells to Bert, and to Daffy who came creeping back to distribute slobbering and repentant kisses over one and all, and set off back over the moor with a couple of gallons of complimentary maggots stowed under the seats.

'Nice man, Bert,' I said.

'Lovely feller,' said John. 'But don't let him fool you: he's a very shrewd businessman. Makes a fortune out of that place. Works for it, mind you. Seven-day week for forty-eight weeks in the year, then a month's holiday in the Bahamas for him and his missus. He's done it by running his farm properly and selling quality. I'd never begrudge a man like that.'

'Nor me,' I said. 'Feel a bit sorry for Daffy, though. He's obviously not the dog for the job.'

'Of course he's not,' said John. 'And after today I think Bert will get a proper guard dog firm in and take Daffy back where he belongs – to the bungalow, where he can look after Mrs Bert and frighten the odd rabbit out on the moor.

'Bert's a hard man in business, and an ace with maggots, but he's got a soft spot that any dog can recognise – even one as lunatic as Daffy. Every man to his own trade, I always say.'

As the Land-Rover bumped and lurched through the buffeting winds over the moor top, and with the sting of ammonia still in my nostrils, I realised that I would not have swapped my five a.m. emergency call for a day's more predictable work at the maggot farm, not even if there was a month in the Bahamas at the year's end.

'Dead right, John,' I said. 'Every man to his own trade . . .'

CHAPTER 7

C.P.

For three generations the Wilder family had owned the *Tadchester Gazette*, first published in about 1850. Although their name was prominently displayed at the head of the paper, the Editor of the *Gazette*, the man who *was* the *Gazette*, was Chris Parfitt, generally known in the town as C.P.

C.P. had had some years in Fleet Street and in publishing before coming down to Tadchester, was wise beyond his years and was one of the great local characters. If you worked for the *Tadchester Gazette*, not only had you to meet your deadlines and send in good copy, you had to have the added qualification of being able to drink at least four pints of beer every lunchtime.

'Any good working journalist,' said C.P., 'needs to oil the machinery.'

I always enjoyed C.P.'s company. He had a kind of canny wisdom and you'd find him any lunchtime in the Tadchester Arms with his pipe and a pint. He and his wife, Joyce, would often come and have a meal with Pam and myself. He wrote beautifully. He was far too good for the literary situation that he was in, but he liked the place: he was a keen fisherman and, being virtually a one-man band, he was able to express his own ideas.

I didn't know what part the Wilders played in the *Gazette*'s affairs, other than to accept any profit that C.P. made for them during the year. C.P. was a first-class journalist, a first-class writer, a great character – one of the old school.

He came to see me one day with a lump in his neck that bothered him. I saw him a few times until it began to bother me. It looked like a gland that was just slightly bigger than it should have been, so I got Henry to look at him. We did the usual blood counts and chest X-rays, all the normal checks.

'Better have it out,' advised Henry. 'That shouldn't be much trouble. Really an ENT job though. Not my or Ron Dickinson's field. You'd better go and have it out in Winchcombe.'

I knew the ear, nose and throat surgeon in Winchcombe well and I asked if, as a favour, he would operate on this friend of mine. So, within a couple of weeks, C.P. was in.

The lump took much more digging out than they had expected, though it proved to be harmless, some sort of old tuberculous gland. The ENT surgeon commented that there was a tiny nerve running through the gland which he had to cut through to remove the gland, but he didn't think it was one of any significance.

C.P. was home a couple of days afterwards, very hoarse from the anaesthetic, but otherwise quite well. I reassured him that his voice would come back in a day or two and that a good pint of beer could well lubricate his vocal cords.

However, his voice didn't come back in a day or two. When it hadn't come back in a week or two, he went back to Winchcombe to be seen by the ENT surgeon. The little nerve that he had had to cut through, not that he had any alternative, wasn't a nerve of no significance: it was the recurrent laryngeal nerve. Its importance is that it supplies one of the vocal cords: if you cut it, that vocal cord is paralysed and the patient can speak only in the quietest whisper.

46

C.P. was sent off to a speech therapist, assured by us that things would be much better. He did, for a time, improve marginally but on the phone he was almost unintelligible. It was very difficult to hear what he had to say and this loss of voice was gradually beginning to destroy him.

'It's terrible,' he whispered. 'I can't even order a beer in a pub that I'm not known in. They can't hear a word I say.

'I don't even know if I can keep my job. Whenever I ring anybody else, particularly in London, they think I'm a heavy breather. I rang a company in Belfast and they set the alarm bells ringing – they thought I was the IRA.'

I encouraged him to persevere with his speech therapy, but little progress was made and C.P. got more and more depressed.

'Can't blame the surgeon,' he whispered. 'He did what he had to do. The lump might have been malignant. Better out than in.'

I knew of nothing more that could be done, and C.P. whispered around the town for almost three years. People, impatient, often turned away before he had made himself understood. Not being able to express himself properly seemed to cut him down. Without the voice, he even shrank physically.

'Until you've lost it, you don't realise how much your voice keeps you afloat in society, protects you from other people,' he wheezed one night in the Tadchester Arms. 'Every minute of the day we're engaged in verbal fencing. By the tone or the volume of your voice, people know how far they can push their luck. And when you've neither tone nor volume the buggers come straight in for the kill.

'Whether it's arguing politics or who was first at the bar, few people have any scruples about shouting you down. Verbal violence. I'd never realised how widespread it is. It's probably saved mankind from a lot of physical violence, but it's not funny when you're in a verbal punch-up with no defence.'

'Aren't you taking all this a bit too seriously?' I asked.

'People knew you when you had a voice. You've not really changed. They know what you're trying to say.'

'There's a big difference,' he said. 'Now they don't have to listen. And a lot of them think that if you can't speak properly, you can't be all there.'

'Not in this day and age, surely?'

'You try it, Bob. Try standing there in the street with the wife, meeting a couple you've known for twenty-odd years. And listen to them saying, "My, he's looking well. Getting over it, is he? That's good." And one of them turns to you and says very slowly and very loudly, "I believe you're doing very well. Yes . . . VERY WELL. Getting over it now, are you?"'

'Then you either give a silly grin, nod politely and say nothing, or you lose your temper. You wheeze away for a bit until you've got your wind up and say, "Of course I'm getting over it, you silly old bugger! But I'm not deaf and daft as well!"'

That was another thing that worried C.P.: losing his temper. With one vocal cord paralysed, it was difficult to regulate the amount of air he took in and breathed out. When he breathed too much out, panic would set in and he would gulp in air to compensate for it. This resulted in hyperventilation and the consequential overdose of oxygen, combined with the adrenalin released by the panic, produced alarming outbursts of bad temper.

'Terrifying Bob,' he said. 'I become completely irrational at times like that. Fight anybody. Bloody silly at my time of life.'

Eventually the speech therapy helped him to control the hyperventilation, and both his temper and voice improved a little. It wasn't enough, however, for someone whose livelihood depended on communication.

He came to see me in the surgery almost exactly three years after his operation. 'I'm off to Liverpool tomorrow,' he whispered, 'to have something done about my throat.'

'That's fine, Chris,' I said. 'But I don't know what *can* be done. What's all this about?

'There's a new technique where they inject liquid Teflon into the paralysed vocal cord. It makes it swell up and brings it back to the middle again, so that the active vocal cord can meet it. That stops all the air escaping and gives you some sort of voice back.'

Most people think of the vocal cords as being like two strings on a guitar, vibrating when air from the lungs is forced through them. But they're more like a split dustbin lid; both halves coming together to make the noise that, with help from the tongue and palate, we take for granted as speech.

But the Teflon injection sounded too good to be true. I checked up with my ENT colleagues. Yes, they said, there was indeed such an operation, a very successful one, but it hadn't yet reached our part of the world. Liverpool was the main centre, where a brilliant ENT surgeon was pioneering the technique.

I felt bad that C.P., rather than me, had found out about the Teflon operation. But it was a very new technique which had originated in the United States as a spin-off, of all things, from research into the use of Teflon as a coating in the space programme.

'See you soon,' said C.P. 'With a pair of non-stick vocal cords.'

'Best of luck, old lad,' I said. 'How are you getting to Liverpool?'

'Driving up,' he said. 'I can't waste time messing around with trains.'

'And how are you getting back?'

'Driving,' he said.

C.P. was certainly getting his confidence back; he was one of the worst drivers I've ever known.

He went off one Tuesday to Liverpool. On the following Friday evening I had a phone call from a voice that I knew but could not place.

'Who's that?'

'It's me,' said the voice.

'Who's me?'

'You've got a short memory. Me. C.P.'

'My God!' I said. 'It's you!'

So it was. C.P. with his voice back – not quite the same, slightly huskier than it used to be, but a firm, clear resonant speaking voice that you could hear perfectly well.

'I don't believe this,' I said. 'What happened?'

'It wasn't the jolliest time I've ever had,' he said. 'They stick a long, fine needle down your throat, into the paralysed vocal cord, and inject the Teflon into it. Every so often you have to say, "Ah", so that they can judge when enough has been pumped in.'

'So it's done under local anaesthetic?' I asked.

'The local anaesthetic is given from the *inside*, so you finish up with a throatful of needles. It's known in the trade as an uncomfortable process, which is the understatement of the century. The Teflon injection itself should last a lifetime, but I'd have it done once a year if I had to. That surgeon's a bloody saint.'

Certainly the operation seemed like a miracle. After talking in a whisper for three years, suddenly C.P. could speak again quite normally. This was medicine at its very best; no drama or heroics, but a delicate and simple procedure performed by

the best and most skilful hands. And it couldn't have happened to a nicer chap.

In spite of C.P.'s confidence, I wondered if the improvement would last or whether it was just temporary. But it did last. Five years later, he was still chatting away quite normally, as are others who have had the same operation, which is now much more widely established.

The cutting of that particular nerve sometimes happens when the thyroid gland is operated on. These days, the few who are unable to speak – and even those unable to speak for many years – can be given back their voices in less than an hour on the operating table.

One of C.P.'s problems was in adjusting to the volume of his new voice.

'I keep forgetting that I don't have to force it any more,' he said one lunchtime in the Tadchester Arms. 'Sometimes I build myself up to make myself heard, suddenly find I'm shouting, and get accused of being aggressive. People who were only too ready to shout me down when I had no voice, now back off and sulk in corners. You really can't win.'

As C.P. left the pub I was joined by John Denton, who was also enjoying a liquid luncheon in the Tadchester Arms.

'I know what he means,' said John. 'I've seen it happen in my own chicken run.'

'What? C.P. in your chicken run?'

'No, you silly bugger. There was this damn great rook once that used to march straight into my henhouse every day and pinch the eggs. Cocky, aggressive, bold as brass, and making threatening noises that had all the hens running for cover.

'One day I'd had enough, and I gave it one from my twelve-bore as it was coming in to land. I only winged it and the thing ran into the henhouse to hide. That was its first mistake . . . and its last.

'When I got in there, it wasn't the proud, arrogant, nest-robbing rook any longer. It was a disabled, vulnerable beast, and all the hens were fighting to get at it, pecking it to death.'

'What's that got to do with C.P.?'

'Only that he's fine now he can use himself again. But there were a few in this pub who didn't hesitate to pile in and peck him when he couldn't peck back. Makes me feel ashamed of myself.'

'Why? You didn't peck him, surely?'

'Yes, I did.'

'And when was that?'

'Five years ago. Just before the operation to get his voice back. When he lost his temper and played hell with me.'

'What for?'

'Shooting that bloody rook.'

CHAPTER 8

Singing for Supper

In between surgery hours I was still plugging away at my writing and had had some small success. I had one brief moment of glory when the *Sunday Express* serialised a humorous book. It was all very exiting. The first instalment was published the Sunday we were returning from a holiday in France and there were copies of the *Sunday Express* being read all over the boat. There were none left in the shop. I was dying to rush up to somebody and say, 'By the way, I wrote the serial.'

Eventually one rather nice lady who we were sitting next to in the cafeteria put hers down and I said, 'Would you mind if I borrowed this for a moment?', and there was my story.

The serialisation brought an approach from a famous lecture agency. I would be in great demand as a speaker, they said. Their list of speakers included leading figures in the land: sportsmen, politicians and authors. I felt extremely flattered, and I'd always fancied myself as an after-dinner speaker. I looked forward to a change in my economic circumstances, thinking how much money I would make, and imagining myself at livery dinners and such, having Lord Mayors and Royalty rolling in the aisles.

I waited expectantly. I had been on the agency's books for two years before I had my first request, which was to speak at a luncheon of food manufacturers next day in London. London, by the next day, was quite impossible.

Six months later were was another request, the possibility of speaking to some library staff in Nottingham. They eventually decided they didn't want me.

Then after three years, success. I was asked to go and speak to the Round Table of a small Lancashire town. I was to receive travelling expenses, plus overnight hotel accommodation and a fee of £150. It sounded too good to be true.

It so happened that I had two lady patients who were born in this town and they filled me in with a lot of background information. I had some difficulty in placing it on the map but eventually found it was on the Yorkshire–Lancashire border, nearer to Manchester than it was to Leeds.

I accepted this invitation, which of course I thought would be the first of many, realising that I would cost the organisers in the region of £230. As I had been a Round Tabler in the past, I was surprised that somebody was going to pay that much for me to speak to them. I imagined that they must all be very keen writers and want to know something about writing.

The agency said the lecture should last threequarters of an hour and I set about preparing it.

I received travel instructions: I was to report to the King's Hotel, where I was to stay, and then to dinner at the Black Stag. Before I left, I rang the organiser to check on the length of my speech. He said, 'Oh no, not forty-five minutes, just your usual. An after-dinner speech – about twenty minutes.' This I knew I could do standing on my head. I could already see them being convulsed in laughter but it sounded a lot of money for me to be paid to go all this way to Lancashire. Although this town featured very largely in the eyes of two of my lady patients, it didn't seem to feature very largely in anybody else's.

I travelled up to Lancashire via London, Leeds and a

branch line going out to Bradford, doubling back through the Calder Valley, following a little river bed. Wherever there was water, there was a mill. We were going through a deep valley with splendid hills reaching up either side.

I said to a travelling companion, 'Excuse me, are these the Yorkshire Dales?'

'Not these,' he said. 'These are bugger all,' and that really set the tone for the rest of my day.

All of my trains were late. One of them broke down. And on my way up the branch line we were standing, packed solid in the carriage.

I arrived at the small station to find that my speaking engagement was in a pleasant little town, nestling at the foot of the surrounding hills. It had a splendid town hall, out of all proportion to the size of the place, and I was told by several people that it was much bigger than Halifax. There didn't appear to be too many places of entertainment: there was a Coffee Club, which closed at 4.30, which was new and obviously the social gathering point of the people; and Tom's Tea Bar, which was a little further down the social scale. The town looked a bit run down and, looking back through population figures, I found that the number had actually halved over the last twenty years.

The hotel was clean, comfortable, and I was the only guest. No one came to meet me, although I understood that they had rung to see if I had arrived, and at the appropriate time I made my way to the Black Stag.

I was greeted by the chairman of the local Round Table who fetched me a drink and introduced me to a puzzled vice chairman who said, 'Where did they get you from?' I was surrounded by a lot of happy, hearty, enthusiastically drinking young men, who didn't seem too interested in me. My earlier, unpaid, speaking engagements had been at places like Women's Institutes, where I was fêted as the guest of honour, and a couple of literary lunches where I had been made a real fuss of. But here I was a professional performer.

Most of the assembled company, ninety in all, were well

liquored before we went upstairs to a packed dining room where there was lively discussion with excellent food and good wine. The man on my right said, 'I'm nervous about you.' He questioned me closely on how I had been booked and what I was going to do. At this stage, I was beginning to wonder also.

Picking up the programme, I saw that it was the twenty-fifth anniversary of this Round Table and I was to give a speech in reply, on behalf of the guests. £230 seemed an awful lot of money for that.

The dinner dragged on and on. At about 9.45 the first speaker – and there were three to precede me – rose. I thought all three speeches would be short and sweet, as the audience was waiting for this famous doctor-writer-broadcaster. Just as the first speaker started, the door burst open and in came a crowd of boisterous, half-dressed ladies. Some were made up as French waitresses and some dressed as French male painters with burnt cork moustaches. They were the 'better halves' of the assembled males, determined not to miss out on their husbands' night out. There was a distinct chill about their arrival but once there, they wouldn't go away. There was a tremendous uproar with shouts of 'Get 'em off. Take 'em down!' One or two were mauled by some of the diners who were now fairly well in their cups.

Eventually, after twenty-five minutes, the girls' leader managed to deliver her speech, which was to present the Chairman of the Round Table with a leather briefcase which he had to open. Inside was a present . . . a pair of knickers – what else? – and the room again resounded with shouts of, 'Get 'em off! Get 'em off!'

Eventually the girls dispersed and the first speaker, the original founder of this particular Round Table, began his speech again. It was very witty and much appreciated, very local in content – when Jack did this and George did that, and when Herbert and Dick did so and so – and he had them in fits of laughter about parochial things and parochial events. His promised 'few words' lasted for threequarters of an hour, but he was very funny.

Meanwhile the rest of the ninety guests were getting steadily more stoned.

The next speaker was a veterinary surgeon, the Area Chairman of the Round Table, who was both poorly sighted and hard of hearing. His hearing aid was in his glasses and when he took his glasses off he could neither see nor hear. This was pointed out to him in very explicit language by the inebriated members of the various Round Tables present. He spoke for only half an hour, again very local stuff, being rude about the people who were stoned and dropping the tone steadily.

By the time he finished it was eleven o'clock and there was a ten-minute break. The ten-minute break stretched until 11.15, when it was the turn of the Chairman of the Round Table to speak.

He was a very pleasant chap who had done his best to hold the evening together. He had a French wife, which explained the attire of the ladies who had burst in upon us. Whilst Chairman of this particular Round Table he had apparently committed the heinous crime of spending a five-week holiday in France that necessitated his missing two Table meetings. During his speech the assembled company spent most of its time boisterously pointing out his French connection and neglected duties.

His speech began by mentioning briefly everyone who was present. I forget what he said about me but it was very little. His main story was about a man on a plane radioing airport control in New York that the pilot had died, the navigator had died, the co-pilot had died and that he – who had never flown before – was manning the aircraft. He told airport control that he was flying at 8,000 feet, and at 700 miles per hour, and upside down.

'Don't worry,' said airport control, 'we'll talk you in. How do you know you're at 8,000 feet?'

'I can see it on the dial,' said the man.

'How do you know you're flying at 700 miles an hour?'

'I can see it on the dial,' said the man.

'And how do you know you're flying upside down?' asked the controller.

'Because of the shit coming out of my collar,' said the man.

This was the joke of the evening. It had the audience in fits. This was the man I had to follow. Eventually, at 12.15, it was my turn to speak. By now those who weren't boisterously drunk had nodded off to sleep. The Master of Ceremonies, who I think had taken a dislike to me, introduced me with some reluctance: perhaps my fee had been debated at some bitter Round Table meeting.

I have used various pseudonyms for my bits of writing and somehow this chap had got hold of all of them and he introduced me by saying, 'Our next speaker, and I've got to read this, reckons he is Dr Robert Andrew, Dr Clifford, Dr Pheasant and, for all I know, Doctor f--- ing Partridge. I don't know what he's going to talk about but he is going to respond to the guests.'

I got up and did my twenty-minute crowd-basher. It had delighted thousands of Women's Institute meetings, adjustments had made it a wow at literary luncheons and literary dinners, it had held its own on distinguished occasions such as the after-dinner speech to the Association of British Medical Publishers, and even the World Business Council at Gleneagles, but it wasn't right for this Round Table dinner.

There was a bit of polite laughing at the beginning, then automatic laughing, plus a lot of barracking. I sweated through my twenty minutes and when it was over, sat down.

'What about your expenses?' said the Chairman.

'Oh,' I said in a generous moment, 'forget them. I've been a Round Tabler in the past and this is my contribution to the evening.' As my expenses were more than £50 this was indeed generous but I realised that I was going to write this off as an expensive experience.

The man who had worried about me bought me a drink and said, 'That was fine.' The Chairman said, 'That was excellent.' But nobody else said anything.

Two people spoke to me afterwards; one tried to be nice and the other spoke because I looked as though I was lonely. Nobody saw me off and I made my way back to the hotel. I read a book, went to sleep and caught my train back to the Calder Valley.

To my surprise, a few days later, there was a cheque for £150 from the Chairman with a note saying, 'Thank you for your excellent speech and for not claiming expenses. Yours in friendship . . .'

So there I was, at home. I noticed that the cheque wasn't a Round Table cheque but his own personal business account. I hoped the poor man hadn't paid it all himself.

What a sell. It must have cost them £10 a minute for me and nobody had listened. I was glad that initially the agent had written to me saying that she had arranged for them to pay me in cash. I had written back to say that I would find this highly embarrassing; could she make sure that I was paid by cheque? I could just imagine at the end of the meal, with ninety people watching, as they peeled off £230 in notes at the end of my boring twenty-minute interlude. They hadn't really needed a speaker at all. They were extremely nice, they just made a mistake. Still it was a great experience for me. I hope it wasn't too expensive an experience for them.

59

CHAPTER 9

Recovering My Zip

It must have been a measure of the state of mind I had unknowingly drifted into when, one Sunday morning over a cup of tea in bed, Pam said, 'You are always sending people away for forty-eight hours. Why don't you take your own advice and see if you can get your zip back. Look, here are some organised trips, "City Weekends all over Europe".'

Pam is persuasive, and the idea seemed a good one at the time, so the next day I booked myself a single passage for a weekend in Salzburg.

It was only as the time grew nearer that I had doubts about what I might have let myself in for. As a logical man, I realised that Salzburg – being further east and north – would probably be cold, wet and sloshy. It was not high enough to have the sun that goes with Alpine coldness. I also rationalised that, as it was between-season time, most things would be shut down.

I couldn't visualise what I was going to do on my own, other than drinking, eating and sloshing about in the cold and wet. However, the idea of two days in a luxury hotel appealed to me. Who knows what adventures might lie ahead? Apart from that, I couldn't get my money back.

As a family, and individually, we never ever seem to be able to do anything in an ordinary way. There is always some natural or man-made disaster that dogs us on our travels. Two days before my planned trip, the British Rail overtime ban started. Although many people blamed it on a Communist plot, I knew that the go-slow was directly related to the fact that I wanted to use the railways. However, I worked out that by careful planning I could make a leisurely journey to Austria and back. There was time; I had chosen my weekend in the middle of a ten-day holiday.

I saw from the tour brochure that I had to be at Luton airport at 7.15 a.m. I booked a room at an hotel adjoining the North London Air Terminal, thus ensuring that there would be no last-minute rushes anywhere. All I would have to do would be to get out of bed and get on the bus.

In spite of the go-slow, if I travelled up in the afternoon before, I should have no problems.

Fate did not mean things to be this way. The practice decided to have a party on the eve of my departure, and for every reason I was unable to miss this. So I eventually went to catch my train at 9 p.m. – which of course didn't arrive until 10.30 p.m. – which got me to the hotel at 3.30. To catch my bus I had to be at the Terminal at 6.30 a.m. Being a cautious man, I not only booked a 6 o'clock call with the night porter, but also rang him from my bedroom before falling exhausted into bed. Checking my watch when the alarm call came, I saw that it was 6.25, giving me five minutes to get packed, shaved, washed, dressed and round to the Air Terminal.

I rushed downstairs, half-shaved, half-clothed, dragging my case, and enquired from the night porter on the way out what had happened to his timing mechanism. His reply was brief, and roughly translated, meant, 'Get stuffed!'

This set the pattern for the day. There are some days when one's aura just does not seem to be functioning, and one's dominant personality doesn't fire on all cylinders.

I made the bus in time and got to the airport in time, so it

61

did look as if I was going to get away. By the time the plane was due to fly out, however, the passengers had not been called, and there was mounting anxiety among the group hoping to get to Salzburg.

Eventually we set off, half an hour late, in a pink plane, to arrive at Munich airport in snow and ice. We had a two-hour bus journey to Salzburg ahead, and at this stage I realised that a cold which had begun the day before had really started to stream, and that a boil had begun to erupt on the left side of my nose.

The first news at Munich was that, because of the ice and snow, the bus journey was likely to take three hours, which it did. The autobahn was blocked by an overturned lorry, and the bus had to go along part of the German Alpine route near Berchtesgarten, through Insole, the venue for the world ice speed-skating championships, and eventually arrived at our hotel late in the afternoon.

The hotel was absolutely luxurious. Cultured and gentlemanly diplomats waited on us at the porters' desk. Hordes of waiters, waitresses and page boys buzzed about and hovered around, helpful and smiling. This was the life.

For the evening, there was a choice between a Mozart concert and a folk-dancing display. Being uncultured, I opted for the folk-dancing, and set off with the courier and a British couple to the Sternbrau, resigned to the spectacle of blonde pigtailed maidens and boot-slapping men in leather shorts. We arrived to be told that the folk-dancing was off, but we could stay for a meal.

All through the meal, the loss of personality dominance dogged me. A round of drinks was served to everyone but me. The waiter had forgotten. Everybody was served with the first course. Except me. My first course arrived with the second, so I was able to allow my wiener schnitzel to cool while I ate my hors-d'oeuvre.

Back at the hotel, our party swelled, and I found myself buying a round of seven brandies and one cup of coffee. I had thought the drinks might be expensive, but this was terrifying

— £24 for seven brandies. One glass of brandy cost the same as I'd paid for a bottle on the plane.

The weather in Salzburg was just as I had anticipated, bitterly cold and windy, with driving snow overhead and slush underfoot. An expedition to the shops not only gave me a severe chill on my bald head (I hadn't brought a hat), but turned the taps full-on for my cold and gave my growing boil a boost. I sat in the hotel with a boil on my nose, a streaming cold, having just paid £24 for seven brandies, having had three and a half hours' sleep, travelled several hundred miles, and missed a folk-dancing evening. *This* was the life?

Mercifully, it was time for bed. I fell fast asleep to wake up with a start at quarter to four, aroused by the noise outside. I looked through the window to see people in cars, people window shopping, people bawling cheerily and loudly at each other. Obviously an old Salzburg custom. I slept fitfully for the rest of the night, but determined to make the most of my holiday the next day.

When I woke up, the atrocious weather had deteriorated, my cold was much worse and the boil was much bigger. Everybody had a companion except me, which was not surprising. I did not have a lot to offer.

I made repeated forays against the blizzard, but the shops were so expensive I couldn't afford to buy anything. I could get a cup of coffee, though, for 50p at a coffee shop fifty yards from the hotel. By having coffee once every two and a half hours I managed to keep my interest and spirits up.

The proffered entertainment of the Saturday night was another Mozart concert or a performance of *The White Horse Inn*. *The White Horse Inn* being nearer, I plumped for that. I couldn't drink any more coffee.

My seat cost me £8, and I was in the second row of a half-empty theatre with a cast that seemed to be composed half of fairly good professionals and half of pretty rotten amateurs. Not speaking any German, I couldn't understand a word, but did recognise one or two tunes, and tried not to let my cold interfere with the dialogue. I had to wait until the chorus

broke into song before I blew my nose. One light relief was to see a male ballet dancer obviously rupture himself catching his partner in a flying swan movement. I was glad somebody else wasn't having the luck.

Back to the hotel, and more brandies. Even whisky was £2.50p a glass, so there wasn't much point in changing my brand. I got into conversation with three young German girls, eighteen-year-olds from a domestic-science college. The Deutschmark was so strong that they had come to this palace of luxury to have a cheap weekend. Bully for them. They wanted to talk, and it seemed my luck had changed, but I was buttonholed in the bar by a German bore who wanted to practise his English. It was not until four o'clock in the morning that I was able, bored out of my skull, to stagger away to my couch.

I was woken at 8 o'clock. By now I was pouring catarrh and could hardly open my left eye because of the boil. I was sneezing, I was cold, and I was a long way from home.

It wasn't snowing this morning, thank goodness, and I was able to wander around the town and see some of its beauty. It was indeed beautiful, and would have been even more beautiful if most of it hadn't been closed.

The autobahn was empty on the way back, Sunday driving not being a habit in Germany. A freezing three-hour stop in Munich, my cold getting worse, and back to London to find no trains running, no hotels with vacancies. I finished up sleeping on the floor of a friend's flat for the night, sharing it with the dog, who obviously wasn't as tired as I was.

At Paddington Station next day, I eventually found a train about to move off, and arrived home exhausted, feeling as if I had been to the North Pole.

Pam was all concern: 'Oh, you poor darling! What a terrible boil!'

The children looked at me with less compassion: 'Serve him right. Swinging weekends at his age!'

Before my ten-day holiday was up, by dint of careful nursing and an alcohol-free diet, I was fit enough to stagger back to work. I was welcomed by Gladys and Grace.

'Good God, Doctor Bob!' said Grace. 'You must tell us this magic formula you have for getting fit in forty-eight hours. I have an old uncle I want to finish off. By the look of you, it might just do the trick . . .'

CHAPTER 10

Planning Ahead

One of the conditions Pam made before I went to Salzburg, was that we booked our summer holiday. The only people who were available for this were Paul, Jane, Pam and I, so I booked an apartment in La Tranche, a French seaside resort south of the Sable-d'Olonne.

We love France. Nothing pleases us more than to wander along the secondary roads of France putting up in little hotels in remote villages, shopping in local markets and eating lunch – crisp French bread, a bottle of wine, cheese and pâté – by the nearest river.

We rarely travel beyond the borders of France as there is so much we haven't seen and we cannot think that there can be anything better. When we have strayed into Spain or Italy we have always been glad to get back to France.

We crossed to Cherbourg, our favourite crossing, and ambled through France spending our first night at Vitré which is a beautiful medieval town with more churches per head of population than any I have seen, and a magnificent castle. We then spent a day wandering leisurely along secondary roads with one more night's stop before arriving at La Tranche itself, to find a clean apartment overlooking the beach with good facilities. There were young French people in the apartment upstairs, who took Paul and Jane off to discos, and there was sailing and windsurfing and swimming. A nice-sized town where you could shop, a large market, plenty of boulevard cafés where you could sit in the sun and watch people go by. There wasn't a great deal of entertainment in the evening but it was always pleasant to stroll into the town and have a coffee or a drink and watch the townsfolk drift by.

There were day trips to La Rochelle, marvellous sea-food meals and plenty of muscadet, the wine of the region. It all went too quickly. We had a really splendid holiday – sunshine and sea, good wine and made friends with lots of French people.

Being a superb organiser, I decided we would cut our holiday short. Too often our holidays had been ruined by the mad dash for the boat so I had planned a hard day's driving to find somewhere in Normandy where we could spend two leisurely days unwinding before a short journey to the boat for our return home.

The journey went splendidly. We were exactly halfway up the Cherbourg peninsula at about four o'clock and started, in no hurry at all, to look for decent accommodation.

By nine o'clock and eighty miles further on, we had found nothing. What we hadn't realised was that this was a French public holiday and every single room everywhere had been booked months in advance.

In despair, worn out and exhausted, I said, 'We'll just have to sleep in the car for the night.'

We had seen a sign 'Camping – Agricultural', and as I wasn't going to park in the road we made off in the appropriate direction. The camp consisted of a field with six caravans and a tap.

I enquired of one of the campers where the farm was, so that we could ask permission to sleep there in our car for the night. In my halting French, supplemented by Jane's A-level vocabulary, we explained our position to the farmer. He picked up the telephone directory and rang friend after friend, to see if they could put us up. This was French hospitality at its best. He tried everyone he could think of, but without success.

He sat thinking for a moment, then he said, 'I have an idea.' He had a *gîte*, a letting house which he had rented to a honeymoon couple. It was a large house with three bedrooms and this was the last night of their honeymoon, so he wondered if they would mind sharing it with four bedraggled, tired Anglaises (the *gîte* not the honeymoon) on their last night.

He came back from the phone, smiling and triumphant.

'They will be pleased to have you.'

Pierre and Margaret were absolutely delightful. Perhaps they were a bit bored after seven days on their own in an isolated hamlet. Certainly they went out of their way to be hospitable.

'Not eaten yet?' This horrified them. Ham, eggs, bread, soup, pâté, all appeared. They produced a bottle of wine and I produced a bottle of duty-free gin, a litre, which I had anticipated taking home. This was a new drink to them and they drank it by the tumberful.

'It's very good,' they agreed. 'Now you must try some of our local spirit.' And this was Calvados.

By now we were almost stoned. Even Jane, who doesn't normally drink at all. But yet more wine and more Calvados were consumed. We looked through the wedding photographs, then the bride fetched her wedding dress from upstairs and eventually the bridegroom brought out his wedding suit, all of which received their full share of admiration. Finally, we all tottered to bed.

We woke in the morning to huge, steaming bowls of coffee, croissants, butter and peach jam. Names and addresses were swapped and later on, when we got back to England, we sent them a wedding present. The farmer would take nothing. How kind the French were.

We still had one more night to go in France and the public holiday was still going on so we decided to start looking for an

hotel at eleven o'clock in the morning and found a moderate
one which had its own dining room. We had lost the incentive
to stray too far. All we were thinking of, after the previous
tiring and alcoholic day, was to get home.

For dinner, Pam decided to become adventurous and have
something from the menu, which, from her French translation,
she thought was sweetbreads. She didn't like the taste of them
very much and they looked like nothing I had ever seen
before. In one corner of the dining room I could see a
television buzzing away. There was a news bulletin, something
to do with the ports. I tried to attract the family's attention.

I said, 'I think there's something wrong. They're shutting
the ports or something.'

'Oh, shut up, Dad,' said Paul. 'Just stop worrying. You worry all the time. You're going to spoil our holiday.'

I *was* worried however, and on questioning at the hotel desk, I found there had been some trouble at the ports and there was a possibility of their being blockaded the next day. My heart sank. We all had pressing commitments on our return to England.

We awoke early and turned the car radio on and found that my fears of the night before were confirmed. The French had blockaded all their ports in an industrial dispute. Motorists were advised not to go into the main ports where they might get stuck and were requested to head for Zeebrugge in Belgium where there was a chance that they might be picked up.

Zeebrugge was 380 miles away, a tortuous route across country and through all sorts of industrial towns like Lille. This was the moment that Jane, poring over her French dictionary, chirped up: 'I know what you were eating last night, Mother. It wasn't sweetbreads, it was brains.'

Whether it was just the thought of this – Pam had already been feeling queasy – or whether they were bad I don't know, but Pam was continually sick all the way from Cherbourg to Zeebrugge. I think she must have been sick at least once every half hour for the whole day, far outstripping any effort of Paul's, who up until then had been the family's champion vomiter.

Paul navigated. We sped on, first on motorways and then, on a direction from Paul, we turned right on to mile after mile of cobbled roads through Lille, all of which looked the same to me. The signposting was poor or non-existent and as far as I knew we could have been going round and round in circles.

'Why did we leave the motorway, Paul?' I asked.

'Oh,' he said, 'I thought we'd been on it too long and got a bit scared. I thought we would be better going through a town.'

It was like going through Manchester and Wigan twice, with no signposts.

Eventually we reached Zeebrugge. There was a queue of cars ahead. I had no idea whether it was short or long. The car in front of me pulled out to make an extra lane. I duly pulled out and followed it. I was met by a crowd of screaming, abusive fellow countrymen, accusing me of trying to jump the gun. I had assumed that we were just squaring up to go on the boat, I hadn't realised that there was a queue of cars two miles ahead of us and I had to back shamefacedly, passing about thirty cars, with the children and Pam hiding in their seats, pretending they weren't with me.

Eventually, after much waiting and inching forward, we got on board a huge ferry boat and arrived at Dover at eight in the morning, having had no sleep. With Pam exhausted from her vomiting, me with a sort of ache in my side, we drove back from Dover just in time for me to start the afternoon surgery.

At supper that night Paul said, 'Good idea of yours that, Dad, two resting days before the boat. It certainly settles you down.'

He managed to duck as I swung a punch at his left ear.

The ache in my side persisted. It wasn't a bad ache but it didn't go away. It was not dissimilar to, but not nearly as bad as two episodes I had had in that region before. These attacks had been what is called ureteric colic and meant that a little stone that I had formed in the kidney was passing down the tube that led from the kidney to the bladder. I had had two of these and the pain is absolutely excruciating. The first one I had had during a ward round when I was in Tadchester, the second was when we were at the furthest outpost of a trans-Saharan safari: I was the medical officer to an expedition taking some rich Americans round the Sahara who were not at all comforted by the sight of the expedition doctor writhing on the floor in pain.

Happily, after a few days of really intense pain, the first two stones passed. They say the pain is worse than childbirth. Men say that anyway – I have never met a woman who had had both a renal stone and given birth. Stones and babies have a similarity in presentation in that they come in waves.

You can be perfectly well, then suddenly, out of the blue, you get a great wave of pain going right down one side of your body. You confirm the presence of the stone by having an investigation called an intravenous pyelogram. Some fluid is squirted into your vein, which for a few seconds feels as if you had been filled with hot mustard. This is a dye which can be watched as it goes through your kidneys and it will show whether your kidneys are blocked and whether there are any stones in your kidney, ureter (the tube from the kidney to the bladder), or even in the bladder itself.

My intravenous pyelogram showed a stone halfway down my ureter, three or four times bigger than any stone I had ever seen before. The surprising thing was that it wasn't causing me as much pain as the others.

I went to Winchcombe to see the urologist.

'Well, Bob,' he said. 'Your stone is probably four times bigger than the maximum size that should pass out of the system on its own. It's not stopping the kidney working at present so I think we can afford safely to watch it. It does mean having an X-ray, perhaps every month, and testing your water regularly. If this one gets stuck, I'm afraid it will be at the junction where the ureter meets the bladder. Then I'm afraid you'll need an operation to have it removed. But occasionally big ones will pass, in spite of their size.'

My stone's progress down my ureter was very, very slow indeed. After eighteen months it had reached the end of the ureter and was poised to go through the tiny little valve into the bladder. I went to my urologist.

'I don't think it's going to go any further, Bob,' he said. 'We'll fix an operation for three weeks' time.'

'Can't you sort of reach up and grab it from there?' I said.

'No,' he said, 'it would do too much damage to the valve in the bladder. We'll fix the operation just the same.'

I was depressed by the news of this forthcoming operation and it must have shown in my attitude to the patients at the next morning surgery. One of my regulars, Mrs Cookson, a dark, energetic lady, interrupted my questioning of her by saying, 'There's something wrong, Doctor.'

'Yes,' I said impatiently, 'try and tell me what it is.'

'No,' she said. 'There's something wrong with you. You know I have second sight. For a change, you tell me what is wrong with you.'

One of Mrs Cookson's claims was that she could communicate with the spirits, particularly those with healing powers.

Reluctantly I told her about my forthcoming operation. She listened intently. When I had finished she said, 'Don't worry. I'm in touch with a spirit who's especially good at moving stones. You've been very kind to me in the past, Doctor. I'll see you don't have to have an operation.'

I did politely remind her that only last year she had had an operation to remove gallstones of her own: what was the spirit doing at this time?

'Don't laugh at me, Doctor,' she said. 'I can only get the spirits to work on other people. You just wait and see.'

She got up and determinedly walked out of the consulting room, brows furrowed, quite forgetting that she had not told me the reason for her visit. I got on with the surgery and the rest of the day's work without another thought about Mrs Cookson's offer of spiritual help.

I went home brooding about the impending operation. During the evening surgery that night I had all sorts of funny feelings down below. A bit more pain, a few aches in different places, a great desire to pass water, then, suddenly, I realised the stone was in my bladder. I rang everybody in triumph – no operation, marvellous. No hospitals for me because I knew that anything that got into the bladder could make the last few inches to daylight without trouble.

In fact, this particular stone, because of its size, didn't and it had to have a little help over the last couple of inches. But, no operation.

Could it have been Mrs Cookson's friend who gave my stone a last push? Who knows? Many unexplained things happen in medicine. Big stones like mine do pass sometimes but it was all rather eerie that it should happen the very day that Mrs Cookson said she was going to get to work on me.

The next time I saw her she was completely unsurprised about what had happened.

'I told you so, Doctor,' she said, 'but I can't do this for everybody so don't go round telling people I arranged it for you.'

I just had to leave it at that and I have had to disguise her under a pseudonym, but if she does have the powers she claims, what an asset she would be to any hospital – I think they would have to make her a consultant straight away.

I went with glee to see my urologist, taking my stone in a pot.

'Well done, Bob,' he said. 'It certainly saved you a lot of inconvenience and a major operation.'

'Yes,' I said, 'I didn't think I was meant to be in hospital.'

I was delighted because an operation would have interfered with all my summer activities, boating, seine-net fishing and whatever. I came home delighted to Pam.

'No hospitals or operations, darling,' I said. 'How about that?'

'Oh good. It's amazing how Nature takes care of you,' she said. 'Why not take this as an opportunity to lose a bit of weight and stop smoking. I noticed you have dropped back to puffing the odd pipe and cigar again.'

'Right,' I said, 'I'll become a reformed character. I am definitely going to keep clear of hospitals from now on.'

Three weeks later I had to change my mind.

CHAPTER 11

The Heart of the Matter

I felt in desperate need of a boat. Our last boat had disintegrated and here we were, living down by the river with no form of water transport. A couple of years back I had gone with Pam's father, Gerry, to Wales to explore the possibility of a boat, but it turned out to be a dud. When we had an unexpected and back-dated extra payment from the practice I went straight to the Sheridan Boat Stores. Without consulting anybody, I bought an eight-foot fibre-glass dinghy, a brand new outboard, oars, rowlocks and a fire extinguisher. They had no trolley for me to wheel it down to the river but arranged to have one made, and deliver it as soon as possible. I boarded the dinghy at the Sheridan Boat House and travelled home in it. One of the boatyard engineers came with me to explain the working of the engine and helped me carry the boat up to the house, which was a bit of a struggle. Pam was out at the time so we stowed it in the garage.

When Pam came home I said, 'I've a surprise for you, darling.'

'I know what it is,' she said. 'It's a new fridge.'

'Not quite,' I said, 'but close. Now, how can we live near a river and be boatless? We've bought a new boat.'

I could see her heart sink. I was running true to form. I had surprised her with the first car, not a Mini-Cooper or venerable MG, but a ten-hundredweight van that suited my seine-net fishing expeditions. Now we had a boat instead of a fridge. But she took it well.

'I expect you're right,' she said, 'when can we have a trip in it?'

'We really ought to wait for a trolley,' I said, 'but I think I might manage it on my back.'

'Are you sure?' she said.

'Nothing to it. It's my day off tomorrow; if it's nice, we'll have a trip down river.'

The day dawned bright and clear and I managed somehow to pack the boat on my back. By bending double, nearly kissing my knees, I could balance it and I staggered down the two hundred yards to the river. Then I went back and fetched the engine, which wasn't quite as heavy. Pam brought the petrol tank and oars, and we had a lovely trip. The tide was in, and we sped up to Tadchester Bridge: we could fairly skim along in this little boat. Then back towards the house to be able to land before the tide shot out and left us with yards of mud to wade through.

We took off the engine and various impedimenta. I hitched the boat on my back again and staggered up the hill towards the house. It really was a struggle: it took me every bit of my strength and energy and, because I was bent, it did make the muscles of my chest hurt. I felt it pushed me to my physical limit and my chest continued to ache afterwards. The pain didn't go away until I had sat down for a bit, so I rested before going out again to fetch the engine and other boating paraphernalia.

'Before we go out on the river again,' I said to Pam, 'we'll wait for the trolley.'

I thought I had strained something. My chest was a bit uncomfortable most of the next day and I was on duty that night. Coming back from a call Up-the-Hill, I felt extremely uncomfortable and I tried to discover which muscle was

causing me so much bother. I twisted this way and that to find a position that would make my driving more comfortable. I got indoors, still in discomfort, went upstairs to spend a penny, came downstairs, sat down and then felt awfully strange. It was difficult to describe: more of a tightness in my chest than a pain, and although it wasn't severe, I was frightened by it. Something was happening to me that I couldn't control. Pam was busily knitting and hadn't noticed my distress until I said, 'I think you'll have to contact one of the partners. I don't feel well. I've got this funny pain. I think I've strained myself or something.'

'Oh, darling,' she said, looking up, 'you do look white. I'll give Steve a ring.'

Steve Maxwell was round in a few minutes. While he was talking to me and taking my blood pressure the pain eased away.

'I'm sorry to be such a bother, Steve,' I said. 'Messing about with that boat. I've called you out for nothing.'

'Bob, my lad,' he said, 'we can't ignore this. We really must

77

send you to hospital and have this checked – and you are going in by ambulance.'

I couldn't believe my ears. This was what happened to *patients*.

'Are you sure?'

'I'm not sure of anything,' said Steve. 'But I want to be. You've had a chest pain, you're overweight, you smoke a pipe; this is a pain brought on by effort. I've got to make sure your heart is all right, and I can't test you properly here. It's Winchcombe for you, my lad, and the heart boys. If you're fine then you can come back and start work tomorrow but we've got to make sure.'

I felt all right now: the pain had gone but, looking back, I expect if a patient had come to me complaining of those symptoms, I would have thought he had had a heart attack.

I arrived at Winchcombe by ambulance, a new experience for me. The ambulance men, whom I knew, pulled my leg, saying, 'We knew we'd get you in the end, Doctor.' I was put in a four-bed ward where there was a monitoring unit wired up to a small television screen where I could watch my heart-beat merrily ticking along. The duty registrar came and examined me.

'Your electro-cardiogram is normal,' he said. 'We've just got to do some blood enzyme tests and keep an eye on you for a couple of days but, all being well, you'll be home on Monday.'

John Bowler, the physician, a great friend and whose overall care I was under, was away for the weekend. His registrar came in on the Sunday and repeated the ECGs. 'I'm afraid we're going to have to keep you a bit longer than I thought,' he said. 'There's evidence that you've had a heart attack. We'll know more when we get the blood tests back.'

'A heart attack!' I said. 'Surely not, Doctor!'

'Yes,' he said. 'I'm afraid they're no respector of persons.'

'But I feel perfectly well.'

'Good,' he said. 'That's the best thing you can do. But we'll get Dr Bowler to see you tomorrow.'

John came in on Monday and chastised me for trying to carry the boat on my back.

'Who do you think you are?' he said. 'Tarzan?'

Happily the blood tests were all right, but there were sure signs that my heart had protested at what I'd done to it, and there might be some underlying disease. I was to stay in hospital for a week and I was certainly to have some time off at home.

It was interesting being a patient, on the other side of the fence. I talked to the other members of the ward, one of whom was particularly ill and had had his heart restarted fourteen times, but was now doing well.

I had no further pain until the following Wednesday, when I suddenly had a recurrence. This was a blow. I rang for the nurse. I hadn't met her before, a rather grumpy staff nurse.

'Take one of these tablets then,' she said, giving me something to hold under my tongue.

'No,' I said. 'I don't want your tablet. I want the doctor who's looking after me, please.' I was a bad patient. She went out, snorting, in search of John. He came in and did further checks.

'Nothing to worry about, Bob, but we will have to have you on a regime. This won't hold up your going home but you've got to take it steadily next week. Start doing a bit more the next week, and from then on I want you really to start pushing yourself.'

It was nice to get home. I spent most mornings in bed where I could watch herons on the river, and salmon fishermen rowing out with their nets. With my telescope I could see that these men were enjoying good fishing, quite a different tale to the one they told when you met them: 'Very poor catches nowadays, doctor, we hardly get a thing.'

I felt well, I was doing an increasing amount of exercise and walking as much as two miles along the river bank in the afternoons, but I was taking a mass of tablets. Happily they seemed to work. What wasn't happy was that I would get chest pains at odd times. Whereas I might walk two miles along the bank without any trouble, I might get pain as I got up in the morning or when turning over during the night.

One evening when Ron Dickinson came for a meal I was boasting how fine I was. Then I walked upstairs and had to call him up because I had a severe spasm of pain.

I was due to see John Bowler for an exercise test a couple of days later. Pam drove me over to Winchcombe. This was going to be the crucial test. Did my heart protest when it was exercised? I had blood-pressure cuffs put round my arm and electrodes stuck all over my chest, and then had to mount a little pulpit. There were bannisters to hold on to and at my feet was a little treadmill, a conveyor belt. The last conveyor belt I had seen was in my mining days.

The machine was switched on and I started to walk along an endless 'path', holding the bannisters.

'Just imagine it's a stroll along the river bank,' said John.

As I walked John watched my ECG tracings. I had been going barely a minute when I began to get pain in my chest. 'Hop off,' cried John. 'That's enough. Come and sit down.'

I now had quite an unpleasant pain in my chest. A nurse squirted an aerosol under my tongue and in a minute the pain had gone.

'Have a cup of tea,' said John, 'and we'll have a talk in my office.'

John Bowler was the best physician I'd ever met. He was a first-class cardiologist and a general physician, as were most of the other physicians in the Winchcombe area, but he had an extra dimension. Somehow he was always able to see the whole picture of a situation. He liked seeing patients in their own homes. Patients loved having him call for a second opinion or special examinations. He was also a literary man and a great reader, in fact the best-read man I knew, with a huge collection of books.

He looked sombre in his office.

'Well, Bob,' he said, 'we have to face facts. I'm very conservative in my diagnoses, but you've obviously got extensive coronary artery disease. Nowadays there's a good treatment for it. It's surgical, and it's one of the commonest operations too. I won't minimise it – it's not a small operation – but it's very successful. If I leave you as you are, then you're not going to do much boating. Your activities are going to be very limited.

'First, we have to arrange for you to have a cardioangiogram [this meant inserting a tube into a main artery and threading it round into the blood vessels that supply the heart so they could be injected with a dye]. That will tell us if you need a coronary bypass operation. If you do, it involves taking a vein out of the leg and making three new arteries for the heart, bypassing any of the narrowed vessels that supply blood to the heart muscle itself. As Ron Dickinson says, it's the equivalent of having a new carburettor fitted.'

'You're the boss, John,' I said, with my heart sinking. I was worrying about being out of the practice . . . all my patients . . . how would the partners manage?

'Now stop worrying,' said John. 'If you'd been run over by a car they would have had to cope. Here's a chance of getting you back to full fighting fitness again. I'll make arrangements to get you up to the Middlesex Hospital in London as soon as possible. We don't do anything like this around here. In the meantime, if you can lose some weight, it will help you and them.'

I weighed in at fourteen stones two pounds at this time.

We had a pretty miserable couple of months waiting to go up to the Middlesex where an extremely nice physician did a cardioangiogram.

First I was well knocked out with an injection and from then on all I really felt was somebody pushing and prodding in my groin; it certainly wasn't a very trying experience. It meant my staying in hospital for two nights. Pam had come up with me. A friend from student days, now a consultant physician at University College Hospital round the corner, very kindly made his flat available for Pam so she could be near at hand.

My physician came the next day with diagrams and

drawings. It all looked awful. He pointed out the state my coronary arteries were in. He said that there was no real alternative but for a coronary bypass operation, but that I should do extremely well. There was quite a waiting list, but they hoped they might operate in about a month's time.

Those four weeks seemed endless, but many people have to wait for months. Things were made worse by the fact that I was having to try and lose weight. My diet was cut to the minimum and seemed to consist mainly of bran. Eventually the time for admission came and I went in on a Tuesday.

It was all bustle and activity in hospital; a physiotherapist came and explained what she was going to do to me immediately after my operation; my physician and surgeon visited me; I had chest X-rays, electrocardiograms, blood tests, urine tests, and was destined for the theatre on the Thursday. Somehow it didn't seem to bother me particularly – it's very much like boarding an aeroplane: you have to put yourself in the care of the pilot. An extremely pleasant grey-haired man and a very good-looking lady assistant came to see me to ask about height and weight. 'We look after the heart-lung machine,' they explained. One of the great advances in medicine is the fact that there is now equipment that can take over the duties of the heart during an operation. I made the mistake of calling the operators of this machine 'technicians' but they are the early members of a new society called the 'perfusionists'. However skilful surgeons have become, without these highly trained people most major heart surgery would be impossible. They also said that I wasn't to worry and that they would look after me. I could have kissed them.

I slept reasonably the night before my operation, was glad to have the pre-medication, then slipped off into a sort of limbo. I don't even recall the anaesthetist giving me an injection. The next thing I remember is waking up with bright lights in my eyes and a tube in my mouth that stopped me from talking. People were speaking to me and I was gesticulating for a pad to try and write messages. I was fully conscious or 'soggy' conscious. I seemed to have a fair number of tubes sticking out all over me. The front of my chest was uncomfortable but not painful. My left leg was bandaged and again uncomfortable, not painful.

Somebody whispered, 'His blood gases are all right. We can take this tube out.' The rubber tube in my throat was removed and I could talk.

The surgeon came and had a long chat with me, I gather only four hours after my operation. Our conversation I remembered quite clearly for days afterwards. The night was a mixture of dreams and night nurses. I was sick once which was unpleasant and I woke next morning in the intensive care unit. I was on continuous oxygen which meant that I had to wear an oxygen mask to keep my blood a bit richer, but I could take it off when I liked and have a cup of tea or other drinks.

Pam and Jane came to see me that afternoon and were absolutely delighted to see me over the operation and almost my old self again. But they looked fearfully at all the tubes sticking out of me.

The next day I was fully alert. The physiotherapist came and banged my chest every few hours. I then enjoyed a comfortable night and the following day all the tubes were taken out and I was sent back to the ward. Exactly forty-eight hours after my operation I was sitting up in my dressing gown having tea and toast. It was quite incredible.

I was encouraged that day to take a few paces. With the help of physiotherapy, over the next four or five days I increased my walking. The physiotherapist constantly enquired whether or not I was breathless or in any pain, of which I was neither, although my chest wound and leg did cause some discomfort. We reached a climax on the sixth day when I climbed two flights of stairs under her guidance.

'You don't need me any more,' she said. 'You're on your own from now on.'

I had cut down visitors to a minimum. I didn't really feel like seeing too many people, but all the children came to see me, as did Pam and one or two close friends. John Bowler did the round trip from Winchcombe in a day, just to see I was OK, and Steve Maxwell came up on behalf of the partners. The Scottish anaesthetist, who had a wonderful brogue, also visited me twice after the operation just to see all was well.

Throughout my stay the nursing was superb. The nurses were literally angels in white – in addition they all seemed terribly good-looking. I don't know who was responsible for their selection at the Middlesex Hospital, but whoever it was he had an eye for form. It was like waking up in the middle of a Miss World Competition. In spite of their good looks they were patience itself and nothing was too much trouble for them. When my heart gave an extra strong beat it wasn't always just because it had a new supercharger. I think it was related to whichever particular lovely happened to be dressing my wound, giving me a bed bath or whatever at the time.

I beamed a silent message to the spirit of Florence Nightingale for having got all this lot going.

What absolutely staggered me were the hours my surgeon and physician kept. I thought we were hard working in general practice but they seemed to work night and day. My surgeon would call in, often as early as seven in the morning before he started his list, just to see all was well, then again at night, perhaps after seeing somebody else.

'I haven't come to see you because you're ill or anything,' he said. 'I just popped in because you're a doctor.' He was a real treasure.

My physician, who was the gentlest and kindest of men with a great capacity for reassuring, for seven days called to see me every morning at eight o'clock. He was immaculately turned out, always with a fresh flower in his buttonhole. These two men, their team and John Bowler represented medicine at its highest and best; my only worry was that if they continued the pace of life, work and dedication that they did, they would all eventually be candidates for the operation they were performing themselves.

I had little pain. There were various preparations that I could have had for it, but they made me feel muzzy so I asked for something much milder which coped with the discomfort. The food was good; I had a small appetite but there was a menu and you could choose what you wanted. There was a TV in my room and when I at last felt well enough, I turned it on – straight into a film about cardiacs and bypass surgery in Australia, where apparently this operation is more common than having your appendix taken out. I switched off hurriedly. I had had enough of bypasses for a while.

The ten days after the operation did drag a bit. I had expected pain, but what pain I did feel was much less than I had anticipated, and I felt hot and a bit strange. The surgeon pointed out that this was my body reacting to the insult of being carved up. Nobody has control of his auto-immune system and it just takes time to settle down: the funny temperatures didn't matter. I was on various drugs to rid my body of excess water and keep the blood from clotting. Each day I was encouraged to walk a little further and be more active. My blood pressure and pulse and heart rates were monitored every four hours until the evening of the ninth day when the nurse came in.

'We're not bothering you tonight,' she said. 'You're off tomorrow.'

On the tenth day, they took all the stitches out, and there seemed to be yards of them. I had a very nice little line down the middle of my chest and a very smart scar the whole length of my leg. I was given the silkiest, most expensive-looking, full-length elastic stocking to wear for a time on the leg. Then home, glorious home.

The family were waiting for me with a bottle of champagne. John Bowler had apologised for not being able to welcome me home, as he was going that weekend to Yorkshire where his mother was very ill, but bless him, that first evening, at the end of motoring all the way from Yorkshire, up the drive came his familiar car. He checked me over completely.

'They've done a marvellous job, Bob,' he said. 'But just you make haste slowly. Ring me at any time if you have any problems or worries. Take it quietly for a couple of weeks, pottering about the house. From then on you are going into full training and there's no reason why you shouldn't be back at work in another ten weeks.'

I spent the first four days at home, just lying in my bed, thanking God that everything had gone so smoothly and so well, looking out over the river watching boats go by. I had landmarks in my progress, like my first bath and my first shower, and I started to come downstairs, gradually increasing my walking, going a bit further every day along the river bank until I was on a two-mile schedule again. It was cold and I had to wrap up warmly against the wind. I was two stone lighter than before the operation and I was determined to try and maintain my new weight.

All the partners came to see me. John Bowler popped in from time to time. Happily I had neither pain nor breathlessness and I now knew nearly every blade of grass along the river bank. I was due to go over to Winchcombe after eight weeks for a test to see how everything was working, and it was good to be alive. Pam and I, who are not really churchgoers, made a couple of trips to St Mary's Parish Church to thank whoever it might be that ordains the way of our lives for having kept a benevolent and kindly eye on me over these last few weeks.

CHAPTER 12

What the Stars did not Foretell

When I had been home eight weeks, faithfully doing my daily exercises along the river bank, I went for a check-up with John Bowler at the Winchcombe Hospital.

'We'll just see how the new plumbing is working, Bob,' he said. 'You've got to have an exercise ECG (electro-cardiogram).'

I remembered my last one, when I had lasted only a few minutes, and hoped to God as they wired me up that I would do better this time. I was slightly embarrassed because for some reason in this particular department of the hospital there wasn't a cubicle to undress in; so I just started taking my clothes off. I didn't mind this in front of John Bowler, but there were also a couple of technicians on hand. I was very conscious that, although I had lost nearly two stone in weight, I still had a few rolls of fat around the middle.

I mounted the conveyor belt, gripped the handles and started my walk. The pace increased, it became harder and harder work, but there were no bad results, no pain and I wasn't much out of breath.

'Cut!' said John Bowler, as if he were directing a film. The roller came to a halt and I hopped off.

'Fine, Bob', he said. 'Everything's working. You *are* unfit you know – your pulse rate was up in just a few minutes – but all's well. You will have to increase the amount of exercise you are doing. You can walk on the flat until you are blue in the face, but that's not enough, you must start doing some hills.'

I got dressed, thankful to have passed this hurdle.

As Pam drove me back to Tadchester, I told her about John's instructions. As we were experiencing one of our worst winters for some years, telling me to increase my walking exercise was like inviting Captain Oates to walk out into the storm.

Pam said, 'There's only one answer: we'll have to have a sunshine holiday somewhere.'

It wasn't as easy as we thought. To get a last-minute sunshine holiday at the beginning of February was nigh impossible. Finances limited us to a choice between Tenerife, Grand Canary, Madeira and Lanzarote. Southern Spain, the Algarve, Majorca or Minorca would have done for me but Pam maintained that she wanted a tan and had checked up on daytime temperatures.

We rang travel agency after travel agency. Nobody could find us anything before the end of March. We were joined in our search by Henry Long, a fellow 'walking-wounded' patient of mine who, a couple of months previously, had had a total knee replacement. We thought it might be a good idea to make a foursome with Henry and his wife.

When I had almost given up and resigned myself to thermal underwear and the beach at Sanford-on-Sea, a travel agent rang to say she had found us a holiday in the Canary Islands, which was not only first class but in addition was cut-price. It sounded too good to be true. We were guaranteed minimum four-star accommodation but would not know which hotel we were to stay at until we arrived at Las Palmas. We had to make up our minds straight away as the booking was for the following week.

I rang Henry Long to break the good news, but his wife, a former air hostess, would have none of it.

'I'm sorry, Doctor Bob,' she said, 'I've heard this story before. I never go anywhere unless I know exactly which hotel I'm going to. You might land up anywhere.'

Feeling mean, but knowing I had to follow John Bowler's instructions about getting some uphill exercise, I chided her for her lack of faith in human nature and travel agents, and booked the trip for Pam and myself.

We arrived at Las Palmas Airport in brilliant sunshine and high winds. A smart courier was efficiently herding people together in groups for different buses. We were to go to a hotel in the southern half of the Island. She gave us the name of our hotel, which meant nothing; it was not even in the brochure of the tour company.

In the half-hour bus trip from the airport our courier informed us that our hotel was one of the largest on the Island. This was encouraging. I've always thought of big as beautiful and I looked forward to breakfasting in bed in a sun-filled room, cutting a dashing, if scarred, figure by the side of the pool, and enjoying long leisurely meals in the dining room, where I would of course eat sparsely and go for the quality of the food rather than the quantity.

The hotel was huge. We were dropped at the door with the vague promise that there were porters inside; however at that particular moment they were all missing. We struggled to the desk with our cases. We were allotted room 795. The numbers went up to 895. We set off through concrete corridors, I dragging a heavy case which I'm sure was against doctor's orders, to find our room, which was as far away as possible from the centre of the hotel.

The room had been an apartment with a kitchen and refrigerator. The kitchen was now out of use and curtained off. We did have a sunlit balcony however – unfortunately, it overlooked a building site. With a hotel of this size, one end of it was bound to overlook a building site of some sort. The bathroom was shabby, with paint peeling off the bottom half of the door; the end of the bath was rusty and the bath and shower taps encrusted. Happily they all worked.

89

My ideas of relaxed dining were brought to a sudden halt. All the meals were self-service; room-service was non-existent. My anticipated leisurely breakfasts and dinners were replaced by meals eaten off trays after patient queuing. George Orwell obviously had a hand in planning this hotel: not only did you have to produce an identity card to get your room key, which was reasonable, but it also had to be shown when you entered the restaurant, where you were given further cards. If you were so indulgent as to order something additional to the set menu – for example, a glass of orange juice or a boiled egg for breakfast – it was marked on this card and you had to pay for it before you were allowed to leave the restaurant. Breakfast and dinner, which were served in the restaurant, were spread out affairs. Breakfast was from eight to eleven and dinner from six-thirty to nine-thirty, but during those times about sixteen hundred people had to filter those two points of entry. I wondered what Pam's father, Gerry, would have made of it all. I think he would have blown the place up.

Breakfast was a buffet of rolls, butter, jams, marmalade, cold meats and cheese, with purchaseable extras such as fried eggs, bacon and boiled eggs. Tea and coffee came from a press-button machine. For the evening meal there was a tremendous salad buffet, usually supplemented by cold meat and ham, and a vast array of various vegetables. A vegetarian's delight. There were two tables where hot food was available, meat and fish. On the first night I could clearly see that the meat dish was sausages and I was told that the fish was cuttlefish. There was no other night when I could identify either the meat or the fish.

When we ventured out of the hotel it was obvious that George Orwell *had* designed the whole area. It was purely a holiday centre, with hotels and apartments stretching for miles. There was no indigenous population, no local markets, no traditional or local work: it was all concrete buildings, supermarkets and shops that all sold the same things. The beach, twenty minutes away, was windswept with rows of umbrellas – not standing up, but lying on their sides as protection against the wind.

Our first purchase was a water heater and a small enamel teapot, which meant that we could make a life-saving cup of tea at any hour of the day or night. The only time we were unable to do this was the last two days of our week when – having then been three days without hot water and trying to heat a sinkful, as opposed to a teapotful – we blew the electricity in the room. Miraculously, the electricity was restored within an hour, but the water situation was not quite as bright.

From the third day the hot water stopped appearing; on the fourth day we had no water at all. As we had been advised not to drink the tap water and there were swimming pools to bathe in, this did not seem too much of a hardship. We were well stocked up with bottles of drinking water but what I had forgotten was that toilets need flushing. Being quick-witted I realised that it wouldn't be too long before our own bathroom became rather high, so I shot down to the toilets just outside the public dining room, to find that at least sixteen hundred other residents of the hotel had been even more quick-witted. The water was restored on the fifth day, and on the sixth day tepid water came through the hot tap, meaning that we could have a semblance of a bath before we returned to the UK.

I tackled our courier on 'minimum four-star accommodation'. She said 'This is the fault of the travel agents. They don't read the instructions properly. Four-star is no better than this anyway.'

Other indignant passengers had all been enticed with four-star promises, including one woman whose daughter was a travel agent and was quite sure that she was giving her mum a treat. Our hotel had firmly emblazoned on its front 'Three Stars', rather Spanish stars at that. Henry Long's wife was absolutely right.

The most irritating thing of all was that the hotel was absolutely ideal – ideal, that is, for somebody recuperating from a coronary bypass operation, who needed to exercise and not to put on weight. My room was exactly three hundred yards from the dining room and reception and there was no room service, so unless I wanted to starve or hoard food in my room, I had to walk a couple of miles a day just for food. The food was mainly salad and being self-service meant that there was nobody pushing you to eat anything.

We were twenty minutes from a splendid beach, splendid in spite of the wind, and there was an uphill climb back of a mile and a half. This was just what the doctor ordered, and, hurrah, it became a little easier each day. The sun shone, Pam got her tan and I came back confident, feeling fitter and for the first time after any holiday, not having put on any extra weight.

Apart from the basic accommodation offered by the hotel, other facilities were first class, but of course you paid extra for them. There was a very good independent restaurant, a steak bar, a beer bar, a disco, and a nightclub. For the young people there were plenty of activities: surfboarding, sailing, wind-surfing, water-skiing, snorkelling, swimming and tennis; and an abundance of nightclubs of the nicest possible sort.

In the brochure of another tour company, our hotel was described as active, lively and ideal for young people. I was lucky, but if Henry and his wife had come, it would have been a complete disaster for them and I would hate to think how anybody who was old and infirm would have managed.

I suspected that this hotel was a dumping ground for the other hotels, and that tour operators would fill up the four-star places and four-star-minus places and anybody left over would go to this monstrosity. Or possibly, as the hotel was so central, it was the other way round. I learnt a lesson, as Henry's wife had, that you are very vulnerable when making last-minute bookings.

For many of our fellow travellers, however, this was the holiday of a lifetime. If the main objective of the holiday was to get laid, this was the place to come. All the unaccompanied ladies on our trip – including two very elderly women – irrespective of size, looks or whatever, had all been very personally propositioned.

As we boarded the bus to return to the airport and home, an English girl who travelled out with us was having difficulty disentangling herself from a tall blond German in the hotel entrance. She eventually made it, and scrambled, breathless and flushed, onto the bus. Here am I, I thought, grumbling that we didn't get the four-star rating we were offered. I bet this girl would give this holiday a minimum of six . . .

CHAPTER 13

Back to Work

I came back after my Canary Islands holiday bronzed and raring to go to work. I felt stiff after my daily trips up the hill but felt I could cope with anything. I was quite happy to go back full-time but both John Bowler and Steve Maxwell said, 'There's no question of your starting full-time staight away. You've got to have at least six to eight weeks feeling your way back into work. You haven't practised medicine for six months; you haven't driven for six months: it's not going to be as easy as you think.'

They were very kind to me about my absence from the practice. It had put an extra workload on them all and had cost them money: they had insisted on paying me in full all the time I was away, as well as paying for the locums.

I started work again exactly twelve weeks after my operation. I was to do part-time until I felt I could cope with full-time duties again. It felt strange going back. Time did funny things: one minute it felt as though I hadn't been there for years, and the next minute I felt that it was only days ago that I had last seen a patient. Patients who were in ante-natal care when I went off, now came back with babies, but with most of the old regulars time had stood still. Conditions, conversations and prescriptions were exactly the same as before.

Most of my work had been covered by a delightful young lady doctor, Catherine, who had won the hearts of them all. I think secretly that most of my patients would have been quite happy to have continued with her, especially the local boys' boarding school. She was an excellent locum, though she only looked old enough to be a schoolgirl herself.

For six weeks I worked Mondays, Tuesdays, Thursdays and Fridays from about ten until six, doing no night calls or weekends. Then I went back to full duties, which presented all sorts of nightmares, and nightmares, by definition, come at night. At first I found it very difficult to cope with night calls: I had lost some confidence, and it was hard to gear up again to go back into action. I used to lie awake when I was on call, wondering whether the phone would ring, what the problem might be and whether I could cope. In my first few weeks back I was called practically every night I was on. One awful night I had four separate calls out. Gradually, however, things started to fall into place. I continued to get chest pains; they had warned me that I could for at least a year. I had to remember that my rib cage had been wired together, and that it would take some time to settle down. Fortunately, the ever-patient John Bowler would always be happy to check me over and say, 'You're doing fine. It's going to take at least a year before everything calms down. Your heart's fine and you've got a new lease of life. Make the best of it.'

In my early days back, I had an example of sheer unselfish courage. It was an urgent night call to a man with a heart attack who lived in an isolated country cottage. I left straight away, but apparently just after I had left the telephone rang again. It was the man's wife. She said, 'I feel certain my husband is dead. I do know Dr Clifford has had a heart operation . . . it's a long way to come . . . so, if he hasn't left yet please tell him not to hurry.' This was courage with a capital 'C'.

I had certain objectives. I wanted to have a break when I'd

been fully back at work three months and a week on the Thames in a cabin cruiser with Joe and Lee Church was just what the doctor ordered. It was a tremendous success, the ever-fit Joe leapt about doing all the heavy work while I steered the boat and Pam and Lee made sure we had a full table. I didn't even have to do the washing up. Joe and Lee were naturalists and gave another dimension to our holiday. They were always pointing things out – kestrels, lampreys and the like.

We travelled from Wallingford to Lechlade and back in glorious sunshine and spotted forty different species of birds in one day. If we hadn't had Joe and Lee with us I doubt if we would have noticed more than a dozen. We were chased into Eynsham Lock by the most huge magnificent cob swan whom we had fed the night before. It flew alongside beating the outboard engines with its wings; we were glad to see the lock gates shut behind us.

'He's a one, he is,' said the lock keeper. 'Think yourself lucky you're not in an open boat. He jumps on the back and plays hell. He just doesn't like engines.'

I felt much better after the holiday and gradually took over my full work load, though it did take at least a year for all my aches and pains to go. By the end of the summer I was trundling my boat up and down to the river – on the trolley, not on my back. Although my boat had triggered off my heart trouble, the problem had been there all the time. Carrying the boat on my back just drew attention to the fact that I had coronary artery disease. In a way the boat was almost a lifeboat: without its warning I could have gone on and had a major heart attack out of the blue. But I was caught before I had any heart damage and was given three new arteries. As Ron Dickinson said, 'You've got the best heart in the practice now – a supercharger.'

I was having a drink with C.P. in the Tadchester Arms about a year after my operation.

'You know, Bob, I reckon your profession's a damn sight

more useful than mine,' said C.P. 'Look what it's done to the two of us. We've both been given a new lease of life, by skilled dedicated men. I wish I'd been a doctor. My work means bugger all by comparison.'

'Rubbish, C.P.,' I said. 'We can't advance in medicine. All we can do is get better at keeping people alive, from then on it depends what they do with their lives. The only area that we can advance in is the arts and your work is invaluable; you're a communicator and the most skilled, humorous and articulate one I know. One of your fishing articles or philosophical tales will do more good than most of my medicines. Wordsworth said that a poet's job was to describe people's experience and enrich them by doing so. A writer's job is exactly the same. You give more help, comfort, humour and hope in your columns than you can ever imagine. What I do abhor about your whole conduct is the utter waste.'

'What do you mean, utter waste?' said C.P., looking bewildered.

I said, 'You waste so much time talking when you could have been drinking another pint.'

'Point taken,' said C.P. 'We'll have to find a pub where they serve quarts.'

CHAPTER 14

Family Engagements

After qualifying at Kingston – where one of his great joys was helping every week in the Citizens' Advice Bureau – Trevor went to Warwick University to do a master's degree in law. It was all very complicated and quite beyond my understanding. I wondered whether he might have preferred medicine after all, but when he helped me once to stitch up a patient in an emergency, it was obvious that he was not a natural surgeon.

He had an urge to write, and wrote very well. He was a beginning-to-end writer; he would sit down and shut himself away and write until he had finished. However, he had no success. He wrote at least two full-length novels, one of which was a rather strange book about a marathon for the physically handicapped, but he did show an ability. Home on holiday one evening he was sitting restlessly at a typewriter.

'I don't know what to write,' he said. 'I don't seem to be getting anywhere.'

'Why not try writing for one of the medical magazines?'

'About what?'

'How about,' I suggested, 'the problems of being a doctor's son?'

He hammered away for the next three hours and then presented me with the following manuscript:

The presumption that a doctor's son will eventually evolve into a doctor by some strange process which even Darwin could not have foreseen, is one that is accepted throughout the world. Even as a child, when the time came to re-enact the battle for Iwojima (or whatever other film John Wayne had appeared in on television the night before), I was always chosen as the first-aid man. This did not particularly distress me at the time because at least it meant that I never got killed, but I found little joy in treating my 'winged' cronies and missing out on the real action. As a protest one day I actually made a charge from the rear, hoping that one of the supposedly slant-eyed urchins from Up-the-Hill would shoot me in a way that would enable me to die like a hero. But the 'enemy' just stared at me with wondrous eyes and said 'You're not supposed to do that,' and I was forced to slink back to the rusty pram that served as our field ambulance.

My contemporaries were not the only ones who accepted this position. Whenever my father introduced me to one of his friends, I would invariably be greeted with the question, 'Going to follow in Dad's footsteps then?' In my very early youth, I would either mumble in the affirmative in the hope that I might receive a raise in pocket-money, or grin widely and make some precocious remark which my father had rehearsed with me the day before.

However, as I grew older, I began to notice things – the fact that my father frequently had to break off in the middle of meals, even on Christmas day sometimes, to visit a patient; the fact that at least twice a week he was called out in the middle of the night; the fact that he was frequently summoned to the door to stem the bleeding of a horrifically wounded patient who looked like an extra from a Sam Peckinpah film. All these things gradually put me off the idea of entering the medical profession.

I confessed my worries to my mother, and she seemed mightily relieved that she would not one day have to answer the phone for two doctors. My father, too, was by no means overcome with distress when he heard my decision. 'Good boy,' he said, tears of genuine emotion running down his cheeks. 'All has not been in vain.'

My rejection of medicine was helped by the fact that I had the least aptitude for science of anyone I have ever known. Having failed my general science O-level at Grade 8 after writing for three hours on the delights of the cuckoo pint, a career in either the arts or the social sciences was assured. As it turned out, law was the unlucky target of my aspirations. This was welcomed by all concerned as it meant that if my younger brother eventually decided to become an architect, there would be three professional men in the family. For my sister it was more difficult. As we all refused to let her join one of our own chosen professions (we were afraid she might do better than us), there were few professions left. My brother's suggestion that she might join the oldest one was instantly and very violently quashed.

One would have thought that my standing as 'the doctor's son' would be forgotten by my friends and relatives. True, my choosing of the law was a temporary haven, but unfortunately my father's patients still presumed that I was conversant with medical lore. Frequently I would be assailed over the telephone with symptoms of obscure diseases and my efforts to explain my lack of knowledge were usually ignored. A typical telephone conversation might run as follows:

Patient: Hello, is that the doctor?

Me: No, I'm afraid he's out at present, can I take a message?

Patient: Who's that?

Me: This is the doctor's son.

Patient: Oh! Well, you'll do. It's my daughter Rosie – she's got this rash on her bottom . . .

Me: Well, actually . . .

Patient: It's really painful and I was wondering if you could have a look at it . . .

Me: I'm not a doctor actually.

Patient: (after a long pause) But you said you were the doctor's son?

100

Me: Well, yes . . .

Patient: Well, that's all right then. Now this rash, it spreads right down her . . . etc. etc.

One can do nothing about fighting this sort of presumption and the only solution is to play along with it. Having been subjected to my father's telephone procedure from a very early age, it was quite easy to pick up such phrases as 'Where does it hurt?', 'Have you tried giving her an aspirin?', and even the word 'Yes' repeated in a thoughtful way at regular intervals. One can usually stall for time until they realise that you are an imbecile and ring off, or, as sometimes happens, my father arrives home, in which case I can say 'I think I'll hand you over to the doctor who specialises in these rashes.' I have even occasionally reprimanded a patient with the old chestnut, 'I wish you had rung earlier when these symptoms were first made apparent,' but my father has discouraged this as he holds the patent for that particular remark.

The crunch came when I actually had to help my father with a case. He was giving me a lift to the shops one day when a neighbour came running out of his gate, shouting that his wife had fallen over and split her head open. As was normal for a doctor's son, I remained in the car and laughed at the names in my father's appointment book, but after a while he came out of the neighbour's house and beckoned for me to follow him in. I obeyed, expecting to be presented with a cup of tea. Much to my horror, I found that I had to help my father do a temporary stitch-up of the lady's head. I won't go into details, but the operation took a lot longer than it usually took my father on his own. Afterwards the lady's husband said, 'I can see you're not going to follow your Dad.'

After that, word must have got round. When I answered the phone, patients would either ask for a proper doctor or even, on occasions, for my younger brother whose medical reputation was as yet untarnished. One lady who heard about the fiasco actually tried to report me to the British Medical Council until someone gently told her that, when it came to medicine, I was as much an innocent as she.

101

I am one of the lucky ones. To all other doctors' sons I have one message – Give in. Put down your towel, your spade or your briefcase and pick up a stethoscope because, whatever you actually want to do in life, everyone else will presume differently and there is no escape. Console yourself with the thought that perhaps, in the future, doctors' children will be presented at birth with licences to practice medicine – at least it will avoid a lot of confusion.

* * *

'I think that's excellent,' I said: 'I'm sure you'll sell it, but if it comes back, send it off to another magazine the next day.'

He posted his manuscript to a medical magazine. Four days later it was back. He posted it to *Pulse* the next day: within a week they had accepted it and paid him thirty pounds for his effort. He was an established writer now, being paid real money.

After leaving Warwick he lectured at the South Bank Polytechnic in London, but law and his conscience were not easily squared. He said that he could only consider academic law, as he felt that there were two laws: one for the people who had money and one for the people who hadn't.

Warwick University had encouraged his enthusiasm for acting, and now it began to show. In the evening he worked at theatres, behind the bar or as assistant catering manager, but the stage was obviously his first love. He lectured on law for two years and then announced: 'Dad, I want to be an actor. Would you see me through acting school? I've got to get this out of my system.'

'Yes,' I said, bravely (wishing he'd never asked). 'You've got to do what you feel you want to, or at any rate give it a try.'

I couldn't imagine Trevor as an actor. He had got rather heavy now and was certainly never very athletic. He had trials for various drama schools and, after a year, found a place in the Ealing Drama Studio. The bad news was that he couldn't get a grant. However, he was adamant that he would pay his fees.

So he arranged a loan with our friendly bank manager and I supported him for the year in London. I thought it was just a phase that would pass and he'd soon get back into law.

We saw several student productions of plays and I must say I thought he acted well. To our great pride he won, in the face of all the other drama students in the country, the first prize in the Carleton Hobbs Radio Award, which meant that as soon as he had finished his drama school he would have six months with the BBC Radio Rep.

He was busily writing at the same time but now his main themes were plays. He won the International Student Playscript Competition and was commissioned by Alan Ayckbourn to write a play for the Scarborough Theatre. New fields opened up for Trevor; he was always fully employed, sometimes in musicals, sometimes in plays. He would appear in bits of television and films. He played a prominent part in one of the Guinness TV commercials, and as well as performing in one of the Granada *Ladykiller* series, he wrote one of the episodes.

The family became Trevor groupies and would travel whenever we could to see him in his productions. I travelled out to the East End one night to see him play a major rôle in *The Ragged Trousered Philanthropists*, an old book long remembered, and did my parental duty by sweating through a three-hour performance of *Hamlet* on the top of the Barbican in a tent that wasn't properly ventilated.

In following Trevor around we discovered new towns that we had always meant to visit. We went to York to see him in *Having a Ball*, to the Aldwych Theatre in London for *Andy Capp*, to Chesterfield to see a rock opera. This was round about Christmas time and we took the opportunity of going as a family, Paul, Gill and Jane coming with us.

The day after the rock opera, we went to Dinnington, the old mining village where I had been a Bevin Boy. The Dinnington folk were still the marvellous, kindly people I remembered. They couldn't take us down the pit but they showed us round the pit top. All the children were fascinated by the mine and the miners.

We went to see my old landlady and her husband, Auntie and Ike Bradley, in their old people's bungalow. It was about thirty-five years since I had been their lodger. Pam had met Auntie and Ike Bradley before and we'd taken Trevor up when he was a baby. We went into the sitting room; there was Ike with Auntie Bradley in a wheelchair, she hadn't been well. There was a budgie, several generations removed from the one in my time.

Paul was the spitting image of me when I was his age. At the sight of him, Auntie Bradley broke down.

'There's our Bob,' she sobbed. The clock had turned back thirty-five years.

Paul and Gill had been going together for four years and Gill came with us on all our family holidays. Her father was now training horses, first in Hong King and later in India, and we used to see him and Gill's mother, Liz, a woman of great beauty, when they were home on leave. Liz was staying with us one Christmas, Eddie being stuck in India, when Paul suddenly said, 'I have an announcement to make.' We all stood silently with our drinks. 'Gill and I are going to get engaged.'

'Oh don't be silly,' said Pam.

'I'm serious,' said Paul, thinking his great moment was being stolen, but we had got so used to them being around together that we thought they were engaged anyway.

'That's marvellous,' we said. 'When are you thinking of getting married?'

'I thought 1995 would be a good year,' said Paul, jumping as Gill kicked him.

I don't know if it was something in the air or whether engagements are contagious, but for a time Steve Maxwell had been behaving rather strangely. For fifteen years he had lived away from the practice in a cottage on a smallholding, taking care of the retired senior partner and his wife and their younger daughter.

I don't know what he did in the evenings; he would never accept an invitation to a meal and never encouraged us to go and see him.

Fairly recently the old senior partner had died and Steve had taken a small flat in Tadchester.

Just after Christmas, one morning during coffee, Steve, who looked as embarrassed as I'd ever seen him look, and he must have been sixty-four or sixty-five at the time, said, 'I have an announcement to make – I'm engaged.'

'That's absolutely marvellous,' we said. 'For real this time, Steve? We remember your last engagement.'

Steve's last 'engagement' had been about ten years previously when a mental patient had tried to announce it in the *Tadchester Gazette*, but fortunately the proprietor had checked with Steve first.

There was some story, true or not, that Steve had promised the old senior partner that he would never marry while he was

105

alive. He had been absolutely marvellous, taking care of the partner's ageing wife and sick daughter and now at last he was going to have some time for a life of his own.

He always took less holiday than we did; he used to spend a fortnight during the first half of the year putting the potatoes in his smallholding and a second fortnight later in the year, digging them up. He worked every Sunday. Perhaps things were going to change now.

He was marrying an ex-schoolmistress from an old Tadchester family who had a removal business and antique shops. Nancy Doone was a lovely lady, just right for Steve. What a waste that he hadn't been able to have a family and children of his own.

John Denton came into the surgery to have one of his many little septic cuts treated a few days later.

'I'm very pleased to see that Dr Maxwell is engaged.'

'Why does it please you, John?' I asked.

'Well,' he said, 'I've always thought what a nice young woman that Nancy Doone was and I said to a pal the other day, last week it was actually, "You know, I think that Nancy Doone isn't long for this world. She must be very ill. That Dr Maxwell's car is parked out there nearly all the time lately." '

Steve was a very private person – and to keep such a secret in a place like Tadchester, you had to be.

CHAPTER 15

It'll be All Right on the Night

For several years Pam had been a leading player in the Tadchester Drama Society, but this year she had opted out of acting to help found a junior branch, the Tadchester Youth Theatre, and direct its productions.

Though Tadchester was a lively enough town in the summer season, there wasn't much for the local youngsters to do after all the holiday attractions closed down in the autumn. The boredom this brought about had led to occasional outbreaks of vandalism and a few confrontations between juvenile or teenage groups. The Youth Theatre was a great idea for getting kids off the streets, and there was no lack of recruits. So many youngsters enrolled, in fact, that the problem was in finding parts or backstage jobs for them all.

The solution was a bumper Christmas pantomime with a cast of thousands – well, dozens – and C.P. helped with the script for *The Potty Panto Cavalcade*, a director's nightmare including characters from *Cinderella*, *Aladdin*, *Dick Whittington*, *Babes in the Wood*, *Sleeping Beauty*, *Mother Goose*, *Humpty Dumpty*, *Little Bo Peep*, *Little Red Riding Hood*, *Robinson Crusoe*, and with a Demon King thrown in for good measure.

Night after night, Pam came in from rehearsals worn out

and in a growing state of despair. The kids had not yet grasped the idea that there was more to putting on a show than just larking about on stage.

'They're not bothering to learn their lines properly,' said Pam. 'And the older ones keep nipping out to the pub for a quick one. Some of them are practically legless by the end of the evening. I shudder to think how the show's going to turn out.'

'Don't worry, darling,' I said, speaking from my encyclopaedic knowledge of showbiz. 'Shakespeare probably had the same trouble. It'll be all right on the night.'

I'm sure Shakespeare did have his problems. But if the first night of *Hamlet* was anything like that of *The Potty Panto Cavalcade*, it's a wonder there was a second.

The lights dimmed over the hushed audience, the front row of which consisted of Tadchester's leading civic dignitaries, with the Mayor and Mayoress in full regalia, chains of office and all. They were certainly doing Pam's company proud. In return, they were certainly given an entertaining evening, though Pam still breaks into a cold sweat every time she thinks of it.

One or two of the props had slight structural imperfections which had not been apparent at rehearsal, but which revealed themselves almost as soon as the curtain went up.

'*I'll cast a spell over all the land,*' said the Fairy Queen, confidently.

'*With just one wave of my magic – Whoops!*'

As she waved her hand, perhaps a mite too vigorously, the sheet-steel star shot off the tip, hit the stage and bounced into the orchestra pit, missing by only half an inch the jugular of the first trombone.

This brought roars of laughter and applause from everybody. Everybody, that is, except the first trombone, who sat there chalk-white with the 'Ffffttt!' of the spinning star still in his ears.

'Sheet-steel?' I said to Pam later. 'A bit robust for a magic

108

wand, wasn't it?'

'I realise that now,' said Pam. 'But one of the boys is an apprentice at Turner's Metals. He volunteered to make the star and have it machine-polished until it glistened. I couldn't say no, could I?'

To the tune of *Jingle Bells*, the Magic Sleigh glided to the centre of the stage, pulled by two lusty lads in the wings, hauling on a nylon clothesline. The Snow Princess stood up in the sleigh, made a moving speech about the Message of Christmas, then declaimed:

'Tis far away I now must go,
'To Santa's land of ice and snow . . .'

This was the cue for the lads to haul on the line and pull the sleigh smoothly into the wings. They hauled a split-second too soon and with more power than was strictly necessary.

As the Snow Princess was curtseying gracefully into a sitting position, the sleigh shot from under her, dumping her ungracefully onto the stage, and careered into the wings. The lads on the rope overbalanced against the hardboard pine forest which masked them from the audience, knocking the thing over and landing in a tangled heap on top of it. Each loudly blamed the other in phrases which caused blushes among the gentler souls in the audience, and a horizontal fist-fight broke out.

The scenery was a problem all through the show. It had been made from whatever scraps the crew of amateur chippies and painters had been able to cadge, and was less than sturdy. It was a bit disconcerting when a castle turret crashed to the boards at an accidental touch from one of the Broker's men. And Peaseblossom's entrance was spoiled when her five-year-old foot felled the Enchanted Oak.

Dick Whittington rose to the occasion, though. As the Enchanted Oak hit the deck, he turned to the audience and observed:

'My, oh my! Oh, what a fright!
'The wind is strong in the wood tonight!'

The sound effects, too, made their contribution to theatrical history. The sound effects engineer, to give him his full title, was an eighteen-year-old who had only recently discovered the euphoria of alcohol. He had dived into the pub before the show for a few swift ones, made them a few large swift ones because of the pressure of time, and thereafter was not at the peak of his form. The result was that several times the cast seemed to be gifted either with extra-sensitive hearing or powers of premonition.

Buttons was explaining to Cindrella why he could not shower her with the luxuries she deserved:

'Alas, dear Cinders, I too am poor.

'Hark! Who's that knocking at the door?'

Whoever was knocking must have been using a sponge, for all the audience heard. Buttons tried again, ad-libbing desperately:

'Hear it, Cinders? Listen once more.

'I'm sure there's somebody at the door.'

Not a sound.

Buttons hissed to the wings for somebody to kick the effects man, and in a lather of sweat made one last attempt:

'Leave the jobs, Cinder. I'll sweep the floor

'As soon as I've found out who's AT THE DOOR!!!'

Knock-knock . . . came a noise.

Knock-knock . . .

Naturally, the door stuck as Buttons tried to open it. After a few frantic tugs, which left the door firmly jammed but threatened to bring down the whole wall of the castle kitchen, he called:

'The door is stuck. Alas! Alack!

'Whoever you are, go round the back!'

As Buttons peered expectantly to Stage Right, enter the Fairy Queen, Stage Left, waving her reconstituted wand ever so gently.

Abanazar had prop trouble, too, when the magic lamp failed to ignite. He rubbed and rubbed, but the disposable cigarette lighter in the spout just refused to function. Full marks for ad-libbers that night.

Abanazar saved the situation by saying:

'This magic lamp's not up to scratch.

'Has anyone out there got a match?'

Much more suitable for a family audience than the legendary old-time professional comic and amateur drunk who hit the same trouble in pantomime in Liverpool. His ad-lib was plausible, if not in the best of taste:

'Oh, dearie me! Oh, what a shame!

'Somebody's pissed on the magic flame!'

Just before the transformation scene which saw Cinders all dressed up for the ball, there was a clopping sound backstage which I first took to be another mistake of the effects man. But then there came the noise of an unmistakable and gargantuan fart, followed a couple of minutes later by an irritated 'Neigh!'

Thank God for the neigh: it illustrated to the coarser elements in the audience, who were still falling about, that the farting sound was not the product of the effects man, but of the Shetland pony borrowed to take Cinders to the ball.

The pony had been kept outside the hall in a horsebox until it was time for its appearance. Although it had been petted and pampered by the kids – perhaps *because* it had been petted and pampered by the kids – it was in a foul mood. The kids had been stuffing it with all sorts of goodies, too, from brussels sprouts to liqueur chocolates, which probably accounted for its digestive aberrations.

Led by its child owner dressed as a coachman, the pony stepped on to the stage, daintily picking up its feet to the sound of oohs and aahs from the audience. It drew a little trap, transformed with cardboard into a vague approximation of a golden coach.

All went well for a start. Cinderella climbed into the coach, arranged her voluminous ball gown about her, and sat down safely. Off moved the pony with a slow and dignified gait. Well, it was slow. It would have been dignified if the brute hadn't farted thunderously at every step, causing a few quavering notes among the orchestra and sending the audience into hysterics again. Finally it gave up all pretence to

good behaviour, lifted its tail and plodded off the stage, leaving piles of steaming dung at regular intervals behind it.

Thank God Pam was backstage, I thought. I don't know how I could have comforted her through the horrendous sequence of catastrophes. Not without bursting out laughing myself. But the Great Shetland Pony Disaster should be the end of it: nothing could be worse than that . . .

Towards the end of the panto was a scene in which the Demon King leapt out of a blinding flash and did a song-and-dance routine, waving his three-pronged fork and swishing his tail. Or rather *her* fork and tail: the role was played by one of the few accomplished solo dancers, a girl who had taken evening classes at the local dancing academy.

Whoof! went the powder in the flash pan. And out leapt the Demon King into the dance. It was at least a minute before she realised that her tail was on fire: whoever filled the pan had been over-generous with the flash powder.

Good little trouper that she was, the girl grabbed the tail

with her free hand and, without breaking step, tried to put out the smouldering end by banging it on the boards and bashing it against whatever piece of scenery she was passing. The waving about only made the tail smoulder more, though; and every time the waving stopped, the thing burst into flames.

Bless her, the girl carried on right to the end of the number. As she launched into the last, long note of the song, she laid the end of the tail on the stage and stood on it. The note didn't last as long as it should have done, but the girl had no trouble in reaching high C once the sole of her slipper caught alight. With a final screech, she leapt off the stage like a rocket and plunged foot and tail into a bucket of water proffered by an enterprising stagehand.

As I made my way backstage to comfort Pam after the show, I bumped into C.P.

'I'm sorry you've had so many disasters,' I said. 'Especially after all the work you put in on the script. I hope it's not spoiled the show for you.'

'Spoiled it?' yelled C.P. above the hubbub of departing patrons. 'Spoiled it? It's *made* it! Absolutely marvellous! We gave 'em Potty Panty right enough! Yes, those cock-ups have made the evening – I'm going to ask Pam how many we can keep in the show!'

'There you are,' I said to the white-faced and almost hysterical Pam, who was trying to sort out what seemed like hundreds of laughing, chattering and shouting kids. 'I told you it would be all right on the night . . .'

CHAPTER 16

Good Clean Fun

One of my favourite people in Tadchester was Philomena Fraser who, with her husband, Jim, ran a ladies' hairdressing business. The salon was always full, not just because Phil and Jim were expert stylists, but because there was always something going on to entertain the customers.

For anybody feeling peckish, there was a selection of Phil's home-made cakes. And on special occasions, a huge cake made by Phil's mother, Alice. When word got around that one of Alice's cakes was due, there was a sudden rush of bookings: no connoisseur of cakes would want to miss one of Alice's.

There was coffee, too, for the customers under the driers. And for those who fancied it, there was sometimes a dash of the hard stuff to give the coffee an extra lift. Few did not fancy it.

'Brazilian mild roast today, ladies,' Phil would announce. 'And if anybody wants it perking up, there's a drop of something all the way from Auchtermuchty. Hands up all those of Scottish ancestry.'

It was amazing how many females of Scottish decent patronised Phil's shop.

During term-time, Phil had to break off to collect her seven-year-old daughter, Laura, from school. Often Laura came back to the salon and entertained the customers with an impromptu fashion show or song-and-dance routine.

Laura had the best collection of stand-up jokes in the whole of Tadchester. 'I'll tell you a joke,' she'd announce, and launch into a non-stop stream of Christmas-cracker chestnuts that had the customers in fits of laughter.

Inevitably, now and again she would go too far and come out with a hair-curling blue joke she'd picked up at school. The fact that she didn't understand it herself was beside the point: it was that week's in joke, and she'd seen her classmates falling about when it was told.

'Right,' said Laura one day. 'There was this lad and he only had . . .'

When she finished there was a stunned silence from under the driers, broken only by a few suppressed giggles. Unfortunately for Laura, one of the customers was her paternal grandmother, Edna.

'Laura!' exclaimed Edna, shocked and embarrassed. 'I didn't hear that joke.'

'What do you mean, grandma?'

'You know very well what I mean. I *did not hear* that joke!'

'Don't worry, grandma,' said Laura. 'I'll tell it again. There was this lad and he only had a little willy and one day . . .'

* * *

On early closing day every week, Phil visited Tadchester Hospital to do the hair of the patients in the ladies' geriatric wards. Her time and skills were free; all she charged for was the wholesale cost of the materials, which came out of an amenities fund run by the Friends of the Hospital.

It was a great boost for the old dears to be fussed over and prettied-up once a week, and Phil's visits were always a great social occasion. She not only did their hair, she regaled them with a non-stop stream of patter and gossip which cheered them up no end and made them feel in touch with the goings-on outside the hospital walls.

115

Every so often Phil would get the patients involved in an Old Time Music Hall session: not just a sing-song around the piano, but a full-scale production in which every one of them could play a part. Even the oldest and most feeble was involved, helping to stitch costumes, making simple props or painting bits of scenery.

One old lady had been particularly troublesome from the moment she arrived. Given to imperious gestures and outbursts of disapproval at her surroundings and companions, forever hinting at a former lifestyle of wealth and luxury, she was a trial to the ward staff, visiting doctors and fellow patients alike.

'I hear you're trying to organise some entertainment for these people, Mrs Fraser,' she said during one of Phil's hairdressing sessions.

'That's right, love,' said Phil. 'Want to join in?'

'Ai should say not,' she sniffed, in a haughty and obviously counterfeit accent. 'Rank amateurs. Wouldn't demean myself.'

'How do you mean?' asked Phil.

'Surely you've heard of me? Florrie Farnham?'

'Florrie Farnham!' exclaimed Phil in a tone which implied instant recognition, but not having the slightest clue who Florrie Farnham might be.

'Florrie Farnham – the Tadchester Nightingale!'

'The Tadchester Nightingale!' exclaimed Phil again, still not having much of a clue but catching on fast. 'Of *course*! Just the kind of talent we need!'

'Well, I don't know that I've got the time . . .' began Florrie. Poor old love; like everybody else in the ward she had all the time in the world.

'Florrie – may I call you Florrie?' said Phil, who called all the other patients by their first names just as they – with the exception of Florrie – called her Phil. 'Florrie – you've got to *make* time. No matter how busy you are, you owe it to everybody in this ward, to all the nurses, to matron, to the doctors, to appear in this show. And if not for them, *please* say you'll do it for me.'

'I'll have to think about it,' said Florrie.

And that was that, until Phil's visit the following week when Florrie turned up for her hairdo clutching a list of songs, the appropriate piano arrangements, some demands for costume accessories and suggestions for lighting.

Phil, meanwhile, had done her homework and discovered that Florrie in her day had been a popular concert singer, never making the big time, but possessed of a good mezzo-soprano voice and well-enough known in the area to make a steady living as a soloist until her kind of repertoire went out of fashion.

I was invited to the Old Time evening and accepted with trepidation. The trepidation was justified by some of the quavering old voices which tried to rise above the out-of-tune piano, but I kept reminding myself that I was not there for my own entertainment. By the time the umpteenth chorus had bitten the dust in an off-key dying fall, I stopped wondering what I was there for and told myself it was all in a good cause.

Then Phil was up front announcing: 'Ladies and gentlemen – a very special treat for you this evening, a lady who I'm sure needs no introduction from me. The one and only Tadchester Nightingale ... Your own – your very own ... MISS FLORRIE FARNHAM!'

The little stage blacked out and was then lit by a single spotlight, which homed in shakily on a glittering diamanté tiara. The spot opened jerkily to reveal a magnificently gowned and amply bosomed figure which stood majestically with one white-gloved hand on top of the piano.

'*Velia* ...' a passable mezzo voice began. And then gained strength and authority. '*Velia ... oh Vee-lia ... The witch of the wood* ...' Suddenly the evening was transformed by the magic strains of that eerie song from *The Merry Widow*.

By the time Florrie had finished, I was blowing surreptitiously into my handkerchief. The rest of the audience, including the nurses, had no such inhibitions; tears were rolling down every cheek.

'Thanks again for a marvellous evening,' I said to Phil a few weeks later. 'I never expected to hear a voice like Florrie's. How's she behaving herself now? Less of a bother since she's been in the spotlight?'

'No chance,' said Phil. 'Last time I did her hair she was demanding top billing and a star dressing room . . .'

*　　*　　*

I doubt if many of the ladies of the geriatric ward would have survived the treat Phil laid on for her customers at the hairdressing salon: a visit to a male strip show.

'My own fault,' said Phil. 'I should never have had those copies of *Playgirl* in the shop: Before I knew it, they were all demanding to see the real thing. Women of the world, they said they were. Or hoped to be.'

So the trip from the salon was laid on. Thirty women, not counting Phil, and one man – the coach driver. Phil's husband, Jim, had wisely contracted out. He'd see nothing, he said, that he hadn't seen before, and it wouldn't do much for him anyway. He'd stay at home with his pipe, the telly and a bottle of Scotch.

Chattering and giggling, the women climbed out of the coach outside a club on the sea front which was plastered with garish posters advertising *All-Star Ladies Night! Positively No Gentlemen Admitted!* Phil checked the arrangements for the return trip with the driver.

'And what are you going to do while we're in there?' she asked him.

'Well, I've no other jobs on meantime,' he said. 'I'll just sit in the cab and have forty winks.'

'Oh no, you won't,' said Phil. 'Mrs Henderson dropped out at the last minute when her husband found out where she was going, so we've an extra ticket. You're coming in with us.'

Ignoring the driver's protests, Phil tied a headscarf over his bald patch, borrowed a spare cardigan from one of the stouter ladies, an ankle-length coat from one of the taller ones, hustled him into the throng, and before he knew it he was sitting at a table in the club.

When he took off the coat he was able to hide his trousered legs and boots under the table. Luckily the auditorium was dim enough for nobody to notice his five o'clock shadow, though the waiters must have wondered why the old girl in the cardigan kept her headscarf on all through the performance.

And what a performance! The respectable married ladies of Tadchester clapped, cheered, whistled in direct proportion to the amount of wine which flowed as the evening wore on.

'By heck,' said Phil. 'Those blokes! Especially Tarzan and the Viking. I'd seen nothing like it. Neither had any of the other women.

'Yes, there were a few red faces in the shop over the next week after they'd sobered up and realised how they'd carried on.

'But it did them a world of good. Women don't get nearly the chances that men do to let off steam and be a bit of a devil. They really enjoyed themselves. And, when all's said and done, it was good clean fun. Well, sort of . . .'

CHAPTER 17

First Aid Frolics

I remember clearly the characters in *The Wizard of Oz*: The Cowardly Lion who was given a medal which showed he was brave; the Scarecrow who was given a diploma to show he had brains; and the Tin Man who was given a heart. I shared their experience: I wrote a funny first-aid book and became an immediate authority on the subject. Once the label was stuck on me, I was an expert. There was no way, in spite of my protests to everybody, that I could not know all, and more, about first-aid.

In my first years at Tadchester, Gladys, who was then heavily involved with the Red Cross, had landed me with the job of medical officer to the Forward Medical Aid Unit. Each hospital group in the country had to provide a doctor, a trained nurse and ten auxiliaries, plus a van with lots of equipment, so that we could deal with the millions of casualties who would come down from London in the event of a nuclear holocaust. There was a national competition with the final four teams reaching the Albert Hall to be introduced to the Minister of Health. I was never, ever sure what we were supposed to do. Whatever it was, we obviously did it better than most others for our team was one of the finalists.

In time, all these units were dropped. Whether it was because the chances of a holocaust were receding, or whether it was on financial grounds, I don't know, but I would suspect that it was the latter.

My fame as a first-aider spread. I did first-aid phone-ins for *Women's Hour* on BBC Radio. They recorded a series of first-aid broadcasts I had done for them and sent it out on the World Service. For years afterwards I would meet people who would say, 'Oh, I heard you in Hong Kong,' or 'Guess whose voice I heard in the kitchen in New Zealand?' or 'What were you doing in Australia?' It's a credit to the frugality of the resources of the BBC that they kept this recording going round the world for many years.

My first-aid book was prompted by experiences of rugby injuries over the years. I remember the excitement of going to meet the great publisher. There he was, sitting behind a huge mahogany desk with Havana cigar, huge horn-rimmed spectacles and clutching an advance copy of my new shiny book. I asked tentatively when it was likely to be published.

'We have decided,' he said between puffs from his cigar, 'on Monday, the 17th of September. We have chosen Monday because on Monday more people read their papers than they do on any other day of the week. There's more book reviewing space on a Monday so you are more likely to get your book reviewed. All in all, books launched on Mondays tend to do better than books published on other days of the week.'

He paused, smiling wisely.

'Correct me if I'm wrong,' I said, looking hesitantly into my diary, 'but the 17th of September is a Thursday.'

'Great,' said my publisher without flinching. 'Thursday's a good day as well.'

It came home to me suddenly that the practice of medicine and the publishing of books had many similarities.

First-aid wouldn't let me alone. Apart from the radio, there was the yearly routine of giving first-aid lectures, attending first-aid examinations, offering first-aid facilities at agricultural shows, horse shows and point-to-point meetings.

Then came the big one: I was asked to produce six films on the treatment of home accidents and first-aid for Westward Television. This I did, thinking that soon I would be an international celebrity, but the films were quite terrible and I had the feeling that they burnt them after they had been made.

At the time, first-aid was beginning to take on a new dimension, not in the normal field like football matches, sports meetings and road accidents, but in the general deterioration of social behaviour. Violence in the streets had grown in every aspect of community life, much more so in the bigger cities, but these have their imitators even in the small communities. Over the years in Tadchester there has been a steady increase in the number of muggings, drunken brawls and aggravated burglaries. We aren't as bad as Winchcombe, Winchcombe isn't as bad as Taunton and Taunton is nowhere as bad as London. But anybody with a bit of knowledge of first-aid can have plenty of practical experience – patching up fellow members of the community who for one reason or another don't want to go either to the Casualty Department or the Police Station.

It is all terribly sad. Although we make great strides, or think we make great strides, for example in abolishing capital punishment and reducing corporal punishment, both of which being considered inhumane, it is now less safe to walk in the streets than it ever has been and man's inhumanity to man increases. It is as if every step society takes forward, it takes two back. I remember the advice given by three old men some years previously, when I asked them for a formula for improving society. Their joint answer was that no system could improve society, only better individuals could make a better society.

There isn't much new in first-aid. I strongly advocate it as a social skill to help cope, not only with the increasing violence in the community, but also with that other monster, the increase in heavy and high-speed traffic. Certainly a knowledge of basic first-aid helps to cut the toll of death and injury on the roads. Not only do people die because first-aid is not immediately available, but also they die because well-meaning amateurs actually harm them by doing the wrong thing.

Once I was just in time to stop a motor cyclist being killed by cod-liver oil. On a trip to see a patient I noticed a motor bike on its side in the road and a crowd on the kerb. From the house opposite was rushing a woman with a bottle in one hand and a spoon in the other. I stopped my car and pushed my way through the throng to find the woman pouring out a hefty dose of cod-liver oil and thrusting it in the face of the unconscious motor cyclist saying, 'Here, give him this, it will do him good.' What it would have done to him in his condition would probably have been to get him in the *Guinness Book of Records* as the first man to have drowned in cod-liver oil.

Drake's College, to which I was a medical officer, gave me a steady run of assorted first-aid injuries. There were broken

123

noses on the rugger field and eyes poked out at fencing or gouged out at judo, and there was one boy who had a predilection for letting off fireworks in his bed, usually managing to lose a finger per firework. When he had managed to blow off three fingers, each in separate incidents, the school felt he should retire from his scholastic pursuits at this particular establishment in case he got over-ambitious and decided to blow the steeple off the chapel instead of a fourth finger.

We had been very lucky at Drake's College. As the system of management was changed, so the staff were increased. Whenever a boy had to go to hospital or to the dentist, one of the nursing staff would take him, saving his form or house master from being dragged out of school. There was a fine motherly matron, a doctor's widow, who was a great stabiliser for the whole school, boys and staff alike. Her assistant had been an outpatient sister at Winchcombe Hospital. In addition there were two first-class State Registered Nurses. They all had had children, and were familiar with the problems of boys and parents. They all knew a great deal more about first-aid then I did, and were able to take a lot of work off my shoulders – as well as always being able to produce a couple of dozen boys as really realistic casualties for my first-aid classes.

First-aiders really need to be of a particular temperament: they must be calm, reassuring, well-informed and terribly enthusiastic about their interests, but the main quality is calmness and not getting over-excited. My best first-aider, Barry Blunden, didn't have this particular quality. In my first-aid classes he did very well, both in theory and practice, as you would expect from a man whose secret ambition was to be a male nurse, but when the crunch came he proved to be a little short of self-control.

He was wakened one morning by a crash outside his house. From the bedroom window he saw a spinning motorbike in the middle of the road and a prostrate form in the gutter. Pulling on his dressing gown and grabbing his first-aid kit he ran out.

He weighed up the situation in a flash. Across the road was parked a neighbour's car and from the position of the bike, it was obvious that the rider had run into it.

'Silly bugger,' muttered Barry. 'What a bloody stupid place to leave it.'

A brief questioning of the barely conscious victim established the areas of pain. Barry diagnosed a broken left arm and possibly a fractured ankle. Swiftly and expertly he applied splints and bandages, only then did he turn and look at his own car parked outside the house. The back was completely stoved in and the rear screen shattered.

As realisation was dawning on Barry, the motor cyclist staggered to his feet.

'Thanks a million,' croaked the man. 'You saved my . . .' Just then his stricken ankle gave way and he keeled over. In an effort to save himself he grabbed the aerial on Barry's car and wrenched the thing off completely before collapsing back in the road.

'You bastard,' yelled Barry. 'Look what you've done to my car!'

It was a full minute before a neighbour ran out and dragged him away from the motor cyclist to whose ribs he was applying a tattoo of well-aimed kicks, certainly not a resuscitation technique he'd learnt from me.

The motor cyclist, Jim Ford, was one of my patients and after a few days he hobbled round to the surgery for a certificate.

'Sorry to hear about your extra injuries, Jimmy,' I said. 'On top of what you'd got, you could have done without having the boot put in.'

'It wasn't as bad as all that, Doctor,' said Jimmy. 'Thank God it was early in the morning. The mad sod had only had time to put his carpet slippers on.'

CHAPTER 18

Alarm Calls

I always rather dread the autumn term at Drake's College. It is the rugby term and we have many more injuries to cope with than we do in the other two terms. There is the intake of new boys which means about eighty routine medical examinations to perform and in every new batch there are usually a couple of boys with an undescended testicle that hasn't been noticed, and at least one who has not realised that he is blind in one eye. It is only rarely that something serious turns up. One particular case, a small healthy looking boy, worried the matron. I don't think she knew quite why she was worried, but worried she was, and I have a great respect for the intuition of those who have been in the medical profession for a long time; so often their suspicions are aroused not by logic or investigations but by an inner sixth sense that tells them something is wrong.

'It's his pulse, Doctor Clifford. It's a bit odd,' said Matron.

This little lad had been under observation for flu, which was one of the other hazards that came this term. I examined him and I thought his heart had a murmur that ought to be further investigated. He was sent to John Bowler at Winchcombe who found that the boy had a serious condition: the

126

main artery in the body, the aorta, was narrowed, the boy had very high blood pressure and needed urgent medical attention. Within a month he was up at the Middlesex Hospital in London in the same unit that had put me right. His main artery was operated on and his life literally was saved. If the first real symptom of this particular condition had gone undiagnosed, it could well have been this little lad's last. I was very grateful for my medical team.

No sooner do we get through all the medicals and follow-ups of medicals than the nursing staff have to cope with rounds of BCG jabs. Tuberculosis is only kept at bay by the routine screening of school children, testing them to see if they are immune to it or have come across it, and if not they are given an injection to build up immunity.

Autumn is also the term in which we give injections against flu. We have to have parents' permission for this and there are usually about half for and half against, and of the half for, the boys themselves say they are definitely sure that their parents have said no, so it often means rechecking, and for the half against, about a quarter swear that their parents have said that they should have it, so this has to be checked too.

Following the long break of the summer holidays, by the end of the term all the boys who travelled or lived abroad have to have all their immunisations brought up to date. This amounts to a good third of the school, so during the last month of the term there is a welter of jabs for cholera, typhoid, and a host of other diseases for which I have to write out certificates and prescriptions. And, of course, this is the term when flu epidemics, in spite of the injections, very often turn up.

Latterly the school has opened a junior school, not in the same premises but in the same grounds. This means that in addition to all the medical problems there are emotional traumas to deal with. As half of the eighty intake are little boys from eight to ten, there are great numbers of the wee chaps sobbing their hearts out for their mums before eventually settling in to this place of learning where they will probably spend the next seven years of their life.

The practice load is always heavy at this time of year, right up to Christmas, but the school medical workload is absolutely frantic. It is heavier in this term than in the spring and summer terms put together. I do three surgeries a week and during December it is like a countdown to sending up a rocket from Cape Canaveral. Whether it is matron or one of the sisters on duty at the surgery they say to me, 'Only seven more to go now, Doc,' then six, five, and so on until the last. If we make it to the headmaster's Christmas party and matron's Christmas lunch it means we have all survived another autumn term, but only just.

The year after I had my operation something was going on in the autumn term that was nothing to do with the medical examinations, BCG, flu or cholera injections, and it was something that was being kept from me. The headmaster and matron and sisters were grim faced; the chats over tea after surgery, although pleasant, weren't relaxed; there was something missing; there was something wrong. This went on for about four weeks. I probed as much as I could but they obviously did not want to include me in whatever trouble was worrying them. I was slightly miffed by this but just had to accept it. It obviously wasn't something medical.

It wasn't until the sixth week of term that I found a complete change of atmosphere. There was the headmaster looking himself, matron beaming and one of the sisters looking relaxed for the first time. On the table by the tea tray were three small cellophane packets containing white powder.

Good God, I thought, they're all on drugs.

Matron smiled, 'What do you think that is, Doctor?'

I picked up a packet and examined it – it could have been anything. From what I'd seen in films it looked like heroin or some other noxious substance of that order.

'Just smell it and taste it,' they said.

'I'm afraid I have no real opinion,' I muttered. 'I've no experience.'

I smelt it. I could smell very little. I tasted it and found it had a slightly soapy tang.

'What is it?' I asked.

'What do you think it is?' they said.

I said, 'I think it could be anything but I would suspect that it is a rather nasty drug that somebody is pushing around.'

'So did we,' they replied, 'and we've been in a terrible dilemma. We knew these were being pushed round the school; we didn't know what they were. We checked with various authorities for the likely signs and symptoms of drug abuse but we could find no boy who even looked as if he might be drugged. It's been a terrible worry. If we'd have reported it to the police they would have turned the place inside out. It was a problem we wanted to solve ourselves. We had the reputation of the school to consider.'

'Have you solved it?' I asked.

'Yes,' they replied. 'After failing completely to identify it in the laboratory, we had the bright idea of sending it to the public analyst.'

'And . . .?' I said.

'It's soap powder. We even managed to find the boys responsible . . . and the packet of soap powder. They were just showing off.'

'And,' said the headmaster, 'there are now four very sore bottoms which make this little escapade unlikely to occur again.'

Running a school isn't easy and I could see what a worry it must have been when those in charge thought that they had uncovered a ring of hard drug pushers in the middle of the school. I think I would have given the culprits a soap mouthwash as well as having tanned their hides.

* * *

There was one other major alarm in Tadchester at this time and it concerned my old friend Eric Martin, the proprietor of Tadchester Electrical Services. He complained of tummy trouble and said it was due to some frozen lobster he had for his birthday dinner cooked by the exotic Zara, his wife and Pam's best friend. The difficulty of having friends who are

129

doctors is like being a doctor's child: you are either neglected or completely over-doctored. I am the over-doctoring sort so Eric was whisked to John Bowler at Winchcombe, in spite of the former's protests that he was quite better. As I had sent him and he was a friend of mine, John Bowler said he would have to have a complete check over. This meant not only chest X-rays, blood counts and a barium meal, but a barium enema which Eric said he wouldn't wish even on his worst enemy. Happily all his tests came back normal, only the barium enema remaining before he would be given a clean bill of health.

To prepare for his barium enema he had had to take some medicine the day before to ensure that nothing would obstruct the barium. The X-ray department posted the lethal ingredients – a packet of granules and two suppositories that looked like bullets in silver paper – and gave him an appointment a week ahead to attend Winchcombe for his X-ray. In the evening of the day he received this little parcel I had arranged to meet him with C.P. and another friend, Joe Church – a sort of sub-committee of the Tadchester Angling Society – to decide what we wanted to go on the agenda of the society's AGM. We were to meet at the Tadchester Arms at six.

On my way there I met the three of them in the street – they were part of a crowd of people who had been cordoned off by the police and fire brigade, standing some hundred yards from the Tadchester Arms. As I arrived an Army bomb disposal team turned up.

'Good God, what's happening?' I said. Up to that time the IRA had taken no notice of Tadchester.

'Some bomb scare,' said C.P. 'It seems bloody ridiculous to me.'

'Well, let's go somewhere else for our meeting,' I said.

'Come back home with me,' said C.P. 'I've got a few cans of lager. They'll only go stale if they're not drunk.'

We went to C.P.'s, had a bowl of his wife's home-made soup and settled down to our meeting. We had almost got it finished when there was a knock on the door from a very unfriendly-looking police inspector accompanied by a captain from the Army bomb disposal unit.

'Mr Christopher Parfitt?'

'Yes,' said C.P.

'Is there a Mr Eric Martin here?'

'Yes,' said C.P.

'May we come in for a minute?'

'Certainly,' said C.P. looking alarmed.

'Are these yours?' said the police inspector, holding out Eric's sachet of laxative granules and the cellophane bag containing his two silver bullets.

'Yes,' said Eric. 'Thanks very much. I must have left them somewhere.'

'Exactly,' said the inspector. 'You left them in the Tadchester Arms at lunchtime. At closing time the landlord found two bullet-like objects and a cellophane bag. With all these scares about explosive parcels being left here and there, he informed us and we had to bring out the fire brigade and the bomb disposal people. Unfortunately there is no way I can prosecute but by God if there was, I would.'

Eric looked a bit shaken and when they'd gone he turned to me.

'It's all your fault,' he said, 'I told you it was just that frozen lobster. None of this would have happened if you hadn't sent me to Winchcombe.'

Eric went off for his investigation the following week. I arranged to pop round that night to see how he had got on. All his tests to date had shown that in fact he was remarkably fit and this last one, although the least pleasant, was just a necessary precaution. I called at his house, was shown in by Zara, and found Eric lying white and shaken on the settee. I had never seen him look like this before.

'You all right, mate?' I said.

'What do you mean, all right?' said Eric.

'I mean, was your test clear?'

'Oh,' he said, 'yes, a hundred per cent clear; nothing

131

medically wrong. I told you from the beginning it was just that frozen lobster.'

'Well,' I said, 'you're looking worse now than you have looked at any time.'

'I know,' said Eric. 'They were right to get the police and the bomb disposal people out when they found that stuff in the pub. Those suppositories were just like high explosives. I'm sure I lost my tonsils as well as the rest of my insides. It has been at least four hours since I've been able to face a glass of ale.'

'Never mind,' I said. 'Think of the headlines for next week's *Tadchester Gazette*. It will read "Clear Out of Tadchester Electrical Services. Proprietor Flushed With Success Over Recent Inter-Departmental Investigations Has Wind of New Developments." '

I ducked as Eric threw a copy of *Angler's Mail* at me.

CHAPTER 19

Wedding Bells

Jane's A-level years passed only too quickly, though perhaps not for her. She went through all the bitter-sweet agonies of adolescence; her hair changing colour right through the spectrum in the search to find the magic colour. From a lovely, fair, auburn shade it progressed finally to jet black which, when she viewed it in the mirror for the first time, made her burst into tears. She was not helped at all when Mick Brown, one of Paul's entourage, wisecracked on his first sight of her, 'I didn't know Betty Boop lived here! She looked quite different, black. Growing it out was a long painful process, and she settled in the end for having her hair sort of half-dyed.

She also seemed to wear clothes that didn't suit her at all, enraging the headmaster of her comprehensive school who always included a note on her report about her bizarre dress and colouring.

At last she sat through the dreaded torture of A-levels, passed, and secured a place on a foundation course in art at Brighton Polytechnic. Almost before we'd realised it, she was off to Brighton and we were down to a household of three; Pam, myself and Paul. Not that Paul really counted as a full-time resident: home was just a place where he stored all his amplifying gear and rested in between work and gigs.

Jane loved Brighton, worked hard in her first year, then moved on to a three-year degree course on the history of design. She came home whenever she could, to watch Trevor in whatever new play he was in, and go and shout for Paul's group whenever it played within spitting distance.

Paul and Gill's engagement didn't seem to make much difference to their relationship; they just seemed to go on as before. Whenever Paul was asked when they were likely to get married, he'd say, 'I've only two stipulations: it mustn't be on the day of the Cup Final, and Trevor must be best man.'

Suddenly, Paul and Gill had to get married in a hurry. Not for the usual Tadchester reason but because both Gill's mother, Liz, and father, Eddie, lived in India and they only came home for a few weeks in the spring of each year. Gill wanted her parents at her wedding, and if it wasn't this particular spring, it would have to be the next one.

By now, Paul was working little on his music, but was trying to write. His job in the electronics factory had no real prospects and he had ambitions to be a sports writer. Gill was a marvellous cook, an accomplished painter, had qualified in an arts course and designed and made jewellery. Her parents in India, she had to arrange her own wedding. She rushed round organising invitations, receptions, wedding dress.

'Good God,' said Paul, 'I never realised getting married was so complicated.'

He was happy with the arrangements, however. The wedding date didn't clash with the Cup Final, Trevor turned down a part in a play to be his brother's best man and Jane was to be a bridesmaid. But to add to the activity, Gill's sister and her fiancé, taking a leaf from Gill's book decided to marry a week after Gill and Paul.

Poor Liz and Eddie were going to lose two daughters in a week, and Liz flew home from India early to help sort things out.

I took Paul on one side to give him some fatherly advice:

'The first thing, Paul, is don't refuse anything anyone offers you, however grotesque, be it a three-legged chair or a one-legged stool. If you turn it down, they'll never, never, give you anything else.'

They were fortunate that they were able to find an end-of-terrace cottage with garage and out-buildings and in a lovely setting. It was two hundred years old and just the place for Gill to do her jewellery and metalwork.

The weather prospects for the wedding day looked poor. It had been a cold, wet and miserable spring. They were to be married at St Mary's Parish Church in Tadchester, with a reception at the Port Vere Hotel, five miles away. This was an old country house set in acres of landscaped gardens with its own private beach. In the evening everybody was coming back to us for a party. Paul and Gill were to spend the first night of their honeymoon in Taunton, then fly off to Paris the following day.

At last the great day arrived. The indefatigable Mick Brown, who was taking a video of the wedding, was up filming from the crack of dawn. He videoed Gill washing and having her hair done, managed to catch Jane in bed, and went on to film the whole ceremony, reception and going-away in the evening. The gods looked kindly on us; this was the one fine day in the midst of an awful spell.

Gill looked like a princess in a dress which she designed herself. Paul and Trevor looked splendid, tall and for once well-groomed in their hired attire. The church was packed. As well as a hundred guests, there were patients who had known Paul since he was a baby. Catherine, my stand-in, very kindly covered the surgery for the day and all the partners turned up. Ron Dickinson distinguished himself by starting the celebrations long before the wedding began. While the photographs were being taken in the churchyard, he decided to make an unescorted, unroped attack on the south face of the church spire. No sherpas or oxygen either, though he looked as if he could have done with both by the time he came down.

The boys made impressive speeches at the reception. Paul

135

wasn't going to be outdone by his actor brother and Trevor not only welcomed Gill into the family but also her incontinent cat, which was going to be boarded with us while they were on their honeymoon.

Pam's brother, Theo, who has the energy of at least three men and spends his life shooting round the world opening more and more companies, organised the rest of the afternoon's entertainment when we arrived home after the reception.

'Come on, lads,' he said, 'it's the cricket season.'

It must have been one of the few games of cricket played in morning dress. The bride, her beautiful white creation tucked into her waist, took her turn at batting like everybody else.

There was eating and drinking and talking and kissing. Relatives that we only saw at funerals and weddings were all saying to each other and to us that we must get together more often. Then, finally, there was Mr Sparks, the taxi man, at the door, ready to take Paul and Gill off on their honeymoon. Mick Brown had organised floodlighting of the whole of the area outside the house so he could video their departure. Then, with shouts, cheers, kisses and goodbyes, they were away at last.

One hour later Mick Brown was back with the video of the wedding and we had a three-hour replay of all the day's proceedings.

The eating and drinking went on for a couple more hours. The guests and relatives that were staying with us went to bed and Pam and I were left sitting in the lounge. Suddenly the house was deathly quiet. Pam looked up at me.

'Darling,' she said, 'I've something to say to you.'

'Are you thinking what I'm thinking?'

'Yes,' she said. 'Life is going to be different from now on.'

Postscript

There is the fable of the old man sitting outside a town, being approached by a stranger.

'What are they like in this town?' asked the stranger.

'What were they like in your last town?' replied the old man.

'They were delightful people. I was very happy there. They were kind, generous and would always help you in trouble.'

'You will find them very much like that in this town.'

The old man was approached by another stranger.

'What are the people like in this town?' asked the second stranger.

'What were they like in your last town?' replied the old man.

'It was an awful place. They were mean, unkind and nobody would ever help anybody.'

'I am afraid you will find it very much the same here,' said the old man.

If it should be your lot to ever visit Tadchester, this is how you will find us.